Cartographic Expeditions ar Culture in the Nineteenth-C Americas

During the nineteenth century, gridding, graphing, and surveying proliferated as never before as nations and empires expanded into hitherto "unknown" territories. Though nominally geared toward justifying territorial claims and collecting scientific data, expeditions also produced vast troves of visual and artistic material. This book considers the explosion of expeditionary mapping and its links to visual culture across the Americas, arguing that acts of measurement are also aesthetic acts. Such visual interventions intersect with new technologies, with sociopolitical power and conflict, and with shifting public tastes and consumption practices. Several key questions shape this examination: What kinds of nineteenth-century visual practices and technologies of seeing do these materials engage? How does scientific knowledge get translated into the visual and disseminated to the public? What are the commonalities and distinctions in mapping strategies between North and South America? How does the constitution of expeditionary lines reorder space and the natural landscape itself? The volume represents the first transnational and hemispheric analysis of nineteenth-century cartographic aesthetics, and features the multidisciplinary perspective of historians, geographers, and art historians.

Ernesto Capello is Professor of History at Macalester College.

Julia B. Rosenbaum is Associate Professor of Art History and Visual Culture at Bard College.

Routledge Studies in the History of the Americas

For more information about this series, please visit: https://www.routledge.
com/Routledge-Studies-in-the-History-of-the-Americas/book-series/RSHAM

Cartographic Expeditions and Visual Culture in the Nineteenth-Century Americas

Edited by Ernesto Capello
and Julia B. Rosenbaum

Routledge
Taylor & Francis Group

NEW YORK AND LONDON

First published 2021
by Routledge
52 Vanderbilt Avenue, New York, NY 10017

and by Routledge
2 Park Square, Milton Park, Abingdon, Oxon OX14 4RN

Routledge is an imprint of the Taylor & Francis Group, an informa business

© 2021 Taylor & Francis

Library of Congress Cataloging-in-Publication Data
Names: Capello, Ernesto, editor. | Rosenbaum, Julia B., editor.
Title: Cartographic expeditions and visual culture in the
nineteenth-century Americas / Ernesto Capello, Julia B. Rosenbaum.
Other titles: Cartographic expeditions and visual culture in the 19th century Americas
Description: First Edition. | New York: Routledge Taylor & Francis Group, 2020. |
Series: Routledge studies in the history of the Americas; volume 17 |
Includes bibliographical references and index.
Identifiers: LCCN 2020031071 (print) | LCCN 2020031072 (ebook) |
ISBN 9780367333263 (Hardback) | ISBN 9780429319211 (eBook) |
ISBN 9781000228793 (Adobe PDF) | ISBN 9781000228809 (mobi) |
ISBN 9781000228823 (ePub)
Subjects: LCSH: Cartography–America–History–19th century. |
America–Territorial expansion.
Classification: LCC GA401 .C39 2020 (print) |
LCC GA401 (ebook) | DDC 526.097/09034–dc23
LC record available at https://lccn.loc.gov/2020031071
LC ebook record available at https://lccn.loc.gov/2020031072

ISBN: 978-0-367-33326-3 (hbk)
ISBN: 978-0-429-31921-1 (ebk)

Typeset in Sabon
by Newgen Publishing UK

Contents

Figures

Contributors

James R. Akerman holds a Ph.D. in Geography and has been Director of the Newberry Library's Hermon Dunlap Smith Center for the History of Cartography since 1996 and Curator of Maps since 2011. His research and publications primarily concern the history of travel mapping, popular cartography, and atlases.

Nancy P. Appelbaum is Professor of History at Binghamton University. Her research concerns how Latin Americans defined and experienced race, region, nation, and migration. Her most recent book, *Mapping the Country of Regions: The Chorographic Commission of Colombia* (2016), follows mid-nineteenth-century geographers as they traverse the mountains, valleys, plains, and forests of Colombia.

Ernesto Capello researches the cultural history of Latin America. He has written *City at the Center of the World: Space, History, and Modernity in Quito* (2011), *Mapping Mountains* (2020), and is completing a history of geodesy and visual culture in the equatorial Andes. He is Professor of History at Macalester College.

Kenneth Haltman, H. Russell Pitman Professor of Art History at the University of Oklahoma, has published extensively on topics in early nineteenth-century material and visual culture including *Looking Close and Seeing Far: Samuel Seymour, Titian Ramsay Peale, and the Art of the Long Expedition* (2008).

Joni L. Kinsey, Professor of Art History at the University of Iowa, is the author of *Thomas Moran and the Surveying of the American West* (1992); *Plain Pictures: Images of the American Prairie* (1996); *The Majestic Grand Canyon: 150 Years in Art* (1998); and *Thomas Moran's West: Chromolithography, High Art, and Popular Taste* (2006).

Carla Lois is Researcher at the Consejo Nacional de Investigaciones Científicas y Técnicas (CONICET), Professor at the University of Buenos Aires, Editor-in-Chief of Brill Research Perspectives on Map History, and Associate Editor of *The History of Cartography Project*, volume 5. Her latest book is *Terrae Incognitae. Formas de pensar y mapear geografías desconocidas* (2018).

Alicia Lubowski-Jahn is an independent curator and arts writer and holds a Ph.D. in art history. She co-curated the exhibition *Unity of Nature: Alexander von Humboldt and the Americas* at the Americas Society in New York City. She has published on various aspects of Humboldt's artistic legacy in the Americas and Europe.

Katherine Manthorne's scholarship focuses on nineteenth-century landscape, travelers, and women artists with a pan-American dimension from *Tropical Renaissance: North American Artists Exploring Latin America* (1989) through *Restless Enterprise: The Art and Life of Eliza Pratt Greatorex* (2020). She is Professor of Art History at City University of New York's Graduate Center.

Katherine G. Morrissey is Associate Professor of History at the University of Arizona where she researches, teaches, and publishes environmental, cultural, borderlands/Southwest and north American West history. Her related publications include *Border Spaces: Visualizing the US-Mexico Frontera* (2018), edited with John-Michael Warner, and *Mental Territories: Mapping the Inland Empire* (1997).

Julia B. Rosenbaum specializes in nineteenth- and early twentieth-century American visual material. The author of *Visions of Belonging: New England Art and the Making of American Identity* (2006), she is Associate Professor of Art History and Visual Culture at Bard College and has also served as Director of Research and Publications at The Olana Partnership.

Acknowledgments

The editors wish to thank the Newberry Library, especially the Smith Center for the History of Cartography and Jim Akerman, for hosting the 2013 symposium that inspired this volume. We also thank the Terra Foundation for their financial support to realize the symposium. Our gratitude further goes to Max Novick and the entire editorial and production teams at Routledge. Finally, we express our deep appreciation to the authors for their excellent contributions and their enthusiasm for the project.

1 Introduction

The Expeditionary Impulse

Ernesto Capello and Julia B. Rosenbaum

Upon returning to Paris after a five-year expedition from 1799–1804 through Central and South America, Alexander von Humboldt, the legendary natural scientist, and the botanist Aimé Bonpland published their *Essay on the Geography of Plants*, a short volume in which Humboldt presented his research studying plants in their natural habitat and first sketched out his theories, proposing a "unity in nature." He also argued for a broader shift within science in general that would prioritize direct experience and observation rather than laboratory-based conjecture. Particularly notable in the text was the inclusion of a color plate, the famous "Tableau physique des Andes et pays voisins" (Figure 1.1), a sprawling pictorial representation that gathered together, in Humboldt's words, "the sum of the physical phenomena present in equinoctial regions."[1]

Flanked by columns of text filled with meteorological, hydrological, and atmospheric data, the Tableau features a landscape scene at the center with both profile and cross-section views of the equatorial Andes, emphasizing the dramatic volcanoes, Cotopaxi and Chimborazo. Much ink has been spilled concerning the originality of this object, with its unique combination of text and image.[2] A recent assessment by Sylvie Romanowski notes that its startling composition "makes the eye circulate, as if to say: The spectacle of nature is one that involves movement, elegant variation, and well-balanced proportions."[3] Humboldt himself called attention to the aesthetic potential of the Tableau, asserting his desire to "[suggest] unexpected analogies ... speaking to the imagination and providing the pleasure that comes from contemplating a beneficial as well as majestic nature."[4] Humboldt also claims that the Tableau "contains almost the entirety of the research I carried out during my expedition in the tropics," a statement that foreshadowed the 40-year cycle of scientific writings inspired by his equatorial journey. As such, the Tableau operates as a scientific and artistic representation that posits the potential of conceptualizing the sublimity of nature. Indeed, it serves as the dialogical frame for Humboldt's oeuvre, as both a source of facts and as a source of inspiration.

The Tableau captures a nineteenth-century urgency not only to define and delineate visible and invisible natural systems but also to obscure. The act of synthesizing, of picturing a world-at-a-glance so intently, necessitates

Figure 1.1 Alexander von Humboldt and Aimé Bonpland. *Géographie des Plantes Équinoxiales: Tableau Physique des Andes et Pays Voisins*. 1805. Courtesy of Bibliothèque Nationale de France.

sacrifices. For one, the Tableau privileges snapshots over processes. Ecological phenomena, from plant growth to volcanic eruption, each of which have their own temporal chronologies, are presented as occurring simultaneously. The Tableau is also a project of selection: while it covers a wide range of data, from barometric pressure to snow latitudes and temperatures, it muddles the variability of daily, seasonal, or yearly change, as well as the idiosyncrasies of microclimates. Further, the Tableau emphasizes individual effort over a collaborative enterprise, silencing the multitude of figures that guided Humboldt. These include the important work of Indigenous laborers without whom the extended research would have been a failure, the crucial input of Spanish American scientists and botanists who helped shape Humboldt's journey, and, perhaps most notably, the design contributions of Francisco José de Caldas, who simultaneously produced an extraordinarily similar tableau of the equatorial Andes to which Humboldt was likely indebted.[5]

In this way, the Tableau points to the difficulties, choices, and complexities that characterized efforts to compile and process materials generated by expeditions. The translation of information from measurement to map and its subsequent transmission through the printed page produced disjunctures of representation. The essays in this volume explore these sites of inconvenience and ragged edges, considering both the development of maps themselves and the production of complementary visual materials. The proliferation of expeditions throughout the nineteenth century might be best thought of as an "expeditionary impulse," our term to characterize the drive among nineteenth-century nation-states to launch these kinds of high-profile investigative ventures. Though nominally geared toward collecting scientific data, cartographic surveys also worked to justify territorial claims and project national ideals. Beyond just maps, expeditions generated vast troves of artistic material, such as sketches, drawings, paintings, and photographs, that were then incorporated into more popular and widely circulating media. In effect, a feedback loop emerged in which the visual documentation reified the sites, places, and topographies depicted.

The expeditions of the nineteenth century had many of the same empirical goals as in previous centuries, but they also bear a number of distinctive qualities. First, this period's scientific and artistic technologies transformed the opportunities available to both artists and cartographers whose role in envisioning the "unexplored" areas of both North and South America was paramount. Second, these exploratory expeditions produced not only primary documents (maps, survey reports) but an even larger body of ancillary materials (tourist brochures, commemorative albums, posters and postcards, etc.). Moreover, this period represented a shift from the relatively artisanal approach of the "gentleman" cartographer to a centralized and state-driven enterprise in which standardized logics of visual representation increasingly displaced the idiosyncrasies of earlier frameworks. Third, and most germane to our project, the public attention that resulted from these secondary or ancillary publications helped to transform cartographic expeditions into ends themselves, wherein a culture of celebrity and popular acclaim formed as crucial a component as territorialization.

We see the expeditionary impulse as a global phenomenon, but one that takes a peculiar shape in the Americas. The great European imperial surveys, from Napoleon's Nile Expedition to the British Trigonometric Survey of India, expanded the reach of cartographic knowledge directly in service to empire. Moreover, especially in Africa, many of these expeditions represented the first attempts to deploy modern cartographic techniques in depicting vast swaths of unsurveyed territory. The Americas, however, had been progressively mapped by European empires since the sixteenth century, culminating in several massive undertakings during the late eighteenth and early nineteenth centuries, from the Mutis expedition in New Granada to the Lewis and Clark expedition in the Louisiana Purchase territory. As such, their basic contours were largely known. Moreover, expeditionary work was undertaken by newly independent nation-states rather than the imperial governments overseeing similar efforts in Asia or Africa. Fundamentally, then, nineteenth-century expeditions through the Americas were engaged not only in charting little known interior territory but also in finding means to represent and control already known spaces for nationalist agendas.

This is not, however, to deny that there were extended tracts of territory that remained unmapped throughout the nineteenth century. Rather, the vast majority of cartographic expeditions tended to extend and revise previous investigations across repeated routes. At the heart of the expedition is the line, the line taken by surveyors and cartographers that represented known ways of crossing territory. Though these lines would be fleshed out across the century, this was a piecemeal process that arguably came to fruition only in the twentieth century.

To take one example, consider the map of the Republic of Ecuador, drawn by the German geologist and defrocked Jesuit priest Theodoro Wolf in 1892, following a 20-year study (Figure 1.2a). While every previous nineteenth-century map of the country had incorporated its Amazonian territory as a vast triangular province contiguous to Ecuador's Andean spine, Wolf presented this space in an inset map that metaphorically and graphically separated it from the country's territorial control (Figure 1.2b). He labeled this space "Región poco conocida y habitada por indios salvajes," that is to say, "Little known country inhabited by savage indians." Wolf intended by this to propel further exploration and cartographic study of Ecuador's Amazon, correctly noting that the scores of cartographic, botanical, and missionary expeditions into the region across the eighteenth and nineteenth century had largely followed the same route down the Napo River toward the Amazon that had been first explored by Francisco de Orellana in the sixteenth century.[6] Therefore, any claims of national control and national geography were largely fictitious. Nineteenth-century cartographic means of depicting lines must therefore be considered not only as acts of measurement but also as political and aesthetic acts. Such techniques of visualization intersect with power and technology, with shifting

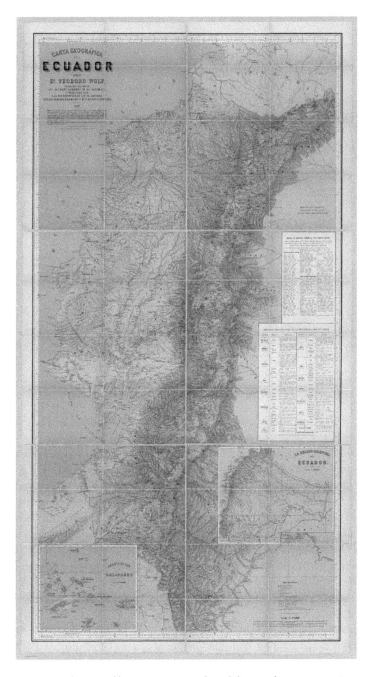

Figure 1.2 Teodoro Wolf, *Carta Geográfica del Ecuador*. 1892. (a) Map, 99 cm × 105 cm. Scale of 1:445,000. (b) Detail. David Rumsey Map Collection, www.davidrumsey.com.

Figure 1.2 Cont.

public tastes, with consumption practices and political conflicts, and become a crucial component of what John Pickles has termed a "scopic regime."[7]

Cartographic Expeditions and Visual Culture in the Nineteenth-Century Americas focuses attention on maps as aesthetic objects produced in dialogue with other aspects of nineteenth-century visual culture, such as methods of printing and production, technologies of display and distribution, and the role of government and commerce in artistic and cartographic production. Several key questions shape this examination: What kinds of nineteenth-century visual practices and technologies of seeing do these materials engage? How does scientific knowledge get translated into the visual and disseminated to the public? What are the commonalities and distinctions in mapping strategies between North and South America? And how does the constitution of expeditionary lines structure space itself?

This volume responds to new approaches in the history of cartography that have developed in the past three decades. Beginning with Brian Harley's pioneering work, map historians have emphasized how maps communicate meaning and inscribe hierarchies.[8] Far from representing neutral representations of geographic space, maps have been shown to be dramatically embedded in power relations. A renaissance in cartographic histories has demonstrated the importance of maps in developing or reifying existing social structures. Two fields have been particularly marked by this rich trajectory of inquiry, namely the history of European imperial relations and that of nation-state construction. These new approaches began to shift the tenor of historical monographs during the late 1990s and early 2000s. Scholars such as Matthew Edney (1997) and Graham Burnett (2001) established the critical role that cartography played in cementing British imperial hegemony in India and Guyana, while Raymond Craib (2004) pursued a similarly influential study for nineteenth-century Mexico.[9]

These social and political histories of cartography began to overlap with a secondary literature in the history of science that emphasized the importance of visual culture for the solidifying of empire. Besides the seminal work of theorists such as Bruno Latour, particularly important studies of Latin America include Deborah Poole's (1997) analysis of the visual economy of the Andes and Mary Louise Pratt's influential *Imperial Eyes*.[10] Two studies in particular should also be mentioned for showcasing the potential of bridging the new cartographic history with art-historical attention to specific objects. The first is Barbara Mundy's *Mapping New Spain* (1996), which focused attention on the sixteenth-century *relaciones geográficas*, an enormous survey of the Spanish empire that featured geographic description including maps.[11] Mundy's analysis of Indigenous-drawn maps of Mexico and Central America stressed the critical role that Indigenous graphic strategies continued to play in the visual culture of New Spain, and the accompanying potential for political resistance to Spanish cultural hegemony. An equally important moment came with Richard Kagan's (2000) synthetic treatment of maps and other forms of urban views in colonial Spanish America.[12] By demonstrating that urban views tended toward the chorographic (predominantly spatial foci) or communicentric (sociocultural emphases), Kagan also helped bridge the new cartographic history, the cultural history of science, and emerging voices in art historical scholarship attending equally to social context alongside object analysis. A plethora of monographs influenced by these approaches has followed over the early years of this century, reflecting the potential of these new areas of inquiry.

These broader patterns were echoed in a slightly different register within the US historiography. As early as 1992, Joni Kinsey's study of the late nineteenth-century artist Thomas Moran and his linkages to the Great Surveys of the American West crystallized the connection between nineteenth-century visual culture and cartographic pursuits.[13] However, the kind of monographs engaging the interplay between visual representation and power that had already been developing in Latin American historiography did not appear until works such as Robin Kelsey's *Archive Style* (2007), Kenneth Haltman's *Looking Close and Seeing Far* (2008), and Michael Gaudio's *Engraving the Savage* (2008) began to more directly engage these subjects.[14] In the wake of their efforts, a variety of new histories of US cartography emerged of which Susan Schulten's *Mapping the Nation* (2012) and Martin Brückner's *The Social Life of Maps in America, 1750–1860* (2017) are perhaps the most universal in their attention to the import of cartographic imaginaries in the establishment of American nationalism (and internal colonialism) during the nineteenth century.[15]

The focus on national or regional histories, however, has tended to obscure a hemispheric approach to cartographic visualities. Martin Brückner's edited volume *Early American Cartographies* from 2011 turned in this direction with examples ranging from the sixteenth to the late eighteenth centuries.[16] Despite the intensity of nineteenth-century expeditions, the resonance across hemispheric examples remains understudied. Moreover, hemispheric studies of visual culture in the Americas leans heavily toward analysis of landscape painting rather than the interdisciplinary approach we pursue here.[17] Our volume brings together art historians, historians, and geographers to address nineteenth-century cartography and visuality in a consciously transnational vein. Moreover, by attending equally to mapping as a process of measurement and mapping as a visual form, we collectively seek to foreground the expeditionary impulse as both a social and cultural phenomenon of the nineteenth century.

Cartographic Expeditions and Visual Culture in the Nineteenth-Century Americas is organized into three main sections, each of which addresses the tensions inherent in visualizing expeditionary work and the strategies put in place to secure knowing and seeing. Rather than follow a strict chronology, the volume moves thematically, taking up what we consider fundamental practices in the presentation and dissemination of cartographic knowledge. Part I, "Seeing and Not Seeing," examines the notion, or better the fiction, of comprehensiveness in scientific mapping. Part II, "Lines and Tracings," looks at boundary making and attempts to explicitly inscribe cartographic lines on the land. Part III, "Art and the Expeditionary Impulse," turns to the expeditionary as an aesthetic form itself.

In "Seeing and Not Seeing," the first two chapters focus on the visual strategies of cartographic practices to master distance and conceptualize broad swaths of land, their contours, and their borders. We might think of these encompassing approaches to visualizing space as a drive for a kind of "comprehensive seeing." Nineteenth-century cartographers and producers of visual material privileged an orthogonal, or "God's eye," perspective to provide a veneer of comprehensibility through scientific measurement. As states and individuals marked boundaries, highlighted topographical elements, charted natural resources, and otherwise attempted to fill in blank spaces on maps, they did not merely flatten certain features; they concealed them. They often rendered invisible, for example, populations and histories in conflict with state desires for control, particularly with regard to Indigenous peoples.

Alicia Lubowski-Jahn's essay opens the section with a discussion of Prussian natural scientist Alexander von Humboldt (1769–1859) and his innovative and influential work in developing graphic systems to visualize and represent statistical data as well as new technologies to disseminate research. Humboldt's promotion of landscape painting, and in particular tropical American vistas, was rooted in a belief in the potential of the genre to represent a holistic view of several unities—the unity of organisms in ecosystems, of nature and human life, of art and science, and of the entire cosmos. Lubowski-Jahn locates Humboldt's efforts within his broader scientific methodology and romantic aesthetics in general. Joni Kinsey, in the second chapter of the section, deepens the theme of holistic visualization with her consideration of geodetic triangulation. Focusing on the Great Surveys of the American West in the late 1860s through the 1870s, she argues that the very practice of triangulation—the process that measured expanses by comparing distances from different points of view—offered a unifying mechanism to integrate diverse assemblages of material, whether map, text, or image. Bringing together separate technologies, "triangulation," according to Kinsey, functioned as a mutually constitutive process enabling an approximation of a comprehensive view.

The final two chapters of the section turn a lens on how these strategies of comprehensive seeing could produce the exact opposite effect, a kind of invisibility, particularly in the case of local and Indigenous populations. Both Kenneth Haltman's and Nancy Appelbaum's chapters focus in on a single map to expose these moments of occlusion. Stephen Harriman Long's *Map of the Country Drained by the Mississippi* from 1822 represented the results of field observations over the course of 18 months when Long was in command of an exploratory expedition organized by the War Department in collaboration with the American Philosophical Society. In his discussion of the map's figuration, Haltman links cartographic technique directly to political objectives and argues that the kind of pictorial metaphor in Long's map facilitated US government control over Native American land in the Midwest. Haltman's analysis of Long's transformation of seemingly empty spaces into legible US territory resonates with Appelbaum's investigation into the Colombian Chorographic Commission, in which she considers the representation of the seemingly "floating" nature of Indigenous communities in opposition to the fixity of the state. How, she asks, did nineteenth-century geographers "see" inaccessible areas that they had only partially glimpsed with their own eyes? Using an original 1857 manuscript map of the Province of Casanare, along with related material produced by Agustín Codazzi, she demonstrates how the same territory appeared emptier of inhabitants and, paradoxically, more certain and known as the same map was reduced in size, detail, and color into a printed map for an atlas.

Despite the impression of comprehensive seeing explored in Part I, the vast majority of nineteenth-century cartographic expeditions in the Americas followed singular routes traveled earlier. Their legitimacy came, in part, through this reiterative engagement with lines traced and then retraced on the earth's surface. The four chapters in Part II, "Lines and Tracings," address the notion of the line and its implications, that is, the multiple ways it could be used by individuals and governments, whether to support a rectilinear order on the physical landscape or to challenge that order, as well as to popularize movement and travel.

The section begins with two chapters devoted to perhaps the most consequential and most contested of lines: international borders. Late nineteenth-century survey teams strove to make abstract lines visible, marking, for example, national boundaries with obelisk-shaped monuments, maps, sketches, and images. At times such efforts occurred concurrently. Katherine Morrissey's essay considers this reification of cartographic lines in her focus on both border photography and the construction of obelisks along the US-Mexico border. She examines the shared visual vocabularies of photography and cartography, tracing the emergence of a specific genre of border monument photographs and the manifestation of power and authority in these media. Carla Lois, on the other hand, emphasizes the instability of mapping efforts and the establishment of official lines in her investigation of a turn-of-the-century boundary dispute between Argentina and Chile. Faced with the difficulty of Chilean claims to control over the Andean cordillera, Argentine geographers, Lois argues, deployed photographs of inaccessible Andean peaks as a strategy not only to demonstrate the impossibility of measuring the border but also to discredit existing maps. Focusing on the interplay among topography, map, and image, she reveals how visual devices advance geographic arguments.

The last two chapters of the section turn from cartographic implications of the line to more public and popular concerns that entail cycles of retracing routes and the development of travel tourism. Katherine Manthorne considers an example from the southern part of the American hemisphere, while James Akerman looks northward to Yellowstone, the world's first national park. Manthorne focuses on the long-neglected Maria Graham, a British writer who in 1824 published an account of her visit to Brazil titled *Journal of a Voyage to Brazil and Residence There, during part of the years 1821, 1822, 1823*. Graham's work, which included her own illustrations, presented a domesticated vision of travel in which expeditionary literature becomes transformed into a "feminine domain." Manthorne argues that Graham's incorporation of on-site drawings, which represent the first Brazilian example of the European aesthetic category of the picturesque, helped her contest the commanding male gaze of previous travelers such as Humboldt and establish alternative destinations and routes for future "female eyes." In the following chapter, James R. Akerman focuses on the case of Yellowstone National Park, created in 1872. Surveyor Ferdinand V. Hayden initially explored the Yellowstone region in the company of photographer William Henry Jackson and the painter Thomas Moran. Tourists followed the first explorers into the park so quickly that, as Akerman contends, the lines between processes of expeditionary mapping and tourist mapping became unusually blurred. Not only did tourism and scientific exploration coexist in the park for many decades, but, as the many representations of Yellowstone demonstrate, tourists, artists, and scientists came to appreciate Yellowstone's dramatic features in largely the same terms. Underpinning all these efforts, as Akerman posits, lay a rhetoric of wonder and an acknowledgment of the inscrutability of natural forces.

The final section of the volume, "Art and the Expeditionary Impulse" picks up on the theme of wonder to address how artists imagined expeditionary ideals. The two chapters address what we might call "after-images," artworks inspired by cartographic explorations but produced largely outside official channels and reports. Each chapter focuses on a single artist and their extended experimentation with visualizing the expeditionary across a host of genres. In Chapter 10, Julia B. Rosenbaum focuses on the artistic production of one of the most prominent US landscape artists, Frederic Edwin Church, and argues for the emergence of a mapping aesthetic throughout his significant body of work. She traces this thematic across Church's career from his monumental canvases that were so popular with audiences to the site of Olana, his home and a 250-acre artwork in itself, shaped by the artist to highlight the dramatic views and topography along the Hudson River and across to the Catskill Mountains and the Berkshires. In Chapter 11, Ernesto Capello examines recursive images of the Arctic in expeditionary materials produced in the nineteenth and early twentieth centuries. In particular, he considers the resonances of the "popular sublime" as expressed in the landscape art and ephemera produced by Albert Operti, a self-fashioned Arctic historical painter who served as resident artist for Robert Peary on two of his polar expeditions and continued producing work for a wider public long after the North Pole had been reached.

Through these case studies, the volume underscores the vibrancy and the power of the nineteenth-century expeditionary impulse and particularly the importance of visual documentation in communicating and shaping exploration narratives. At times spectacular, at times disarmingly "scientific," these maps, drawings, prints, architectures, and ephemera grafted meaning onto landscapes near and far. Such visual dissemination not only offered national legitimacy, it also involved the consumption of newly mapped and remapped landscapes. Across all this material, the viewer was ultimately invited to participate in a little piece of the expeditionary experience itself.

Notes

1 Alexander von Humboldt and Aimé Bonpland, *Essay on the Geography of Plants*, ed. Stephen T. Jackson, trans. Sylvie Romanowski (Chicago: University of Chicago Press, 2008): 78.
2 While the Tableau is usually referred to as the "Chimborazo" image, the composition includes a profile and cross-section view of the equatorial Andes, but its total spread crosses the entirety of South America. As Humboldt himself notes, the image generalizes and abstracts distances, such that "the projection of the Cordillera is represented to scale only for heights, but that this same scale cannot be used for Distances" (p. 85). Indeed, the vast Amazonian plains of central and eastern South America are signalled only by the white vertical strip to the far right. See Humboldt, *Essay*, 82–86. See also Karl S. Zimmerer, "Mapping Mountains," in Jordana Dym and Karl S. Offen (eds), *Mapping Latin America: A Cartographic Reader* (Chicago, IL: University of Chicago Press, 2011), 125–130.
3 Sylvie Romanowski, "Humboldt's Pictorial Science: An Analysis of the Tableau physique des Andes et pays voisins," in Humboldt, *Essay*, 163.
4 Humboldt, *Essay*, 79.
5 Authors who have considered the visibilities, invisibilities, and absences in the Tableau include Mary Louise Pratt, *Imperial Eyes: Travel Writing and Transculturation*, 2nd Ed. (London: Routledge, 2007); Rachael Z. Delue, "Humboldt's Picture Theory," *American Art* 31, no. 2 (Summer 2017): 37–40; Romanowski, "Humboldt's Pictorial Science"; Alicia Lubowski-Jahn, "A Comparative Analysis of the Landscape Aesthetics of Alexander von Humboldt and John Ruskin," *British Journal of Aesthetics* 51, no. 3 (2011): 321–333; Georgia Riley De Havenon et al.,

Unity of Nature: Alexander von Humboldt and the Americas, Kerber Culture (New York: Americas Society; 2014). On Caldas's relationship with Humboldt, see Jorge Cañizares-Esguerra, "How Derivative was Humboldt?" in *Nature, Empire, Nation: Explorations of the History of Science in the Iberian World* (Palo Alto, CA: Stanford University Press, 2006), 112–128 and also Mauricio Nieto Olarte, "Caldas, la geografía y la política," in Mauricio Nieto Olarte (ed.), *La obra cartográfica de Francisco José de Caldas* (Bogotá: Universidad de los Andes, 2006), esp. 40–42.

6 Ricardo Padrón, "Cumandá and the Cartographers: Nationalism and Form in Juan León Mera," *Annals of Scholarship* 12, nos. 3/4 (1998): 217–234.

7 John Pickles, *A History of Spaces: Cartographic Reason, Mapping and the Geo-Coded World* (London: Routledge, 2003).

8 A selection of his essays can be found in J.B. Harley, *The New Nature of Maps: Essays in the History of Cartography*, ed. Paul Laxton (Baltimore, MD: Johns Hopkins University Press, 2001). Besides seminal essays such as "Silences and Secrecy: The Hidden Agenda of Cartography in Early Modern Europe," "Maps, Knowledge, and Power," and "Deconstructing the Map," the collection also includes J.H. Andrews's critique of Harley's methodological critique of cartographic positivism. On broader approaches to map history in general, see also Pickles, *History of Spaces*; Denis Wood with John Fels, *The Power of Maps* (New York: Guilford Press, 1992); Denis E. Cogrove (ed.), *Mappings* (London: Reaktion Books, 2001); and Emanuela Casti, *Reality as Representation: The Semiotics of Cartography* (Bergamo: Bergamo University Press-Sestante, 2000).

9 Matthew H. Edney, *Mapping an Empire: The Geographical Construction of British India, 1765–1843* (Chicago, IL: University of Chicago Press, 2009); D. Graham Burnett, *Masters of All They Surveyed: Exploration, Geography, and a British El Dorado* (Chicago, IL: University of Chicago Press, 2001); Raymond B. Craib, *Cartographic Mexico: A History of State Fixations and Fugitive Landscapes* (Durham, NC: Duke University Press, 2004). Craib's book has also inspired other national histories of cartography in Latin America such as Magali M. Carrera, *Traveling from New Spain to Mexico: Mapping Practices of Nineteenth-Century Mexico* (Durham, NC: Duke University Press, 2011) and Nancy P. Appelbaum, *Mapping the Country of Regions: The Chorographic Commission of Nineteenth-Century Colombia* (Chapel Hill, NC: University of North Carolina Press, 2016).

10 Bruno Latour has written extensively about this issue for several decades now. See, for example. Bruno Latour, *Science in Action: How to Follow Scientists and Engineers through Society* (Cambridge, MA: Harvard University Press, 1987); Bruno Latour and Catherine Porter, *We Have Never Been Modern* (Cambridge, MA: Harvard University Press, 1993); Bruno Latour, *Pandora's Hope: Essays on the Reality of Science Studies* (Cambridge, MA: Harvard University Press, 1999). See also Pratt, *Imperial Eyes* and Deborah Poole, *Vision, Race, and Modernity: A Visual Economy of the Andean Image World* (Princeton, NJ: Princeton University Press, 1997).

11 Barbara E. Mundy, *The Mapping of New Spain: Indigenous Cartography and the Maps of the Relaciones Geográficas* (Chicago, IL: University of Chicago Press, 1996).

12 Richard L. Kagan and Fernando Marías, *Urban Images of the Hispanic World, 1493–1793* (New Haven, CT: Yale University Press, 2000).

13 Joni Kinsey, *Creating a Sense of Place: Thomas Moran and the Surveying of the American West* (Washington, DC: Smithsonian Institution Press, 1992). See also

Joni Kinsey et al., *Thomas Moran's West: Chromolithography, High Art, and Popular Taste* (Lawrence, KS: University Press of Kansas, 2013).

14 Robin Earle Kelsey, *Archive Style: Photographs and Illustrations for U.S. Surveys, 1850–1890* (Berkeley, CA: University of California Press, 2007); Kenneth Haltman, *Looking Close and Seeing Far: Samuel Seymour, Titian Ramsay Peale, and the Art of the Long Expedition, 1818–1823* (University Park, PA: Pennsylvania State University Press, 2008); Michael Gaudio, *Engraving the Savage: The New World and Techniques of Civilization* (Minneapolis, MN: University of Minnesota Press, 2008).

15 Susan Schulten, *Mapping the Nation: History and Cartography in Nineteenth-Century America* (Chicago, IL: University of Chicago Press, 2012); Martin Brückner, *The Social Life of Maps in America, 1750–1860* (Williamsburg, VA: Omohundro Institute of Early American History and Culture, 2017).

16 Martin Brückner, *Early American Cartographies* (Chapel Hill, NC: University of North Carolina Press, 2012).

17 See, for example, Peter John Brownlee, Valéria Piccoli, and Georgiana Uhlyarik (eds), *Picturing the Americas: Landscape Painting from Tierra Del Fuego to the Arctic* (New Haven, CT: Yale University Press, 2015) and Katherine Manthorne (ed.), *Traveler Artists: Landscapes of Latin America from the Patricia Phelps de Cisneros Collection* (New York: Colección Patricia Phelps de Cisneros, 2015).

Part I
Seeing and Not Seeing

2 Alexander von Humboldt

The Aesthetic Science of Landscape Pictures

Alicia Lubowski-Jahn

The Prussian naturalist and explorer Alexander von Humboldt (1769–1859, Figure 2.1) expressed two main goals for his Latin American expedition (1799–1804) through the "torrid zone"—the Spanish American colonies of modern-day Venezuela, Colombia, Ecuador, Peru, Mexico, and Cuba. One of these was to describe the forms of tropical nature. He praised the aesthetic merit of the tropical zone above all others on account of its biodiversity and vitality. The other goal was to investigate the New World in terms of the integration and unity of the natural world. He rejected the pursuit of isolated facts in favor of the processes that connected them. On the brink of his American exploration, he wrote: "The discovery of a group of uninhabited islands is less interesting than the knowledge of those laws, which link together a considerable number of insulated facts."[1] Humboldt utilized his interest in the pictorial and the aesthetic to relay in his Americas publications these two main pursuits of his expedition. Artists and draughtsmen meticulously worked Humboldt's field sketches and plant specimens into a total of 1,425 finished black and white and color plates published in the South American volumes.[2] Just as the German artist Albrecht Dürer (1471–1528) expressed that "the measurement of the earth, the waters, and the stars has come to be understood through painting,"[3] Humboldt too would rely heavily on pictures to formulate key scientific ideas about the nature he observed on his Americas journey.

This chapter examines Humboldt's formulation of this second expeditionary goal—the observation of the unity of nature—using the model of painting. It explores the interrelation of painting (particularly landscape painting) and natural landscape in the context of Humboldt's belief in nature's unity, a pioneering mode of ecological thinking.[4] This chapter defines Humboldt's vision of nature's ecological web as an intensely picturesque aesthetic construct. That is to say, Humboldt would rely on pictures and visual analogies to describe his belief in the web of nature in its diversity. To value Humboldt as simply a naturalist whose findings influenced the way artists painted the natural world ignores the fact that Humboldt's own scientific approach was intensely pictorial and aesthetically defined.

Humboldt's use of visual imagery and aesthetic analogy participates in the historically close ties between art and science in the nineteenth century. Figures

Figure 2.1 Friedrich Georg Weitsch (1758–1828). *Portrait of Alexander von Humboldt* (1769–1859). German naturalist and geographer. 1806. Oil on canvas, 126 × 92.5 cm. Inv. A II 828. Photo Credit: bpk Bildagentur / Nationalgalerie, Staatliche Museen zu Berlin / Photo: Klaus Goeken / Art Resource, NY.

such as Charles Willson Peale (1741–1827), John Ruskin (1819–1900), and Frederic Edwin Church (1826–1900) exemplify the pursuit of dual artistic and scientific endeavors.[5] Celebrated naturalists such as Humboldt, Ernst Heinrich Haeckel (1834–1919), and Charles Darwin (1809–82) have been recognized for their artistic influence on landscape painting and other genres. Yet Humboldt was not solely a scientist whose understanding of the natural world influenced landscape painters; rather, the influence was mutual, for the paradigm of the picture of nature itself was a crucial part of his scientific thinking and a motivation for the prolific visual output that accompanied his Americas volumes.

The explorer-scientist promulgated what he termed the field of physical geography (*la géographie physique*): the mapping of abiotic factors (meteorological, geologic, etc.) and the biodistribution of plants and animals in a particular environment as well as the study of the interactions between organisms in their habitat. Plant ecology—the collective spatial interrelation of plant species in an environment—was foremost in his physical geography. A journal entry before his departure for the South American continent stated that, although he aimed to classify new plants and animals and to analyze the phenomena of magnetism, electricity, and heat, his chief purpose was to "study the interaction of all the forces of nature … I must find out about the unity of nature."[6] Humboldt's encyclopedic or cosmological mastery of vast scientific subjects and belief in nature's unity defined him as a *Homo Universalis* and encompassed a generalist, pre-specialized scientific approach.[7] Nature's unity, its harmonious integration or connectivity, is a major theme of Humboldtian science with a far-reaching and long-lasting impact on landscape art and the natural sciences. Humboldt is celebrated today as a forerunner in the science of ecology.

Portrait and Landscape Pictures as Models for Humboldt's Holistic Vision of Nature

Pictures function as metaphors for many of Humboldt's pivotal scientific views of nature. In particular, Humboldt drew on both the portrait and heroic landscape genres as constructs for how one might fathom a natural landscape and express his vision of nature's unity. Certainly Humboldt succeeded in luring explorer-artists to depict his purportedly newfound tropical American landscapes, but a link between pictures and his natural science runs even deeper in his very conception of nature as pictorial.

Pictures function as an analogy for several of Humboldt's contemplations on nature's wholeness. Humboldt's description of vitality (in German *Lebenskraft*) in the allegorical fable "Vital Force or The Rhodian Genius, a Tale" of 1795 relies on a metaphor of a painting, which is titled "The Rhodian Genius."[8] The young Humboldt sought to define the make-up of the "force" behind nature's order, a postulation that he later hedged in favor of physical, rational empirical enquiry. The story describes *Lebenskraft* in non-theological terms.[9] Nature's interrelations are not sustained by a divine force or pantheon of gods but rather by scientific, observable chemical and mechanical rules and operations.[10]

Humboldt uses the metaphor of two paintings (albeit not landscape paintings) in "The Rhodian Genius" tale to describe the vital force that organizes nature's conditions of unity and death.[11] The fable instructs that *Lebenskraft* regulates the diversity of all forms in a state of peaceful unity.[12] As the story explains, these complex subjects represented by two allegorical paintings are only deduced by a wise, old philosopher, whose characterization resembles that of Humboldt.[13] The use of visual arts analogies to define the scientific concept of animating force and the absence of this force indicates the importance of painted images in Humboldt's science.

Humboldt also drew on the model of another type of picture, physiognomy portraiture, to describe nature's patterns, and as a concept for rendering nature's true face or character. Writings on human physiognomy in the late 1760s by the Swiss theologian Johann Caspar Lavater (1741–1801), which infiltrated landscape art, influenced Humboldt's writings on the physiognomy of plants, groups of plants and landscapes (or, in modern-day terms, the biodistribution of plant and animal life), as well as his regard for the depiction of natural scenery in landscape paintings.[14] Humboldt's contact with the Leipzig naturalist, amateur painter, and theoretician Carl Gustav Carus

(1789–1869) further informed his understanding that an artistic landscape could be painted with physiognomic accuracy. Humboldt succinctly states in *Cosmos: A Sketch of the Physical Description* (*Kosmos: Entwurf einer physischen Weltbeschreibung*) (1845–62): "As in different organic beings we recognize a distinct physiognomy, ... so there is also a certain physiognomy of nature exclusively peculiar to each portion of the earth."[15] Whereas Lavater conceived of distilling the essential character of a human being through a physiognomic portrait to establish a link between outward appearances and a human's morality or personality, Humboldt's discipline of physical geography strove to describe the distinctive features of particular regions, above all the American tropics.

Humboldt's experiments in graphic representation, which the geography scholar Anne Marie Claire Godlewska has described as "eloquent graphic arguments about dynamic relationships in space, distributions, and interactions," further visualized the scientist's central interest in the unity of nature and the comparison of phenomena.[16] Humboldt pioneered so-called "vegetation maps," which formulate the interconnection between plant distribution, geographic environment, and physical conditions.[17] Humboldt's graphic portrayal of his new science of plant geography represents a combined effort to register precise measurements visually and to create a reductive formulation (a type of abstraction or silhouette). They represent a kind of fusion between cartography and landscape painting that Edmunds V. Bunkse terms an "artistic geography."[18] The color cross-section of the Chimborazo volcano, published as *Geography of Equatorial Plants: Physical Tableau of the Andes and the Neighboring Countries* in the "Essay on the Geography of Plants" (1805–7), is his boldest attempt to portray the geography of plants (phytogeography) in graphic form (see Figure 1.1 in Chapter 1).

Humboldt's use of graphical images to represent scientific data in this *Tableau physique* is indicative of his intense interest in the visual arts as well as his pursuit of what Sylvie Romanowski has characterized as "an analytical as well as a holistic, visually oriented science."[19] Humboldt had landscape painting in mind as well in the text that accompanied the map, the *Essay on the Geography of Plants*. In the essay, he listed 15 general plant groups "whose aspect is most interesting to the painter of landscapes."[20] Vegetation is also the central protagonist in Humboldt's definition of the aesthetic quality of the tropical zone. In one portion of the Andean image, the schematic features of Chimborazo and neighboring Cotopaxi are depicted as a naturalistic landscape illustration while the other part of the mountain profile charts the Latin names of plants corresponding to their elevation or elevational range. Text columns flanking the image register the vertical scale (in meters and toises) and still more scientific readings taken on site at elevational gradients—including atmospheric, geological, agricultural, and other observations. Cloud layers, sky grades, green vegetation, exposed rock, the snowline, and smoke help define the different botanical and geographic layers of the Andes.[21] The "profile" map of the Andean mountain's ecology conveys the density and range of life in the equatorial tropics across geographic positions.[22] For Hanno Beck, Humboldt's background in mining, accustomed to representing a mine from the side, influenced his innovative profile maps.[23]

Definition of the Ecological Unity as a "Picture of Nature": Classical Ideal Landscape Painting

The science historian Chunglin Kwa has emphasized the novelty of Humboldt's description of the American natural landscape and visualization of plant geography with a "painterly gaze."[24] Humboldt, for example, uses the fine-arts term a "picture of nature" (in German *Naturgemälde*[25] or *Bild der Nature*) to describe an interlinked vision of the world and its phenomena. The scientist succinctly equates the entire realm of the "Cosmos" with a "sole picture of nature":

> The fundamental principle of my work on the Cosmos, as enunciated by me more than 20 years ago, in the French and German lectures I gave at Paris and Berlin, comprehended the endeavor to combine all cosmological phenomena in one sole picture of nature.[26]

This holistic goal of synthesis is also expressed in painterly terminology in Humboldt's *Aspects of Nature*. He writes, for example: "The unbounded riches of Nature occasion an accumulation of separate images; and accumulation disturbs the repose and the unity of impression which should belong to the picture."[27] As in a picture that can combine various elements together in a composition, Humboldt describes the cohesiveness of the natural world.

Just as a natural landscape might evoke certain organizational qualities of pictures, Humboldt was sensitive to the ways in which pictures and other "delineations" of nature were capable of organizing nature. Humboldt's observations on heroic landscape painting highlight the genre's affinity to nature's own organizing mechanisms. He explicitly heralds landscape painting's capacity to condense, compress, and abstract the scale of nature. For Humboldt, the model of the heroic or ideal landscape painting provided the closest analogy for his perception of the natural landscape.

In *Cosmos* Humboldt presents an art-historical review of landscape painting specifically in the context of its scientific objective, its "influence on the study of nature," through an aesthetic motivation and method of describing nature, what he called "delineations of natural scenery."[28] He ranks the classical heroic landscape as the highest expression in the painted landscape genre. For Humboldt, the heroic landscape style achieves a synthesis of "truthful imitation" and "free creation": "The grander style of heroic landscape painting is the combined result of a profound appreciation of nature and this inward process of the mind."[29]

The heroic landscape genre was of presumed classical origin and defined as the visual counterpart of pastoral poetry. The painters Nicolas Poussin (1594–1665), Gaspard Dughet (1613–75), and Claude Lorrain (c.1600–82) were praised as its greatest exponents. In Humboldt's *Personal Narrative of a Journey to the Equinoctial Regions of the New Continent*, he remarked too how the atmospheric conditions observed along the Rio Sipapo (Amazonas, Venezuela) evoked landscape paintings by these artists:

> These vapours, circulating around the rocky ridge, soften its outline, temper the effects of the light, and give the landscape that aspect of calmness and repose, which in nature, as in the works of Claude Lorrain and Poussin, arises from the harmony of forms and colours.[30]

In both *Aspects of Nature* (1808) and *Cosmos* (1847, vol. 2), Humboldt instructs landscape painters on how to combine empirical observation with artistic grandeur as defined by the tradition of the classical heroic landscape.

Humboldt specifies how the contemplation of nature's outward forms through experiential observation merges with an internal reflection on nature, an impression created by the human imagination. Humboldt's instructions for landscape painting maintain a principle of balance between imaginary and observed reality and describe a distillation process, in which only what is most essential should be retained.[31] The process prescribes the execution of firsthand *in situ* sketches of nature followed by a synthesis of these impressions by the artist's imaginative faculties to produce a work of art. Beginning with sketches, which Humboldt emphasizes must be "correctly-drawn," "well-proportioned," "colored," of "a large number," and "separate,"[32] the landscape painter merges the contemplation of nature's outward forms with an internal reflection. Furthermore, he advises that an artist should not use substitutes for direct observation of nature.[33]

The second step in Humboldt's approach was transforming these firsthand, detailed, accurate, and plentiful impressions of different "views" or "characteristics" of nature into a finished composition. Humboldt clearly asserts that the artist does not slavishly imitate nature but rather improves it with his imagination. He describes a process of idealizing landscape through the exercise of the imagination on the direct observation of nature:

> It requires for its development a large number of various and direct impressions, which, when received from external contemplation, must be fertilized by the powers of the mind, in order to be given back to the sense of others as a free work of art. The grander style of heroic landscape painting is the combined result of a profound appreciation of nature and of this inward process of the mind.[34]

Thus, a landscape painting is an abstract totality of partial aspects. Humboldt's description of a landscape painting as an interrelation of the most relevant elements is analogous to his ecological understanding of nature as organisms and habitats harmoniously interacting according to underlying, unifying laws of physical phenomena.

Although it was typical to enlist a draughtsman on a scientific journey, Humboldt did not bring a traveling artist on the American expedition. The earlier voyages of Captain Cook in the Pacific Ocean, the first commencing in 1768,[35] had set a precedent in scientific travel illustration for an empiricist mode of portraying non-European lands and people. Humboldt's representation of tropical American landscape participated in this broader shift from an allegorical to a descriptive view of the non-European world based on direct experience. Yet unlike Captain Cook and this earlier age of circumnavigation centered on the recording of coastal views and charts, Humboldt's inland journey would document the continental interior.

Humboldt's familiarity with the heroic style of landscape combined with a scientific, direct study of natural forms is evident in the group of artists in both Rome and Paris that he ultimately selected to design the illustrations to his publication *Views of the Cordilleras and Monuments of the Indigenous Peoples of the Americas (Vues des Cordillères et monumens des peuples indigènes de l'Amérique)* (1810 and 1814).[36] Unaccompanied by a traveler artist, Humboldt produced his own sketches and relied on other illustrations for *in situ* visual documentation (Figure 2.2). The explorer was well served by the drawing instruction he received in his youth from the Polish-German artist Daniel Chodowiecki (1726–1801). Upon his return to Europe, he commissioned artists to translate his personal sketches and collected data into finished drawings and etchings.

Rather than strict naturalism and measured empiricism, Humboldt's team of artists experimented with an encounter between classicism and American nature and a desire to exalt the American vistas through the heroic style of the classical ideal landscape. This integration of science and the ideal landscape is exemplified by the Tyrolian landscape painter Josef Anton Koch (1768–1839) who contributed three drawings to the publication. Humboldt met the expatriate artist on a visit to Rome in 1805. Koch's drawings are all executed after sketches by Humboldt and indicative of the artist's specific geological expertise, and his mastery of waterfalls and Swiss Alpine scenery (Figure 2.3).

The later tropical landscapes of the American artist Frederic Edwin Church similarly adapt firsthand observation of American nature into an idealized vision. Church's landscapes have been understood as sublime, panoramic landscapes quintessentially expressive of Humboldt's belief in a unified and magnificent natural world. Humboldt's prescription for a heroic landscape validated Church's personal working method, a combination of meticulous on-site sketches enhanced by his creative imagination. Church's vision of the Andes encompassed the geographic contrasts of the vertical Andean ecology that Humboldt had esteemed and depicted in his Mount Chimborazo tableau (Figure 2.4).

Humboldt's exaltation of the biodiverse Andes would beckon scientific travelers and landscape artists to paint and chart its microcosmic vistas. Humboldt championed the landscape genre's ability to capture plant geography—nature's dynamic interrelation of species—in contrast to the fragmented approach of Linnean classification and botanical illustration, with its isolated, uprooted specimens. Darwin, adhering to Humboldt's beliefs, noted in his *Journal of Researches* that "a traveler should be a botanist, for in all views plants form the chief embellishment."[37]

Several nineteenth-century landscapes of tropical rainforests represent an association of precisely rendered, dense plant species in their natural habitats. These plant groupings reflect Humboldt's appreciation of the aesthetic character of mapping vegetation in its zone and of the qualities of individual tropical vegetal forms. Humboldt influenced the artistic styles of several German scientific explorers—including the naturalist and ethnologist Maximilian zu

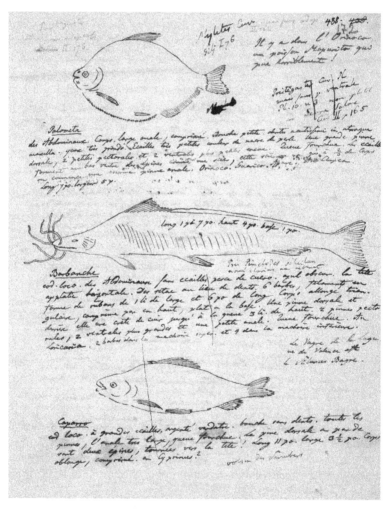

Figure 2.2 Alexander von Humboldt (1769–1859), *Fish*. Sketch with handwritten notes; Formerly from the Staatsbibliothek zu Berlin—Preussischer Kulturbesitz, Dep. 36, Travel Diary IV, fol. 172 recto, now privately owned. Photo Credit: bpk Bildagentur / Private Collection / Photo: Ruth Schacht / Art Resource, NY.

Figure 2.3 Drawn by Joseph Anton Koch (1768–1839) in Rome, on the basis of a sketch by Humboldt. Engraved in Stuttgart by Christian Friedrich Traugott Duttenhofer (1778–1846). *Passage du Quindiu, dans la Cordillère des Andes* (Quindiu Pass in the Cordillera of the Andes). Plate V from Alexander von Humboldt, *Vues des Cordillères et monumens des peuples indigènes de l'Amérique* (Paris: Chez F. Schoell, 1810–13). Private Collection.

Wied-Neuwied (1782–1867), the zoologist Hermann Burmeister (1807–92), and the Polish-born zoologist and naturalist Friedrich Heinrich von Kittlitz (1799–1874).[38] These scientific illustrators recognized their scientific knowledge as an aid in their ability to accurately represent tropical vegetation.[39]

Picturesque Descriptions of American Nature

Although Humboldt, as scientist, more frequently uses the trope of the picturesque to refer to an aesthetic style and a vista that is worthy of the scientific traveler's attention along a journey, he also describes tropical nature that appears like a "picture," i.e., like the artistic mode of representation. In his writings on American culture and nature, there are examples of the scientist comparing natural scenery to visual artistic models (although Humboldt referenced books more often). Notably, the steep and sinuous coastal landscape of the Laguna Grande (or Laguna del Obispo) on the road toward the

Figure 2.4 Frederic Edwin Church (1826–1900). *Study of Mount Chimborazo, Ecuador.* United States, 1857. Brush and oil paint, traces of graphite on paperboard: 344 × 522 mm. Gift of Louis P. Church, 1917-4-1296-b. Photo: Matt Flynn. Photo Credit: Cooper Hewitt, Smithsonian Design Museum / Art Resource, NY.

city of Cumaná (Venezuela) evoked for Humboldt the scenery of Leonardo da Vinci's (1452–1519) *Mona Lisa* painting of about 1503–6:

> There are some pasture grounds at the bottom of the bay. We traced the sinuosities of this arm of the sea, which, like a river, has dug a bed between perpendicular rocks destitute of vegetation. This singular view reminded us of the back-ground of the fanciful landscape, with which Leonardo da Vinci has decorated his famous portrait of Gioconda.[40]

Humboldt also likened the experience of exiting the mouth of the dark Caripe Cave (or Cueva del Guácharo) in Venezuela directly to the view of a "painting":

> We followed the course of the torrent to go out of the cavern. Before our eyes were dazzled by the light of day, we saw, without the grotto, the water of the river sparkling amid the foliage of the trees that concealed it. It was like a picture place in the distance, and to which the mouth of the cavern served as a frame.[41]

Humboldt compared the summit of Mount Chimborazo not only to the serene peaks of Mont Blanc and Monte Rosa but also to an architectural model: Michelangelo's dome of St Peter's Basilica.[42] The majesty, symmetrical perfection, and gleaming snow of the volcanic peak evoked St Peter's spherical shape and white travertine marble. While Humboldt was resolutely secular in his description of nature's grandeur, the spiritual analogy of Mount Chimborazo with the holy site of St Peter's dome likely appealed to Frederic Edwin Church's vision of God revealed in nature in his own renderings of Mount Chimborazo (Figure 2.4).

Humboldt as Art Historian: The Evolution of the Tropical Landscape

In the second volume of *Cosmos*, Humboldt describes the development of the landscape painting tradition in the broader context of descriptions of nature and inducement to travel and study nature firsthand. Along with other arts (such as prose writing, poetry, and landscape gardening) and popular displays (such as parks, panoramas, and daguerreotypes), Humboldt analyzes landscape painting in relation to these arts and as a method of representing natural scenery.

Humboldt's art-historical review of landscape painting is far from purely aesthetic. Indeed, his description of landscape painting extends his argument regarding the link between art and science. Scientific achievements are visible in landscape painting's forms and, reciprocally, the poetic feeling of admiring art inspires the pursuit of scientific investigation. Although this connection between art and science is presented in general terms, Humboldt implicitly champions his own scientific-artistic contribution and geographic discoveries. For Humboldt, the combination of the tropical terrain of his inland Latin American trek and the talent of the young generation of German artists he directly fostered would produce the ideal landscape art.

Humboldt concludes his survey of physiognomic views of tropical vegetation in *Cosmos* with artists of his own generation and nationality, whom he states have outdone the British painter William Hodges (1744–97), who accompanied Cook as draughtsman on the second circumnavigation, and the natural history artist Ferdinand Bauer (1760–1826). Among those who represented Latin American tropical nature, he commends Johann Moritz Rugendas (1802–58), Charles Othon, Frédéric Jean-Baptiste, Comte de Clarac (1777–1847), Ferdinand Bellermann (1814–89), and Eduard Hildebrandt (1818–69) (Figure 2.5).[43] He actively mentored the careers of these artists, understood the weight of his published endorsement, and was sure to mention the strength of the Prussian royal collection in holdings of these artists.[44] It was a collection that he vigorously fostered: "These views of tropical vegetation, which designate the 'physiognomy of plants,' constitute, in the Royal Museum at Berlin, a treasure of art which, owing to its peculiarity and picturesque variety, is incomparably superior to any collection." The artworks' extraordinary representation (in Humboldt's words, "masterly" and on a "grander scale") of the "physiognomy of plants," of "tropical" scenery, and of the "interior" regions of continents not only reinforced a Humboldtian scientific attitude toward nature, but purportedly a personal discovery of a geography that he saw as previously visually "unrepresented."

Figure 2.5 Johann Moritz Rugendas (1802–58). *A rider leads his mule through dense tropical forest.* Oil on board. 1831–4. 30.2 × 20.6 cm. Inv. VIII E.2462. Photo Credit: bpk Bildagentur / Kupferstichkabinett, Staatliche Museen, Berlin / Photo: Volker-H. Schneider / Art Resource, NY.

The visual arts were vital to Humboldt's argument for the value of his expedition as a (scientific) "discovery" of America. The promotion of tropical American landscape painting in Humboldt's project functioned as agent and proof of his scientific and territorial "discovery." For Humboldt, the fact that tropical American habitats had not been previously seen through the European visual arts was testament to the fact that they had not been discovered. His emphasis on the absence of visual iconography of the interior of the American continent, both the lowland tropics and the high Andean tropics, suggested what Europe would see and discover for the first time through his vision and that of a new generation of landscape painters. European chroniclers had illustrated America beforehand but, according to his argument, they had done so in a deficient manner (focusing only on coastal regions and without scientific accuracy). Although not a landscape painter, the portrait and still-life painter Albert Eckhout (1610–65), for example, was heralded by Humboldt as the first European artist to depict tropical American nature with a scientific eye *in situ*.

Humboldt's presentation of a new tropical American repertoire of nature to landscape painters is fundamentally linked to his positioning as a discoverer of *terra incognita*. His belief in the relationship between landscape painting and science as well as his interest in capturing expressly tropical American nature in art is part of a colonialist cartography and imperialist aspirations.[45] The absence of an iconography in European landscape painting that depicted American tropical nature (of the specific kind and place Humboldt witnessed) supported a claim that the scientific explorer was the true discoverer of America. Humboldt created a narrative that discarded Christopher Columbus's first discovery and centuries of European colonization by nations other than Germany and positioned himself as the first to see and represent America accurately. The theme of Humboldt eclipsing Columbus's achievement is evident in nineteenth-century German poetry, Humboldt biographies, Christopher Columbus plays, and Humboldt commemorative portraiture.[46] In the context of Germany's lack of colonization in the Americas and the Latin American independence wars then in progress, Humboldt's promotion of an unseen (and thus undiscovered) South America fed Germany's imperial fantasy.

Conclusion

As we have seen, the metaphor of a landscape painting was integral to Humboldt's scientific conception of a natural landscape, and especially the ecological relationships between its phenomena. Relevant to this interrelation of painting and natural landscape in Humboldt's oeuvre was his sensitivity to landscape painting that does not provide a model or metaphor for natural scenery. In a certain sense, Humboldt reacted to what he understood to be unrepresented by European landscape artists through his impassioned promotion of the iconographic category of tropical American landscape. What he perceived as absent from European landscape painting was equally important to his scientific discourse and discovery as those pictures that accurately captured nature. Humboldt's historical survey of European landscape painting suggests that the lack of a physiognomy of *tropical* nature in its repertoire served to underscore the importance of his personal scientific "discovery" of the American tropics.

In conclusion, Humboldt's concept of ecological unity relied on the model of a picture and was expressed through multiple forms of visual display. Humboldt's Latin American expedition gave him the opportunity to celebrate the beauty of tropical nature as well as to visualize the unity of its biodiversity. For Humboldt, a unitary vision of the natural world could be conveyed by the pictorial representation of landscape. The Prussian scientist's promotion of landscape painting, in particular scenes of tropical American vistas, was rooted in a belief in the potential of landscape painting to represent a holistic view of several unities—the unity of organisms in ecosystems, of nature and human life, of art and science, and of the entire cosmos. Just as the twentieth century saw the waxing of support for Humboldt's science, his philosophy of interconnected unity resonates in today's globalized age.[47]

Notes

1 Alexander von Humboldt, *Personal Narrative of Travels to the Equinoctial Regions of the New Continent during the Years 1799–1804*, trans. Helen Maria Williams, 7 vols. (Philadelphia, PA: M. Carey, 1815 [orig. pub. 1807]), 74.

2 Douglas Botting, *Humboldt and the Cosmos* (New York: Harper & Row, 1973), 213.

3 Christopher S. Wood, *Albrecht Altdorfer and the Origins of Landscape* (London: Reaktion Books, 1993), 46.

4 The scholars Aaron Sachs, Laura Dassow Walls, Malcolm Nicolson, Donald Worster, Kathryn Whitford, Margarita Bowen, and others have characterized Humboldt's interdisciplinary mode of scientific exploration as a precursor to ecological philosophy. The science of ecology postdates Humboldt's lifetime. The term ecology (from *oikos*, the Greek root meaning "house") was coined in 1866 by the German evolutionary biologist and natural philosopher Ernst Heinrich Haeckel (1834–1919), a follower of Darwin. Derived from Carolus Linnaeus's descriptions of the "economy of nature" in the *Systema Naturae* (1735) and the essay "The Oeconomy of Nature" (1749), ecology describes the interaction and relationship of organisms and their environment. Haeckel describes his scientific specialty in 1866 as "the comprehensive science of the relationship of the organism to the environment" and in 1885 as "the study of the reciprocal relationship between organisms and their environment." Ernst Haeckel, *Generelle Morphologie der Organismen*, 2 vols (Berlin: G. Reimer, 1866), 2: 286–287. For various definitions of ecology close to Haeckel's see S.K. Agarwal, *Fundamentals of Ecology* (New Delhi: Ashish Publishing House, 2008), 1–2.

5 Eugene C. Hargrove, "The Historical Foundations of American Environmental Attitudes," in Allen Carlson and Sheila Lintott (eds), *Nature, Aesthetics, and Environmentalism: From Beauty to Duty*(New York: Columbia University Press, 2008), 32. Ruskin appreciated Church's landscapes and commented not on the Cotopaxi volcano itself, but on Church's depiction of clouds: "Church's Cotopaxi is an interesting picture. He can draw clouds as few men can, though he does not know yet what painting means, and I suppose never will, but he has a real gift of his own ..." John Ruskin and Charles Eliot Norton, *Letters of John Ruskin to Charles Eliot Norton* (Whitefish, MT: Kessinger Publishing, 2006), 151.

6 Humboldt to his friend Karl Freisleben, June 1799?, in *In the Beat of a Heart: Life, Energy, and the Unity of Nature*, ed. John Whitfield (Washington, DC: National Academies Press, 2009), 209. Quoted also in Gerard Helferich, *Humboldt's Cosmos: Alexander Von Humboldt and the Latin American Journey that Changed the Way We See the World* (New York: Gotham Books, 2004), 23.

7 Susan Faye Cannon, *Science in Culture: The Early Victorian Period* (New York: Science History Publications, 1978).

8 Alexander von Humboldt, "Die Lebenskraft oder der rhodische Genius, eine Erzahlung," *Die Horen*, part 5 (1795): 90–96.

9 Throughout the nineteenth century, vitalist positions (expressed in terms such as "anima," "entelechy," "soul," "archeus," and "vital force"), in contrast to biochemical observations and reactions (such as catalysis, enzymes), continued to engage the advance of organic chemistry and biochemistry.

10 Humboldt's "forces" behind nature's order were never defined in theological terms, and readers certainly speculated on his religious beliefs and whether or not he was an atheist. Humboldt's theological standing and ambiguity in defining the "hand" behind nature's order were ignited by the publication *Cosmos: A Sketch of a Physical Description of the Universe.*

11 The tale first appeared in the short-lived literary journal edited by Friedrich Schiller (1759–1805), *The Horae (Die Horen)* in 1795, and again was published as a chapter in the 2nd edition of *Aspects of Nature* (1826). It was first translated in English in 1849. See Alexander von Humboldt, *Aspects of Nature in Different Lands and Different Climates*, trans. Mrs. Sabine, vol. II (London: Longman, Brown, Green, and Longmans, 1849).

12 Humboldt's chemical and electrophysiological experiments also informed his writings on the "vitality" (*Vitalität*), "excitability" (*Reizbarkeit*), and "life force" (*Lebenskraft*) behind nature, which appears as a leitmotif in his writings. Humboldt studied animal bioelectricity, discovered by the Italian physicist Alessandro Volta (1745–1827) and the Italian anatomist and physician Luigi Galvani (1737–98), and published the pivotal *Experiments on the Stimulated Muscle and Nerve Fiber with Thoughts about the Chemical Process of Life in the Animal and Plant World (Versuche über die gereizte Muskel- und Nervenfaser nebst Vermuthungen über den chemischen Process des Lebens in der Thier-und Pflanzenwelt)*, 2 vols (Berlin: Heinrich August Rottman and Posen: Decker, 1797) and "Observations on the electric eel of the new world" ("Observations sur l'anguille électrique [Gymnotus electricus, Lin.] du nouveau continent") (1808).

13 The philosopher's royal patronage and profession as a natural philosopher brings to mind Humboldt himself: "yet the philosopher found that the proximity of princes takes even from men of the greatest intellectual power part of their spirit and their freedom. He devoted himself unceasingly to the study of natural things, their forces or powers, the origin of animals and plants, and the harmonious laws in accordance with which the heavenly bodies, as well as the grains of hail and the flakes of snow, assume their distinctive forms." (Humboldt, *Aspects*, 2: 254).

14 Lavater's work *Physiognomical Fragments, for the Promotion of the Knowledge and Love of Mankind (Physiognomische Fragmente zur Beförderung der Menschenkenntnis und Menschenliebe)* was first published in German (Leipzig: Weidmann & Reich, 1775–8). Reissued in several editions, the popular scientific text was translated into French in 1781; followed by a 1789 English edition, which was illustrated by the Anglo-Swiss painter J.H. Fuseli (1741–1825). Editions of Lavater's writings circulated in England, Germany, and France, and exercised particular influence upon the work of notable scientists like Franz Joseph Gall (1758–1828), who studied phrenology, Carl Gustav Carus (1789–1869), who studied craniology, and Goethe, who pioneered studies in osteology and morphology (the word "morphologie" was invented by Goethe). Ellis Shookman, "Pseudo-Science,

Social Fad, Literary Wonder: Johann Caspar Lavater and the Art of Physiognomy," in Ellis Shookman (ed.), *The Faces of Physiognomy: Interdisciplinary Approaches to Johann Caspar Lavater* (Columbia, SC: Camden House, 1993), 5. John Neubauer, "Organic Form in Romantic Theory: The Case of Goethe's Morphology," in Larry H. Peer (ed.), *Romanticism across the Disciplines*(Lanham, MD: University Press of America, 1998), 207–230.

15 Humboldt, *Cosmos*, 2: 97.

16 Anne Marie Claire Godlewska, *Geography Unbound: French Geographic Science from Cassini to Humboldt* (Chicago, IL: University of Chicago, 1999), 253. For further reading on Humboldt and geography see Godlewska, "From Enlightenment Vision to Modern Science? Humboldt's Visual Thinking," in David N. Livingstone and Charles W. J. Withers, *Geography and Enlightenment* (Chicago, IL: University of Chicago Press, 1999), 236–280.

17 Years later, in an essay of 1817, Humboldt developed the idea of a "climatic system" and "isothermal" lines measuring mean variations in atmospheric temperature. As in the comparison of different climates of the globe by distinguishing principle vegetation patterns in *Aspects of Nature*, Humboldt would later measure meteorological distinctions with "isolines" to define different regions: "comparisons among the climates of eastern and western shores of continents and among coastal, continental, and island climates." Humboldt, "Sur des lignes isothermes et de la distribution de la chaleur sur le globe," *Memoires de physique et de chemie de la Societe d'Arcueil* 5 (1817): 102–112. Quoted in Theodore S. Feldman, "Late Enlightenment Meteorology," in Tore Frängsmyr, J.L. Heilbron, and Robin E. Rider (eds), *The Quantifying Spirit in the 18th Century* (Berkeley, CA: University of California Press, 1990), 177.

18 Bunkse, "Humboldt and an Aesthetic Tradition in Geography," 127–146.

19 Alexander von Humboldt and Aimé Bonpland, *Essay on the Geography of Plants,* with a new introduction by Stephen T. Jackson, trans. Sylvie Romanowski (Chicago, IL: University of Chicago Press, 2009), 173.

20 Ibid., 73.

21 Mary Louise Pratt's comparison of Humboldt's cross-section of Chimborazo with a sixteenth-century illustration of the Cerro de Potosí also highlights the pervasive association of wealth and paradisiacal abundance with the microcosmic Andes. Mary Louise Pratt, *Imperial Eyes: Travel Writing and Transculturation* (London: Routledge, 1992), 129. Jorge Cañizares-Esguerra has further explored the origin of this idea of an Edenic, microcosmic Andes as non-European. See Cañizares-Esguerra, *Nature, Empire, and Nation: Explorations of the History of Science in the Iberian World* (Stanford, CA: Stanford University Press, 2006), 112–128.

22 Following Humboldt's example of an interdisciplinary historical and geographic survey, the Peruvian Mariano Felipe Paz Soldán (1821–86) also published geographic atlases (1865 and 1888) and historical studies of Peru and the Republic of Argentina (including modern-day Uruguay and Paraguay). Mariano Felipe Paz Soldán, *Geographic Atlas of Peru (Atlas geográfico de la República del Perú)* (Paris: Libreria de Augusto Durand, 1865), sponsored by the Peruvian government of Ramón Castilla, was illustrated with 45 maps and city plans and 23 architectural, city, and ethnographic lithographic views. The *Atlas* also included a large folio thematic map "Cuadro General de Alturas Comparativas del Peru," which was clearly influenced by Humboldt's thematic distribution maps and comparative geography.

23 Hanno Beck, "Alexander von Humboldt's Contribution to Cartography," in Wolfgang-Hagen Hein (ed.), *Alexander von Humboldt: Life and Work* (Ingelheim am Rhein, Germany: C. H. Boehringer Sohn, 1987), 239–248.

24 Chunglin Kwa, "Alexander von Humboldt's Invention of the Natural Landscape," *The European Legacy* 10, no. 2 (2005): 149.

25 Nicolaas A. Rupke notes the insufficiency of E. C. Otté's English translation of *Naturgemälde* as "delineations of nature" rather than as "painting of nature" in her edition of *Cosmos*. Whereas my analysis in this chapter highlights Humboldt's use of the fine arts metaphor of the "picture of nature" in relation to his own ecological philosophy, Rupke has emphasized Humboldt's use of poetic constructions as a tool for popularizing science. That is to say, Humboldt's aestheticism can also be regarded as motivated by a desire to bring science to a broad audience. Alexander von Humboldt, *Cosmos: A Sketch of a Physical Description of the Universe*, with a new introduction by Nicolaas A. Rupke, trans. E. C. Otté (Baltimore, MD: Johns Hopkins University Press, 1997), 1: xiv. Michael Dettelbach has similarly commented on Humboldt's sensitivity to the popular culture of his day in the second volume of *Cosmos*, noting Humboldt's evaluation of novel public entertainments, such as panoramas and dioramas, in relation to the promotion of science. Ibid., 2: xxvii.

26 Humboldt, *Cosmos*, 3: 6–7.

27 Humboldt, *Aspects*, 1: viii.

28 In his circular reasoning on the mutual reinforcement of landscape (art) and science, Humboldt falls one step short of the English painter John Constable (1776–1837), who proclaimed that landscape painting in itself was a branch of science. See Beryl Hartley, "The Living Academies of Nature: Scientific Experiment in Learning and Communicating the New Skills of Early Nineteenth-Century Landscape Painting," *Studies in the History and Philosophy of Science* 27, no. 2 (June 1996): 149–180.

29 Humboldt, *Cosmos*, 2: 94–95.

30 Alexander von Humboldt, *Personal Narrative of a Journey to the Equinoctial Regions of the New Continent*, trans. Helen Maria Williams (New York: AMS Press, 1966), 5: 44.

31 Humboldt, *Aspects*, 2: 29.

32 Humboldt, *Cosmos*, 2: 95.

33 Humboldt characterizes cultivated nature as misleading: "The deceptive aid of hot-house forms and so-called botanical delineations." Ibid.

34 Ibid.

35 Cook was commissioned by the Royal Society of London to undertake three journeys with the main objectives of recording the transit of the planet Venus around the Sun, locating the mythical continent of Australia (Terra Australis), and discovering the Northwest Passage. The first voyage was undertaken between 1768 and 1771, the second between 1772 and 1775, and the third between 1776 and 1779.

36 Humboldt describes his ambition that the imagery in *Views of the Cordilleras* will ignite in others a desire to travel to America:

> "I shall think I have accomplished my purpose, if the feeble sketches contained in this work should lead other travellers, friends of the arts, to visit the regions which I traversed, and to retrace accurately those stupendous scenes, to which the Old Continent offers no resemblance."

Alexander von Humboldt, *Researches Concerning the Institutions and Monuments of the Ancient Inhabitants of America. With Description & Views of some of the most Striking Scenes in the Cordilleras,* trans. Helen Maria Williams, 2 vols (London: Longman, Hurst, Rees, Orme & Brown, J. Murray & H. Colburn, 1814), 1: 41.

37   Darwin draws on a musical metaphor to describe a vision of nature's totality in its diversity that is characteristically Humboldtian: "there is a growing pleasure in comparing the character of the scenery in different countries, which to a certain degree is distinct from merely admiring its beauty. It depends chiefly on acquaintance with the individual parts of each view: I am strongly induced to believe that, as in music, the person who understands every note will, if he also possesses a proper taste, more thoroughly enjoy the whole, so he who examines each part of a fine view, may also thoroughly comprehend the full and combined effect. Hence, a traveller should be a botanist, for in all views plants form the chief embellishment." Charles Darwin, *The Voyage of the Beagle (Journal of Researches, 1845),* ed. Leonard Engel (New York: Doubleday, 1962), 500.

38   Renate Löschner and Birgit Kirschstein-Gamber, *Viagem ao Brasil do Principe Maximiliano de Wied-Neuwied* (Petrópolis, Brazil: Kapa Editorial, 2001), 2: 12–13, 15, 41.

39   Kittlitz, who participated in a Russian expedition to the Pacific Ocean, authored *Memoires of a Trip through Russian America, Micronesia, and Kamtchatka (Denkwürdigkeiten einer Reise nach dem Russischen Amerika, nach Mikroneisien und durch Kamtschatka),* 2 vols (Gotha, Germany: Justus Perthes, 1858).

40   Humboldt, *Personal Narrative* (1966), 3: 22.

41   Ibid., 3: 136.

42   Humboldt heralded Chimborazo's majesty by likening its appearance to St Peter's dome: "The granitic summits are flattened hemispheres; the trappean porphyry forms slender cupolas. Thus on the shore of the South Sea, after the long rains of winter, when the transparency of the air has suddenly increased, we see Chimborazo appear like a cloud at the horizon; it detaches itself from the neighbouring summits, and towers over the whole chain of the Andes, like that majestic dome, produced by the genius of Michael Angelo, over the antique monuments, which surround the Capitol." (Humboldt, *Researches,* 1: 239).

43   Broadening his geographic scope, Humboldt also did not fail to mention an artist representing North American territory. In a footnote (in the category of "fidelity" to North American nature), he praises drawings and the aquatint engravings by the Swiss artist Karl Bodmer (1809–93) in Maximilian zu Wied's *Travels in the Interior of North America 1832–1834* (1839–41). Bodmer's representation of the "interior" of North America can also be seen as indebted to Humboldt's promotion of inland scientific exploration and survey. The Polish-born German artist and naturalist Heinrich von Kittlitz (1799–1874) is mentioned in a broader geographic context of exploration. Humboldt, *Cosmos,* 2: 92–93.

44   Ibid.

45   The idea of a landscape view or a map as a record of geographical prospecting and a delineation of European colonial dominion is well developed in the writings of Mary Louise Pratt and D. Graham Burnett. Mary Louise Pratt, *Imperial Eyes: Travel Writing and Transculturation* (London: Routledge, 1992). D. Graham Burnett, *Masters of All They Surveyed: Exploration, Geography, and a British El Dorado* (Chicago, IL: University of Chicago Press, 2000).

46   Susanne Zantop, *Colonial Fantasies: Conquest, Family, and Nation in Precolonial Germany, 1770–1870* (Durham, NC: Duke University Press, 1997), 168–185.

47   For speculation on Humboldt's dismissal in the twentieth century and his resurrection in the twenty-first, see Laura Dassow Walls, "The Search for Humboldt," *Geographical Review* 96, no. 3 (July 1, 2006): 473–475.

3 Triangulating the View
Art and the Great Surveys of the American West in the 1870s

Joni L. Kinsey

The voluminous visual imagery from nineteenth-century federal surveys of the American West is daunting, encompassing a myriad of expeditions that traversed a vast terrain, included scores of individuals, and produced thousands of images depicting hundreds, if not thousands, of sites through a wide range of different media. Even focusing on one of the more well-documented locations can entail looking at maps, topographical outline sketches, finely rendered drawings, photographs of several sizes, stereographic views, heliotypes, lithographed and wood engraved illustrations published in disparate government reports and popular publications, chromolithographs, and paintings in watercolor and oil, from intimately scaled scenes to truly monumental canvases. The effect is kaleidoscopic both in the array of media and the shifting points of view. Coupled with the extensive survey reports that address everything from major land forms to the composition of soil, and cover a temporal range extending from the landscape's primordial origins to their future potential for an expanding nation, these materials offer a remarkably thorough portrayal of the western territories of the United States during the formative era of expansion. No single view or individual report could encompass the vast space and all of its offerings, but multiple representations suggest the richness of the whole.

Even with the recognition that different perspectives are fundamental to the process of assessing an enormous, multifaceted terrain, the sheer number and variety of the nineteenth-century survey images discourage attempts to deal with them comprehensively. The concept of *triangulation*, however, a basic tenet of topographical surveying, can help reconcile the uniqueness, diversity, and cumulative impact of these myriad representations. Not unlike the central notion in the American motto *e pluribus unum* ("out of many, one"), triangulation offers a way of understanding the relationships of the images and their collaborative construction of a comprehensive perspective.

One of Carleton Watkins's photographs from the 1870 Clarence King survey (Figure 3.1) seems almost a visual allegory of triangulation. The photograph depicts three men, one lounging in the foreground, another with his back turned to us, painting a landscape just inside a makeshift tent, and a third peering through a surveyor's transit that is pointed away from the others' line of sight, the man's legs mirroring the tripod upon which his instrument rests.

Figure 3.1 Carleton Watkins (1829–1916), *Expedition Camp,* Mount Shasta, 1870, photograph courtesy of the Department of Special Collections, Stanford Libraries. MSS Photo 405, Amy White Photo Album, p. 68.

Immediately above, balanced on a wagon just beyond the split rail fence, is another tripod, possibly supporting a camera or a draped surveying instrument, and curiously commanding the apex of the composition. There it reiterates the splayed legs supporting the transit just below, and more subtly those of the easel that supports the painting to the right.

The three men, three tripods with their trios of legs, the triangular tent, and even the conical forms of the evergreens in the background pepper the image with pyramids, trios, and triangles. It is a scene of looking, seeing, and transcribing, of locating, identifying, and conveying. The two men at work, and the draped device above, are three elements that transform terrain into comprehensible pictorial representations. Added to this more invisibly, of course, is the photographer who has captured this scene, standing behind the lens through which we see. The lounging man seems at rest, but at the same time is preoccupied with watching, thinking, and reflecting as he joins his companions in the conceptual process of surveying; he is a kind of Emersonian muse who personifies the triad of the knowing *I*, the seeing *eye*, and the affirming *aye*, a visible surrogate for us, the viewers, who join the visual team and their work of perception, representation, and interpretation.

The tripartite configurations in Watkins's photograph, each representing a different mode of graphic interpretation of the western terrain, embody the essential principle of surveying and mapping, the spatial and visual process of triangulation. The painter, topographer, and the camera demonstrate the triangulation of visual assessment, assembling information for three different modes of graphic representation that translate the facts of the terrain into pictorial media from different points of view. Each provides unique, albeit limited information to viewers far from the scene, but together their varied vantages provide a fuller portrayal of their subject.

Triangulation in topographical surveying enables accurate measurements across large expanses by first ascertaining the distance between two separate stations and then sighting a third through a transit or theodolite to determine the angles of each of their stations to that distant point. With the distance between the two initial stations and their angles to the far site established, relatively simple geometric calculations can figure the distance to the third position. A series of triangulations can accurately measure an enormous area.[1] "Plane table" surveying also employs triangulation of fixed sites, both near and far, through a related but less technological and mathematical method of mapmaking. Surveyors draw scaled maps and site plans using a stable, level board and a simple device called an alidade that allows them to "sight" distant landmarks and make corresponding marks on paper that are based in the triangular relationships of those geographical features. The marks are then connected by lines that create a diagram.[2] Triangulation measurement and plane table surveying were jointly employed throughout the nineteenth century, and along with elevation and section drawings of vertical features and strata, resulted in a far easier and more accurate, systematic, and comprehensive mapping of the American continent than would have been otherwise possible. Triangulation as a practical method was fundamental to this process of making the landscape comprehensible.

The technique of triangulation in land surveying originated in the sixteenth century when mathematical principles were introduced to improve more rudimentary processes of physically measuring terrain with ropes, chains, and poles.[3] It was not systematically utilized in either Europe or America until the early–mid-nineteenth century when it developed into a precise science that, when allied with drawing techniques, could provide scaled diagrams (either maps or site plans) of uncharted territory.[4] But as new technologies during the same period expanded the possibilities for both image making and the dissemination of images, a metaphorical idea of triangulation also emerged, one that used different viewpoints embodied in multiple types of portrayals to gain a fuller understanding of that terrain. Since that time, especially after World War II, triangulation has been recognized as a methodological approach in a variety of disciplines, in which a range of perspectives help "to map out, or explain more fully, the richness and complexity … [of a subject] by studying it from more than one standpoint."[5] Seen in this regard, triangulation is no less critical metaphorically than it was practically to the visual work of nineteenth-century American western federal surveys. Some of their imagery was literally produced through the systematic process of triangular land surveying, but *all* of it was part of a larger process that presented the West in multiple visual formats and led to a more complete understanding of the region.

As the historian of science Martin Rudwick has explained, methods and concepts for studying the earth that emerged in the nineteenth century were not only augmented by but "perhaps made possible" by visual imagery. "Geology," he writes,

> involved the visual representation of a far wider range of different kinds of phenomena than other sciences: not only specimens that could be sorted in a "cabinet" or museum, but also the configuration of topography, and the penetration of that topography to form a three-dimensional picture of the structure of the earth's crust. As the science emerged, even that structural goal became inadequate, and the causal and temporary interpretation of the observed structural configurations required—*and was perhaps made possible by*—the development of ever more abstract, formalized, and theory-lade modes of representation. About 1840, these forms of visual communication in geology no longer functioned as supplements to verbal description and verbal concepts; still less were they merely decorative in function. They had become an essential part of an integrated visual-and-verbal mode of communication.[6]

Thus by the middle of the nineteenth century written descriptions and even maps were considered insufficient for thoroughly or definitively presenting the complexity of land; more and different types of diagrams and views were required to provide a general sense of the terrain and to develop in-depth understanding of it.[7] As the 1870 *Manual of Topography and Text-Book of Topographical Drawing for the Officers of the Army and Navy, Civil Engineers, Academies, Colleges, and Schools of Science* made clear, "even the best description of a terrain could give no satisfaction without some kind of illustration," and "Such representation shows the characteristics of a country at a glance. They are finished in less time than a good description ... [and] they explain and display the representation more exactly and comprehensively than a mere word could do."[8]

When in 1806 Lewis and Clark returned from their three-year exploration of the Louisiana Purchase, the potential for triangulation, either technically or metaphorically was not yet fully understood in the United States. President Thomas Jefferson had provided an exhaustive list of information he desired about the territory, and the Corps of Discovery brought back a wealth of specimens in response to his instruction, but their written accounts were meager in comparison to later expeditions, the maps rudimentary, and the party had no artist to make a pictorial record of the sights they encountered.[9] Recognizing these deficiencies, subsequent federal expeditions included traditional visual artists and eventually photographers, along with survey cartographers and topographical draftsmen (who employed the techniques of scientific triangulation in their work) to make an array of images of the regions they traversed. Subsequently these views were published in increasingly elaborate illustrated government expedition reports and made available to the general public through an array of books, magazines, photographic portfolios, stereographic sets, and art exhibitions, adding significantly to perceptions of the West in an era of critical change and expansion.

One of the most important factors in the visual productivity of nineteenth-century American federal surveys was the development of the Corps of Topographical Engineers, successors to the Revolutionary era's Topographical Corps that was established as an autonomous organization within the Army in 1838. Responding to a rising demand for roads, canals, navigable waterways, as well as comprehensive information about new territories, the Corps implemented a scientific system of topographical surveying and recordkeeping that placed a high value on visual imagery.[10] It utilized that system in many ways, but most notably in what has been called the "Great Reconnaissance," a series of ambitious surveys of the West throughout the mid-1800s, most of which were staffed by personnel specially trained in surveying, cartography, topographical drafting, and art by the United States Military Academy at West Point, New York.[11]

Because military engineering was a key component of West Point training, technical drawing had been taught since the academy's founding in 1802, but with the appointment in 1834 of painter Robert Walter Weir (1803–89) art became even more important in training the Corps of Topographical Engineers.[12] An accomplished painter and member of the National Academy of Design, Weir taught at West Point until 1867, supervising a rigorous curriculum in which art was taught in conjunction with surveying and trigonometry, and cadets were required to attend two hours of classes every day in "the art of shading and finishing geometrical figures with India ink, sketches from nature, and elements of topography with the pen and pencil, and with India ink and colors."[13] An important textbook was *A Treatise on Topographical Drawing* (1837) by Seth Eastman, a career army officer and noted western painter who taught art alongside Weir at the academy from 1833–41.[14] Filled with diagrams and technical descriptions for creating topographical drawings through the principles of triangulation, the book was one of the first on the subject in the United States, and as its introduction explains, it was designed to "aid in establishing a uniform and permanent system of topography in this country."[15]

As a later West Point report noted, "appointments to the Corps of Topographical Engineers were … occasionally made according to proficiency in drawing," and over the century their surveys were accompanied by greater numbers of artists, demonstrating the Corps's interest in and reliance on a wide range of visual documentation.[16] Publications reporting on the Corps's western expeditions were increasingly illustrated not only with maps and technical topographical drawings but also with rendered landscape views of impressive artistic value as well as practical usefulness. Dozens of these publications were issued, but especially voluminous are the 12 tomes of the Pacific Railroad Survey reports from 1853, which include over 700 illustrations, including lithographed scenes of the West by some 15 artists who accompanied the four expeditions that comprised the survey.[17] The lavishness of such publications was sometimes controversial; congressmen objected to the cost and what they regarded as frivolous art in documentary reports. As one representative argued on the House floor, "Elegant views of scenery ... have no business in Government publications and ought not be sanctioned."[18] To refute such critiques survey leaders were careful to emphasize the *scientific* importance of the plates, a strategy with its own legitimacy but also one that rationalized the sheer pleasure the illustrations provided. As the explorer George Gibbs advised his friend Henry Schoolcraft before he embarked on an extensive study of Native Americans,

> Make your reports to each Session upon the material & the tangible, and above all things have them full of plates. Congress will print them of course & pay for the engraving without writhing ... So long as those devils can count on an illustrated work every session, so long will they make the appropriation ...[19]

Many developments during the period of the Great Reconnaissance contributed to the surveys' increasing interest in imagery and its dissemination. Innovations in paper manufacturing, steam-driven presses, and plate-making techniques lowered costs for illustrated publications.[20] The invention of lithography around 1800 had introduced a new, inexpensive reproductive technology, and the rise of wood engraving by the 1850s provided another. John Charles Frémont took quick advantage of the 1839 invention of photography on his initial expedition in 1842, the first of many federal surveys that would rely on the camera to augment more traditional landscape views and maps. This practice only increased as photographic processes were refined and became better suited to fieldwork and image reproduction after 1860.[21] Lending the exciting addition of color to published reports (although some had included hand-colored illustrations all along), was chromolithography, a complex method of color printing that was in common use in the United States by mid-century. Although expensive, it was used in some of the more elaborate federal survey publications by the 1870s, both for landscape scenes and complex maps.[22]

Just as important as these technological innovations in image making and reproduction, the art world in the United States was maturing during the nineteenth century. New art academies, museums, and galleries in major cities accompanied a concerted emphasis on landscape as a leading subject for paintings, and the number of accomplished painters who could captivate viewers with their portrayals of American scenery increased accordingly. About the same time, at mid-century, the commercial popular press began publishing a host of illustrated magazines and books, some of which included art that had originated in the western surveys. The venues for different types of imagery were increasing rapidly, offering national and international audiences views of landscapes beyond their immediate experience.

Of all the visual work of the nineteenth-century federal surveys, the imagery that emanated from the post-Civil War "Great Surveys" (the expeditions that succeeded the Corps of Topographical Engineers in surveying the West) was by far the most varied, accomplished, and influential.[23] Led by civilian geologists Clarence King, Ferdinand Hayden, John Wesley Powell, and Lt. George Wheeler, these undertakings were multi-year endeavors that ranged over a broad expanse of the American West from 1867 to 1879 and produced a truly startling array of visual results, from colorful maps, topographical drawings, and large-scale photographs, to some of the most important land-scape paintings of the era.[24] Studying even one of the surveys in any depth is challenging since each ranged over an enormous expanse of territory during a dozen years, utilized the services of shifting personnel, and produced an array of imagery in varied formats that were published in different venues and often unsystematically archived. Tracking the expedition itineraries, locating images for each location and occasion, sorting through a dizzying amount of accompanying information and scholarship, and then interpreting the intriguing relationships within and among the visual objects and their creators can feel like a parallel, but entirely different kind of exploration, one that traverses time and space, idea and image, science and art, in a host of fascinating, but sometimes bewildering ways.

This plethora of pictures takes on new meaning, however, when regarded as a whole seen from many angles. Like the pre-Civil War expeditions by the Corps of Topographical Engineers, the Great Surveys utilized scientific tri-angulation methods for ascertaining distances, making accurate maps, and constructing topographical sketches, but they were also engaged in an even more elaborate mode of triangulating as they assembled a rich constellation of visual material. Recognizing that each type of image could represent only a limited dimension of the larger subject, the survey leaders wisely relied on the multivalent synergism of allied triangulated views. Part of this emphasis was undoubtedly essential, as Rudwick explained, to the actual science involved, one reliant on different visual methods for recording geological and geograph-ical data, but it was also due in part to the fact that the Great Surveys were vying with each other for annual congressional appropriations to fund their work, and spectacular visual imagery was useful in making those appeals and in eliciting public support for their efforts.

All of the Great Surveys included multiple view makers; some remain well known and others have been almost completely forgotten. Some were remark-ably talented and others more limited in their abilities. Some were regular fed-eral employees, a few were guest artists who traveled with the expeditions only for short periods, and others were post-expedition artists who transformed fieldwork into publishable form.[25] Their images range in type, style, format, and aesthetic quality, but their contributions to the impact of the Great Surveys was prodigious, especially when regarded, as they were intended to be, as a

Figure 3.2 Gilbert Thompson, *Colorado Canyon, Arizona, Wheeler Survey*, 1872, graphite on paper. Courtesy of the US Geological Survey. https://library. usgs.gov/photo/#/item/51ddc28de4b0f72b44720c09

disparate yet integrated whole, offering a multi-dimensional perspective on a vast and even more multi-dimensional subject.

The theoretical implications of the issues of point of view and vantage lie beyond this study, but scholars are beginning to note the significance of these in western art, what Kenneth Haltman has called "looking close and seeing far," and which Robin Kelsey has described as "archive style."[26] But the connections of these issues to triangulation have been overlooked, even when they are a literal part of the art itself. Some Great Survey sketches, for example, offer visible evidence of their connections to the technical process, as in Gilbert Thompson's view of Colorado Canyon from the 1872 Wheeler expedition (Figure 3.2). The sketch is titled, numbered, and inscribed "SW" followed by "The Elbow," and "215°," enabling the drawing to be paired with a topographical map or at least field notes with the same coordinates to provide a panoramic perspective of the site.[27] Sometimes such sketches were more elaborate, as in John Weyss's view, *El Vado de los Padres, Colorado River,* also from the Wheeler expedition (Figure 3.3). Complete with three triangulation notations and rendered more thoroughly than contour notation, these sorts of drawings provided both technical and aesthetic information and they could later serve as the basis for a more elaborate works of art, whether in print form for the published report or in paintings.

Figure 3.3 John E. Weyss, *El Vado de los Padres, Colorado River*, c.1872, graphite on paper. Courtesy of the US Geological Survey. https://library.usgs.gov/photo/#/item/51ddcf45e4b0f72b44721b51

Perhaps the most revolutionary addition to the confluence of images that represented the nineteenth-century West was photography. The development of the wet-plate collodion method by the 1860s enabled the creation of multiple prints (daguerreotypes could not be duplicated), and made photography a viable graphic tool for surveys. Creating photographs in the field was arduous, however, entailing the hauling of bulky cameras, heavy sheets of glass for the negatives, darkroom tents that had to be erected and taken down at every shoot, numerous glass bottles of chemicals, and a laborious process to prepare the materials and utilize them on site.[28] Despite these challenges photography was highly valued for the veracity of its imagery. As survey leader George Wheeler wrote, "The camera affords the greatest aid to the geologist. Only with infinite pains could the draughtsman give expression to the systematic heterogeneity of the material."[29] And Ferdinand Hayden noted the advances from previous survey imagery:

> Twenty years ago, hardly more than caricatures existed, as a general rule, of the leading features of overland exploration … the truthful representations of photography render such careless work so apparent it would not be tolerated at the present day.[30]

Photographs provided surveys with an unrivaled form of representation that could be used for cross-referencing descriptions, maps, and topographical drawings, as an aid to the construction of other forms of art such as paintings, as a promotional tool by the survey leaders, and a form of education and popular entertainment. Hundreds of original photographic prints from the surveys were disseminated in both large format versions and as stereographs, but until the development of the halftone method in the 1880s that enabled the reproduction of continuous tone images on a printed page at a reasonable cost, photographs could appear in publications only when manually inserted as original prints or when reproduced through photolithography or heliotypy—all very expensive processes. Some of the Great Survey reports did use these, but more often they included less costly lithographs or wood engravings that were based on photographs or field sketches. All of the methods (other than hand-colored views or chromolithographs), resulted in black and white images, but even with this limitation their almost magical ability to mirror the visible world made photographs a highly valued addition to traditional hand-drawn scenes.[31] As Hayden noted,

> We have found them most essential in the preparation of our geological reports and maps, and we have also found them to be very attractive to the public. These photographic views are used in schoolbooks, journals &c. and the demand for them for the purpose of engraving is very great. We all know that it is through the eye that we acquire most of our knowledge, and these pictures help the eye very much, giving, as they do, clearer conceptions of mountain forms than pages of descriptions could do.[32]

Clarence King, the first of the Great Survey leaders to utilize photography, hired Timothy O'Sullivan for his initial season in 1867.[33] King was already very familiar with both visual aesthetics and photography. Before traveling west in 1862, for example, he had been a founding member of the Society for the Advancement of Truth in Art, an American Pre-Raphaelite group dedicated to the theories of the English aesthetician, John Ruskin.[34] The grandson of an artist, King remained faithful to Ruskin's ideas throughout his life and also collected art.[35] Firsthand encounters with landscape photography came in 1862 when King, fresh from Yale's Sheffield Scientific School, joined the California State Geological Survey, which had already recognized the value of photography in western exploration.[36] That expedition's geologist, William Brewer, wrote that year that Carleton Watkins's recent photographs of Yosemite were "the finest I have seen."[37] Watkins joined the California survey in 1865 and King watched him work firsthand.

Anticipating later uses of photography by the Great Surveys, Watkins privately published an album of original views in 1863, and the California survey leader Josiah Whitney used his photographs to illustrate the expedition's 1865 report.[38] Shortly afterward, in early 1866 Whitney sent King and topographer James T. Gardiner to supervise a secondary expedition into western Arizona, accompanied by the little-known photographer Charles August Brinley.[39] The following year, when he began his own survey of the 40th Parallel, King was well aware of the merits and challenges of field photography.

Timothy O'Sullivan was, of course, an excellent choice for the position. His experience making Civil War views for Mathew Brady had prepared him for the rigors of fieldwork and the oppressive conditions that he experienced in the western desert where scarcity of food and water sometimes led to grueling extended marches. The stark, haunting quality of many of O'Sullivan's views are due, to a considerable degree, to the challenging and barren specter of a terrain which Mark Twain described as having "not a sound—not a sigh—not a whisper—not a buzz or a whir of wings, or a distant pipe of bird—not even a sob from the lost souls that doubtless people that dead air."[40]

The graphic personnel on the King survey varied annually. In 1868 in addition to employing O'Sullivan and topographical draftsmen, King added a painter whose work would add color to the visual results of his expedition and perhaps augment them with a Ruskinian interpretation of the scenery they were encountering. John Henry Hill was a friend from New York who had helped found the Society for the Advancement of Truth in Art, and although Hill would stay only for a single season (perhaps because he likened Nevada to hell), he surely validated King's interest in accommodating traditional artists on the survey.[41] In 1869 Andrew Joseph Russell briefly joined the King team. Russell had been a painter in Nunda, New York, a Civil War photographer, and most recently a railroad photographer for the Union Pacific. He spent three weeks in Utah's Uinta Mountains with King, making 25 large plate and 59 stereo views.[42] That summer as well, the painter Gilbert Munger arrived as a guest artist and would remain with King through 1870 when Carleton Watkins replaced O'Sullivan as the primary photographer for the survey.[43] Scholarship by Michael Schroeder and Gray Sweeney has resurrected the almost forgotten Munger, who spent some of his time painting large canvases, what his fellows called "four footers" in the open air.[44] While his work does not rival that of the better known survey painters, Munger exhibited his western scenes widely, and they appeared as chromolithographs in King's reports. Often mirroring O'Sullivan's photos, his views are a vivid demonstration of visual triangulation as they depict landscape in complementary ways.[45]

The other three Great Survey leaders were a little slower than King to recognize the potential of varied graphic documentation, but in time all of them made the most of the possibilities. Powell hired E.O. Beaman as photographer for his study of the Colorado River watershed in 1871, and had already enlisted the services of Frederick Samuel Dellenbaugh as topographic artist. Beaman left after only one season and Powell struggled to replace him before finally assigning the position to John (Jack) Hillers, a boatman who had learned photography in the field. Powell made good use of these men's work, distributing sets of their pictures to congressmen in his appropriation appeals, and publishing thousands of stereographs that publicized his survey's discoveries and provided an important source of income.[46] These stereographs brought the western landscape directly into the parlors of American homes across the nation and had a major impact on the public's awareness of the Great Surveys' work.

Lt. George Wheeler was even more ambitious in his use of photography. By the time he got underway in 1871, King, Hayden, and Powell had all been in the field for several years with their artists and photographers, and they were receiving considerable attention. Wheeler needed to distinguish his efforts from theirs, especially because he was heading that summer up the Colorado River, a route only recently traversed by Powell and one documented two decades earlier by the Corps of Topographical Engineers.[47] Recognizing that sophisticated imagery could help set his survey apart, Wheeler hired O'Sullivan (who had left the King expedition) for three seasons (1871, 1873, and 1874), and William Bell for one (1872), and besides using their work to illustrate his final reports, he also issued it in a series of deluxe photographic albums and sets of stereographs (Figure 3.4), some of which included as many as a hundred views.[48] Photographic albums had been issued by others, but Wheeler produced six different kinds, with an especially elaborate one in 1874 that included 50 prints, 35 by O'Sullivan and 15 by Bell.[49] In the end Wheeler's survey may be best remembered for these extraordinary images.

Of all the Great Surveys Ferdinand Hayden's most spectacularly demonstrated the power of the allied arts. Hayden had begun his explorations in 1867 but did not hire William Henry Jackson as photographer until 1870, the same year he also published some of A.J. Russell's photographs in an album titled *Sun Pictures of Rocky Mountain Scenery*.[50] That summer Hayden's expedition ventured into eastern Wyoming with a team that included not only Jackson and topographer-artist Anton Schönborn, but also the well-known eastern artist, Sanford Gifford, who briefly joined the group as a guest.[51] Gifford found the area uninspiring, but even the little art he created helped Hayden understand the

Figure 3.4 Timothy O'Sullivan, *Camp Beauty, Canyon de Chelle*, 1873, stereograph, Wheeler Survey, Boston Public Library, Print Department. www. digitalcommonwealth.org/search/commonwealth:gt54kw31h

advantages that paintings could offer his survey, complementing photographs with their color and providing significantly more dramatic effects and aesthetic appeal than topographical drawings.[52] Hayden was surely also aware of the unprecedented success of Albert Bierstadt's monumental canvas, *The Rocky Mountain Lander's Peak* (1863) that had resulted from the artist's experiences with the 1859 Frederick Lander expedition. That painting toured throughout the east and sold for a record $25,000 in 1865, propelling Bierstadt to national fame and demonstrating how paintings, especially the stunning "Big Pictures," could promote interest in and support for western exploration.[53] In subsequent years, although not directly commissioned by the government, several major canvases resulted from the western surveys, aesthetic spectacles that comprise the apex of the triangulated arts of the federal expeditions.

Hayden's historic survey of the Yellowstone region in 1871 brought just such an opportunity for significant artistic work and it resulted in a new synergism of the allied arts. Joining Jackson that summer was topographic artist Henry Wood Elliott, and the painter Thomas Moran who came as a guest.[54] Jackson and Moran worked especially well together and their art appeared not only in Hayden's official reports, but also in a wide variety of articles about Yellowstone and the survey in magazines and books.[55] More important, after the expedition Hayden used Moran's watercolor field sketches and Jackson's photographs to help convince Congress to establish Yellowstone as the first national park, and the persuasive power of these images contributed significantly to the ease and speed of the bill's approval. At the same time, Moran was painting his first great canvas, *The Grand Canyon of the Yellowstone* (Figure 3.5), finishing it just weeks after the park bill was signed into law.

Figure 3.5 The Grand Canyon of the Yellowstone by Thomas Moran (1837–1926), 1872, oil on canvas, mounted on aluminum. US Department of the Interior Museum, Washington, DC. INTR 03001.

After a lavish unveiling in New York, he immediately shipped the enormous picture (7 × 12 ft.) to Washington where Congress quickly purchased it for $10,000, the first landscape by an American artist to be so honored.[56] The painting remains among the most dramatic examples of art emanating from the nineteenth-century federal surveys.

This confluence of events—the expedition through a remarkable region, the subsequent publicity, the landmark legislation, and the historic purchase of a monumental painting connected to his expedition—was hugely beneficial to Hayden's enterprise. His appropriation tripled for the following year, inspiring the other Great Survey leaders to emulate his success by seeking out painters to accompany their expeditions.[57] After the mesmerizing impact of the *Grand Canyon of the Yellowstone* it is not surprising that all four Great Survey leaders wrote to Thomas Moran asking him to join *their* expeditions in the summer of 1872, but he turned each of them down due to other obligations.[58] That year Hayden took William Henry Holmes and Clarence King got Moran's famous rival, Albert Bierstadt. The following year Alexander Wyant accompanied Wheeler, while Moran joined John Wesley Powell and Moran was with Hayden again in 1874.[59] Art had proven itself a powerful ally of science.

Of all of these associations, those that involved Moran proved the most fruitful. After traveling with Powell's survey in Utah and Arizona in 1873 the artist created a 7 × 12 ft. companion to his spectacular Yellowstone canvas, titled *The Chasm of the Colorado* (1873–4), the first of hundreds of views he would paint of the Grand Canyon over the following half century. Like its predecessor *The Chasm* was quickly purchased by Congress for the Capitol.[60] Immediately afterward, with Hayden once more, Moran traveled to Colorado to see the Mountain of the Holy Cross, an extraordinary peak that inspired his third great western canvas. Although not sold to Congress, *The Mountain of the Holy Cross* (1875) comprised the last component of a great triptych, which exemplifies the monumentality, challenges, and redemptive power of the West.[61] Moran also produced hundreds of illustrations for popular publications from his experiences with the Hayden and Powell surveys, and several significant groups of watercolors for notable patrons, including 25 for Louis Prang of Boston, who published 15 of them as a set of exceptionally fine chromolithographs in a deluxe edition in 1876.[62]

Despite the headlines Albert Bierstadt had garnered with his record-breaking sale of *The Rocky Mountains, Lander's Peak*, the painter failed to sell a painting to Congress after several attempts and he was jealous of Moran's success in the Capitol.[63] In 1872, banking on the combination of spectacular California scenery, his extraordinary talent and celebrity, and his new association with the well-connected Clarence King, Bierstadt transformed his field studies from the King survey into a 6 × 12 ft. painting titled *King's River Canyon* (1873, now called *Autumn in the Sierras*) that he obviously hoped would rival Moran's Yellowstone scene in its appeal to Congress. King's opinion of the work remains unclear, but he was a devoted Ruskinian who preferred the style of the English landscapist J.M.W. Turner over Bierstadt's Dusseldorfian mode. Revealingly, in his 1872 book, *Mountaineering in the Sierra Nevada*, King crafted a tale about an artist who spoke what may have been the geologist's true feelings toward his real life guest painter. The fictional artist exclaimed:

> It's all Bierstadt, and Bierstadt, and Bierstadt nowadays! What has he done but twist and skew and distort and discolor and belittle and be-pretty this whole dog-gonned country? Why, his mountains are too high and too slim; they'd blow over in one of our fall winds. I've herded colts two summers in Yosemite, and honest now, when I stood right up front of his picture, I didn't know it. He hasn't what old Ruskin calls for.[64]

Although King did not get his great Ruskinian artist, *King's River Canyon*'s multi-city eastern tour brought some publicity to his survey even though it did not sell to Congress.[65] (Two Bierstadt works, albeit non-western historical subjects, were acquired for the Capitol in 1874 and 1878.[66]) The failure of the *King's River Canyon* painting to find federal patronage, and its subsequent retitling effectively obscured Bierstadt's relationship with the Great Surveys, and his contribution to King's survey ultimately remained relatively inconsequential. Instead, King distinguished his expedition with scientific discoveries and publications, including volumes adorned with 41 lithographs after O'Sullivan's photographs, spectacularly colored maps, and ten chromolithographs from Gilbert Munger's paintings.[67] These reports set a new standard with their emphasis on visual effects in large quarto-sized atlases, with each type of imagery offering a different perspective on the 40th Parallel.

Wheeler's attempt to rival the other surveys' alliance with high art proved a disappointment. In 1873 he managed to entice New York painter Alexander Wyant to accompany a branch expedition of his survey through Arizona and New Mexico, with Timothy O'Sullivan as leader. Wyant kept a sketchbook/diary of his experience that offers insights into the travails of their grueling trek across the desert.[68] In the end, after weeks of arduous travel in searing heat and sometimes limited water and rations, the challenges proved too much for the artist's delicate constitution and he suffered a stroke which permanently paralyzed his right arm. Remarkably, Wyant eventually taught himself to paint with his left hand and continued his artistic career in subsequent years, but the attack curtailed his work with the Wheeler survey.[69] His field diary contains some sketches and he was photographed painting at the White House Ruin at the Canyon de Chelly, but his affliction prevented him from becoming the pictorial champion of the Wheeler expedition.[70] The lack of monumental paintings prevented that survey from becoming as well known as Hayden and Powell's and also may have contributed to Wyant's relative obscurity in art history.

One of the most intriguing aspects of the idea of "triangulating the view" is the intersection of comparable views from different years, surveys, and media that offer almost infinite possibilities for perceiving the American West. In the nineteenth century, one of the more notable public opportunities for witnessing such an array of federal expedition imagery was at the 1876 Centennial Exhibition in Philadelphia. In the Government Building, alongside artifacts brought back from the West, photographs from all four surveys were displayed as framed art. In Memorial Hall Thomas Moran's *Mountain of the Holy Cross* was prominently displayed in the central art gallery, and in the Art Annex were L. Prang & Co.'s newly published chromolithographs from Moran's work that had originated in the Hayden and Powell surveys.[71] At this major national exposition the rich variety of visual images from the Great Surveys offered tens of thousands of Americans the chance to view the West in a range of complementary and competing formats as the nation celebrated its hundredth birthday.

Connections between similar images from different surveys comprise an especially compelling twist on the idea of triangulation. Moran, for example, made extensive use of the survey photographs in composing both illustrations and paintings, including all three of the works in his great western trip-tych of the early 1870s. He had personally helped compose some of those photographs, working side by side with Jackson in Yellowstone and Hillers in both Utah and the Grand Canyon, helping them create the best possible images, but he acquired many other photographs for reference, including O'Sullivan's views of Shoshone Falls from the King and Wheeler expeditions. Examining correspondences between photographs and Moran's finished art reveals a great deal about his working process and demonstrates yet another dimension of the surveys' imagery impact in different arenas.[72]

Some of the Great Surveys overlapped with each other in the same ter-ritory, enabling different photographers to document the same sites. Jack Hillers's views of the Grand Canyon from the Powell survey, for example, have important connections to O'Sullivan's and Bell's views of the canyon from Wheeler's expedition. The conceptual dimensions of such relationships multiply with the addition of time as a variable, as in the fascinating work by Mark Klett and others who, in the late 1970s began seeking out the spe-cific vantage points of Great Survey photographs from a hundred years before. Rephotographing the same scenes so as to correspond with their predecessors as exactly as possible, the photographers reveal changes, sometimes subtle, sometimes dramatic, that have occurred in the intervening years. Since the pub-lication of *Second View: The Rephotographic Survey Project,* the process of rephotography has developed significantly, most notably through Klett's sub-sequent efforts and those of Byron Wolfe, which combine multiple views from the past with their own contemporary photographs and create a rich visual, historical, and conceptual interplay (Figure 3.6). In all of these geological time is the preeminent issue, but no less significant is the temporal dialogue among the different views of the same sites, produced years and decades apart, a lit-eral re-membering of separate images into a multivalent portrayal of a single place.[73]

One of the most dramatic sites of such triangulation across the Great Surveys was Idaho's Shoshone Falls, visited by both King and Wheeler in 1868 and 1874 respectively, and portrayed in an array of media after that. Timothy O'Sullivan accompanied both of those expeditions, and his views of the torrent, separated by six years, offer our earliest visual perspectives on that

Figure 3.6 Mark Klett (b. 1952) and Byron Wolfe (b. 1967), *Moran and Condor, Bright Angel Trailhead*, 2007, composite photograph. Collection of the artists.

remote cataract (Figure 3.7). Then, in 1876, based on one of these photos, Moran's watercolor of Shoshone Falls was reproduced in the L. Prang & Co.'s deluxe portfolio of chromolithographs of the West. At the time Moran had never seen the falls and his view is a virtual copy of O'Sullivan's work, artistically enhanced and in vivid color. But then, in a dramatic enactment of the time/space continuum of the allied arts, and probably aware that Shoshone Falls was being considered for national park status at the turn of the century, Moran finally traveled to the falls in 1900 and made it the subject of his last monumental canvas, today in the Gilcrease Museum in Tulsa, Oklahoma (Figure 3.8).[74] In that work the vestiges of O'Sullivan's vantage remain, intermingling with Moran's own interpretation of the site.

The Shoshone Falls park proposal was never enacted, and within only a few years of Moran's great painting, a dam just above the falls effectively bespoiled the spectacle of the "Niagara of the West" to such a degree that the cataract is little known today.[75] This diminishment, however, renders the early portrayals of the waterfall in its glory even more important than they would otherwise be. From O'Sullivan's first photographs to Moran's 6 × 11 ft. opus, the pictures fulfill the promise of the federal surveys' triangulation of visual imagery by providing us perspectives on a site that we could not otherwise achieve.

Ultimately, of course, visual triangulation in the nineteenth-century federal surveys of the American West became more than just a tripartite conjunction of imagery, expanding into a multivalent configuration of portrayals of many sorts across media, place, and time (Figure 3.9). Together these create a rich and remarkable representation of the West, no less for us today than for

Figure 3.7 Timothy O'Sullivan (c.1840–82), *Shoshone Falls, Snake River, Idaho. Mid-day view. Adjacent walls about 1000 feet in height*, 1874, photograph, Wheeler Survey, Library of Congress, LC-DIG-ppmsca-10071 www.loc.gov/pictures/item/2007684844/.

Figure 3.8 Thomas Moran (1837–1926), *Shoshone Falls on the Snake River*, 1900, oil on canvas, overall image 71 × 144½ × 4¾ in. (180.3 × 367 × 12.1 cm), from the collection of Gilcrease Museum, Tulsa, Oklahoma, GM 0126.2339.

Figure 3.9 William Henry Holmes, *At Work. Summit of Mt. Evans*, 1873, graphite and watercolor on paper. Courtesy of the US Geological Survey. https://library. usgs.gov/photo/#/item/51dc8b48e4b097e4d38398ca

audiences of the past. What the men charged with surveying that enormous and still remote portion of the young nation quickly came to understand was that its "singularity" could not be realized from a single perspective. America required multiple viewers, utilizing multiple arts and technologies to triangulate a clear vision of the land and all of its enormity and variety.

Notes

1 J.A. Bennett, "Geometry and Surveying in Early Seventeenth Century England," in "Measuring All Aspects of Land: Some Aspects of the History of Surveying." Special issue, *Annals of Science* 48, no. 4 (1991): 346. For a thorough discussion of the process see Alfred E. Phillips, *Surveying: A Manual of Practical Instruction in the Art of Plane Surveying, Including Plotting, Leveling, Triangulation, Line Running, Cross-Sectioning, Traversing, and Other Details of Field Work* (Chicago, IL: American School of Correspondence, 1908).

2 Bennett, "Geometry and Surveying in Early Seventeenth-Century England," 347–354, and G.L.E. Turner, "Introduction: Some Notes on the Development of Surveying and the Instruments Used," *Annals of Science* 48, no. 4 (1991): 314–315, 317.

3 An early treatise that discussed triangulation was Gemm Frisius's 1533 edition of Apianus's *Cosmographica*. Cited in Bennett, "Geometry and Surveying in Early Seventeenth-Century England," 346.

4 Martin J.S. Rudwick, "The Emergence of a Visual Language for Geological Sciences, 1760–1840," *History of Science* 14 (Sept. 1976): 149–195.

5 Louis Cohen, Laurence Manion, and Keith Morrison, *Research Methods in Education,* 6th ed. (London: Routledge, 2007), 141. For a historiography of the

term in recent interdisciplinary methodology see Todd D. Jick, *Administrative Science Quarterly* 24 (Dec. 1979): 602–611.

6 Rudwick, "Emergence of a Visual Language," 151–152. The emphasis in the quotation is mine.

7 For a wide-ranging and philosophical history of related ideas, see Barbara Maria Stafford, *Voyage into Substance: Art, Science, Nature, and the Illustrated Travel Account, 1760–1840* (Cambridge, MA: MIT Press, 1984).

8 J. Enthoffer, *Manual of Topography and Text-Book of Topographical Drawing for the Officers of the Army and Navy, Civil Engineers, Academies, Colleges, and Schools of Science* (New York: D. Appleton & Co., 1870), 107–108.

9 See my "I Wished for the Pencil of Salvator Rosa: The Artistic Legacy of Lewis and Clark," *South Dakota History* 34, no. 1 (Spring 2004): 28–61, also published in James Ronda and Nancy Tystad Koupal (eds), *Finding Lewis and Clark: Old Trails, New Directions* (Pierre, SD: South Dakota Historical Society Press, 2004), 80–113.

10 The Corps was abolished and its duties incorporated into the Corps of Engineers in 1863. See Frank N Schubert (ed.), *The Nation Builders: A Sesquicentennial History of the Corps of Topographical Engineers, 1838–1863* (Fort Belvoir, VA: Office of History, US Army Corps of Engineers, 1988), 78.

11 The term derives from Edward S. Wallace, *The Great Reconnaissance: Soldiers, Artists, and Scientists on the Frontier, 1848–1861* (Boston, MA: Little Brown & Co., 1955), but is widely used. The best source on this era is still William H. Goetzmann's, *Army Exploration in the American West, 1803–1868* (New Haven, CT: Yale University Press, 1959).

12 David Reel, "The Drawing Curriculum at the U.S. Military Academy During the 19th Century," in "West Points, Points West." Special issue, *Western Passages* (Denver, CO: Institute of Western Art, Denver Art Museum, 2002), 51–59; Michael Moss, "Robert Weir as Teacher," in *Robert W. Weir of West Point: Illustrator, Teacher and Poet* (West Point, NY: West Point Printing Office, 1976). In addition to his work at West Point, Weir is known for a number of significant paintings, most notably *The Embarkation of the Pilgrims* for the rotunda of the US Capitol. See William H. Gerdts et al., *Robert Weir: Artist and Teacher of West Point* (West Point, NY: Cadet Fine Arts Forum of the United States Corps of Cadets, 1976).

13 "Historical Sketch of Department of Drawing," *Centennial of the United States Military Academy at West Point, New York, 1802–1902* (Washington, DC: Government Printing Office, 1904), 294.

14 Eastman had graduated from West Point in 1824 and in 1830–33 was stationed at Fort Snelling in Minnesota where he made numerous drawings of the local area and the Native American inhabitants. In 1833–40 he taught topographical drawing at West Point and after other postings at various locations went on to publish hundreds of illustrations in Henry Rowe Schoolcraft's monumental work, *Historical and Statistical Information Regarding the History, Conditions, and Prospects of the Indian Tribes of the United States*, 6 vols (Philadelphia, PA: J. B. Lippincott & Co., 1851–57). Eastman's book is *Treatise on Topographical Drawing* (New York: Wiley & Putnam, 1837).

15 Eastman, *Treatise on Topographical Drawing*, iii.

16 "Historical Sketch of Department of Drawing," *Centennial of West Point*, 294. This document is extremely detailed in regard to the art instruction over the years at West Point, with thorough descriptions of each course, its activities, goals, and results, pp. 290–310. There is still no thorough single study of the many artists who accompanied these surveys. For a useful overview of some of them see Patricia

Trenton and Peter H. Hassrick, *The Rocky Mountains: A Vision for Artists in the Nineteenth Century* (Norman, OK: University of Oklahoma Press in association with the Buffalo Bill Historical Center, 1983).

17 Hard copy versions of this series can be found in any government documents library in all 50 states, but the set has now been digitized, including the images. A good portal with a useful introduction to the volume's complexities can be found at: www.cprr.org/Museum/Pacific_RR_Surveys/. See also Ron Tyler, "Illustrated Government Publications Related to the American West, 1843–1863," in *Surveying the Record: North American Scientific Exploration to 1930* (Philadelphia, PA: American Philosophical Society, 1999), 156–158. One of the most notable of the Pacific Railroad Survey artists was John Mix Stanley. See Peter H. Hassrick and Mindy N. Besaw, *Painted Journeys: The Art of John Mix Stanley* (Norman, OK: Oklahoma University Press, 2015).

18 Representative Davis of Maryland, *Congressional Globe*, 34th Cong., 1st sess., 1856, 806; cited in Robin Kelsey, *Archive Style: Photographs and Illustrations for U.S. Surveys, 1850–1890* (Berkeley, CA: University of California Press, 2007), 63.

19 George Gibbs to Henry Rowe Schoolcraft, March 29, 1847, Henry R. Schoolcraft Papers, Library of Congress, roll 36; cited in Brian W. Dippe, *Catlin and His Contemporaries: The Politics of Patronage* (Lincoln, NE: University of Nebraska Press, 1990), 176–177.

20 Rudwick discusses many of these same issues in regard to European scientific publications in "Emergence of a Visual Language."

21 See Martha Sandweiss, *Print the Legend: Photography and the American West* (New Haven, CT: Yale University Press, 2002), 92.

22 See Peter Marzio, *The Democratic Art: Chromolithography, 1840–1900: Pictures for a Nineteenth-Century America* (Boston, MA: David R. Godine in association with the Amon Carter Museum, 1979) and my *Thomas Moran's West: Chromolithography, High Art, and Popular Taste* (Lawrence, KS: University Press of Kansas, 2006).

23 The Corps of Topographical Engineers was incorporated into the Army Corps of Engineers in 1863 and although the Corps continued some of its surveying work, the four "Great Surveys" took over much of that responsibility after the Civil War until 1879 when the founding of United States Geological Survey consolidated them into one agency.

24 The best book on the Great Surveys remains Richard A. Bartlett, *Great Surveys of the American West* (Norman, OK: University of Oklahoma Press, 1962), but see also William H. Goetzmann, *Exploration and Empire: The Explorer and the Scientist in the Winning of the American West* (Austin, TX: Texas State Historical Association, 1993), 355–601.

25 For an overview of many of the artists who accompanied the Great Surveys see Trenton and Hassrick, *Rocky Mountains*; and William H. Goetzmann and William N. Goetzmann, *The West of the Imagination*, 2nd ed. (Norman, OK: University of Oklahoma Press, 2009). Kelsey, *Archive Style* provides a more theoretical perspective on the work of some of these artists. Studies of the more notable individuals include my *Thomas Moran and the Surveying of the American West* (Washington, DC: Smithsonian Institution Press, 1992); Anderson and Ferber, *Albert Bierstadt: Art and Enterprise*, 40–45, 49–53; and Michael D. Schroeder and J. Gray Sweeney, *Gilbert Munger: Quest for Distinction* (Afton, MN: Afton Historical Society Press, 2003). For the photographers, see especially Sandweiss's excellent *Print the Legend*.

26 Kenneth Haltman, *Looking Close and Seeing Far: Samuel Seymour, Titian Ramsay Peale, and the Art of the Long Expedition, 1818–1823* (University Park, PA: Pennsylvania State University Press, 2007); Kelsey, *Archive Style.*

27 Thompson's images can be seen on the United States Geological Survey website: www.sciencebase.gov/catalog/item/51ddc28de4b0f72b44720c09.

28 These difficulties are described in detail through primary documents quoted in Peter E. Palmquist, *Carleton E. Watkins: Photographer of the American West* (Albuquerque, NM: University of New Mexico Press for the Amon Carter Museum, 1983), 16–18.

29 Engineer Department, United States Army, *Report Upon Geographical and Geological Explorations and Surveys West of the One Hundredth Meridian*, vol. 3. Geology (Washington, DC: Government Printing Office, 1875), 85; cited in Sandweiss, *Print the Legend*, 304.

30 F.V. Hayden, *Ninth Annual Report of the United States Geological and Geographical Survey of the Territories   for the Year 1875* (Washington, DC: Government Printing Office, 1877), 22; quoted in Sandweiss, *Print the Legend*, 181.

31 For a thorough discussion of these issues, see Sandweiss, *Print the Legend*, especially chapter 7, "Western Photography and the Illustrated Book," 276–324.

32 F.V. Hayden, "Statement to the Committee on Public Lands, May 14, 1874," *Notes Relating to Surveys in the Western Territory of the United States* (Washington, DC: Government Printing Office, 1874), 35; quoted in Sandweiss, *Print the Legend*, 181.

33 Toby Jurovics et al., *Framing the West: The Survey Photographs of Timothy H. O'Sullivan* (New Haven, CT: Yale University Press, 2010), 15.

34 Thurman Wilkins, *Clarence King: A Biography* (Albuquerque, NM: University of New Mexico Press, 1988), 41–43, 55, 68, 174.

35 Ibid., 329–331, 174n.

36 Ibid., 52.

37 Diary of William Henry Brewer, January 31, 1862, Brewer Diaries and Journals, 1860–1864, Bancroft Library, University of California, Berkeley; cited in Palmquist, *Carleton Watkins*, 18.

38 Watkins's portfolio was titled *Yo-Semite Valley; Photographic Views of the Falls and Valeey of Yo-Semite in Mariposa County, California; Executed by C.E. Watkins, San Francisco.* Palmquist, *Carleton Watkins*, 210. Josiah Dwight Whitney, *Report of Progress for 1860–1865.* Vol. 1 of *Geological Survey of California* (Philadelphia, PA: Caxton Press of Sherman & Co., 1865); cited in Palmquist, *Carleton Watkins*, 24.

39 Wilkins, *Clarence King*, 81–85. For more on Brinley, see Peter Palmquist and Thomas Kailbourn, *Pioneer Photographers of the Far West: A Biographical Dictionary, 1840–1865* (Palo Alto, CA: Stanford University Press, 2000), 122.

40 Mark Twain, *Roughing It*, chapter 18 (1872; repr., New York: Signet Classic, 1980), 116.

41 Wilkins, *Clarence King*, 122–123, and Trenton and Hassrick, *Rocky Mountains*, 157.

42 Glenn Willumson, "'Photographing Under Difficulties': Andrew Russell's Photographs for the King Survey," in Jurovics et al, *Framing the West*, 178, 180.

43 For Watkins's participation in the King Survey, see Palmquist, *Carleton Watkins*, 38–42.

44 Michael D. Schroeder and J. Gray Sweeney, *Gilbert Munger: Quest for Distinction* (Afton, MN: Afton Historical Society Press, 2003), 39. See also Trenton and Hassrick, *Rocky Mountains*, 157–159.

45 Schroeder and Sweeney, *Gilbert Munger*, esp. 40–49.

46 In 1872, for example, Powell commissioned Hayden's photographer, William Henry Jackson, to print 4,288 stereographs taken by his photographer, E. O. Beaman, and made similar orders with others after that. The profits from stereograph sales surely contributed to the survey budget, but Washington insiders joked that Powell financed his home there through picture sales. Records for the figures are sporadic, but Powell's income for photographic sales alone for the first six months of 1874 totaled $4,100. See my *Thomas Moran and Surveying the West*, 199, n. 17.

47 The Joseph Christmas Ives expedition of 1857–58 had included two artists, F.W. von Eggloffstein and Henrich Baldouin Möllhausen, and Ives himself experimented with photography and drawing on the expedition. For more on their work, see Ben W. Huseman, *Wild Rivers, Timeless Canyons: Balduin Möllhausen's Watercolors of the Colorado* (Tucson, AZ: University of Arizona in association with the Amon Carter Museum, 1995).

48 Wheeler's William Bell should not be confused with Dr. William Abraham Bell who was also briefly a photographer with the Kansas Pacific Railroad about the same time, but who went on to become vice president of the Denver and Rio Grande Railway. For more on William A. Bell see my *Thomas Moran and Surveying the West*, 153–160. The hundreds of the stereographs from the King survey and the Wheeler surveys are catalogued in the five appendices of Jurovics et al., *Framing the West*, 200–221.

49 See Jurovics et al., *Framing the West*, 29–30, and Sandweiss, *Print the Legend*, 185–195.

50 Jackson's own memories of his experience with Hayden are found in William Henry Jackson, *Time Exposure: The Autobiography of William Henry Jackson* (1940: repr. Albuquerque, NM: University of New Mexico Press, 1986), 186–250. Ferdinand Vandiveer Hayden, *Sun Pictures of Rocky Mountain Scenery* (New York: Julius Bien, 1870).

51 Schönborn was a German-born artist who had been with Captain William Raynolds on the last major western expedition of the Corps of Topographical Engineers in 1859 and was Hayden's chief topographer during that survey's important exploration of Yellowstone in 1871. He is not better known in part because he committed suicide that fall. See Marlene Deahl Merrill, *Yellowstone and the Great West: Journals, Letters, and Images from the 1871 Hayden Expedition* (Lincoln, NE: University of Nebraska Press, 1999), 219–221, and Trenton and Hassrick, *Rocky Mountains*, 107–112. Gifford's participation with the Hayden survey was as a guest and the expedition focused that summer on eastern Wyoming. See Kevin J. Avery and Franklin Kelley (eds), *Hudson River School Visions: The Landscapes of Sanford Gifford* (New Haven, CT: Yale University Press in association with the Metropolitan Museum of Art, 2003), 67–69, 196–198.

52 The most well-known of Gifford's few images from the 1870 Hayden survey is *Valley of the Chugwater* which corresponds very closely to a Jackson photograph of the artist painting the scene. See Avery and Kelley, *Hudson River School Visions*, 196–198.

53 Nancy Anderson and Linda Ferber, *Albert Bierstadt: Art and Enterprise* (Brooklyn, NY: Brooklyn Museum, 1990), 26.

54 The literature on this expedition is large, but for a useful anthology of primary documents see Merrill, *Yellowstone and the Great West*. For a wider consideration of these and other images of the park see Peter H. Hassrick, *Drawn to Yellowstone: Artists in America's First National Park* (Seattle, WA: University of Washington

Press in association with the Autry Museum of Western Heritage, 2002). For a discussion of Elliott's work for Hayden see Trenton and Hassrick, *Rocky Mountains,* 160–166.

55 For Jackson, see Peter B. Hales, *William Henry Jackson and the Transformation of the American Landscape* (Philadelphia, PA: Temple University Press, 1988). For Hayden's publication of Jackson's photographs see Sandweiss, *Print the Legend,* 196–204. For the publication of Moran's work, see my *Thomas Moran and Surveying the West,* 79–92; my chapter, "Moran and the Art of Publishing," in Nancy Anderson (ed.), *Thomas Moran* (New Haven, CT: Yale University Press in association with the National Gallery of Art, 1997), 311–312, and my *Thomas Moran's West.*

56 See my *Thomas Moran and Surveying the West,* 43, 64–67.

57 The Hayden survey's congressional appropriation in 1871 had been $25,000; after the Yellowstone trip it rose to $75,000 while the other surveys were forced to carry on with much less. Bartlett, *Great Surveys of the American West,* 59.

58 For Hayden's letters to Moran see Kinsey, *Thomas Moran and Surveying the West,* 103–104, 201, n. 31. For a discussion of other survey leaders' invitations see Thurman Wilkins, *Thomas Moran: Artist of the Mountains* (Norman, OK: University of Oklahoma Press, 1998, 2nd ed.), 106, 340, n. 5, based on the transcript of a letter from Moran to his wife, May 20, 1872, in the Fryxell Collection, American Heritage Center, University of Wyoming.

59 For King and Bierstadt see Anderson and Ferber, *Albert Bierstadt,* 48, 51–52, 220. For Wheeler and Wyant, see Doris Ostrander Dawdy (ed.), "The Wyant Diary: An Artist with the Wheeler Survey in Arizona, 1873," *Arizona and the West* 22 (Autumn 1980): 255–278. For Moran's work with Hayden and Powell, see my *Thomas Moran and Surveying the West,* 94–149.

60 These works were moved to the Smithsonian in the 1960s, where they hang with another Yellowstone painting Moran created in 1893. Kinsey, *Thomas Moran,* 189, n. 58.

61 Ibid., 141–160. The idea that Moran's three monumental western paintings of the 1870s should be regarded as a triptych is the thesis of my first book. See Kinsey, *Thomas Moran and Surveying the West,* 174–175, for a summary. These three paintings were finally united for the first time in the National Gallery of Art's major retrospective of Moran's work in 1997, a triumphant trio that was the centerpiece of the exhibition. See www.nga.gov/exhibitions/moran/triptych.shtm.

62 See Kinsey, *Thomas Moran and Surveying the West,* 79–92; Kinsey, "Moran and the Art of Publishing," in Anderson, *Thomas Moran,* 311–12, and Kinsey, *Thomas Moran's West.*

63 Bierstadt's ambition to sell his paintings to Congress is discussed in Anderson and Ferber, *Albert Bierstadt,* 40–45, 49–53.

64 Clarence King, *Mountaineering in the Sierra Nevada* (1872; repr. New York: Penguin, 1989), 179–180.

65 Anderson and Ferber, *Albert Bierstadt,* 54, 220–221, 227–228.

66 *Discovery of the Hudson River* and *Settlement of California, Bay of Monterey, 1770.* These remain in the Capitol collection today.

67 Jurovics et al., *Framing the West,* 21, 226, n. 48.

68 The diary is in the Special Collections of Northern Arizona University but has been published in Dawdy, "The Wyant Diary," 255–278. Some of the sketches contain topographical notations indicating the degree of angles from the point of view.

69 Relatively little has been written about Wyant although he was well regarded in his time. One of the best sources on his work is David Cleveland, *A History of American Tonalism: 1880–1920* (Manchester, VT: Hudson Hills, 2010), 67–76. Wyant's malady in 1873 remains mysterious; Cleveland calls it a heart attack, but it seems more like a stroke since it resulted in partial paralysis. Wyant's last entry in his Wheeler expedition diary is a scrawled "It was struck between day and dark."

70 The photograph and caption are reproduced ibid., 266.

71 Jurovics et al., *Framing the West*, 36; Sandweiss, *Print the Legend*, 184; Kinsey, *Thomas Moran and Surveying the West*, 142–143, 150; and Kinsey, *Thomas Moran's West*, 187–190.

72 All these issues are extensively discussed in my *Thomas Moran and Surveying the West*.

73 Interest in rephotography has increased in recent years, with many projects by an array of practitioners and a growing bibliography on the subject. See especially Mark Klett et al., *Second View: The Rephotographic Survey Project* (Albuquerque, NM: University of New Mexico Press, 1984); Klett et al, *Third View, Second Sights: A Rephotographic Survey of the American West* (Santa Fe, NM: Museum of New Mexico Press in association with the Center for American Places, 2004); and Jason Kalin, "Remembering with Rephotography: A Social Practice for the Invention of Memories," *Visual Communication Quarterly* 20 (July 2013): 168–179.

74 The proposal for Shoshone Falls National Park is found in US Department of the Interior, *Annual Reports of the Department of the Interior* 56th Cong., 2nd sess., House Document 5 (Washington, DC: Government Printing Office, 1900), 403–405.

75 For more on this see my recent article, "Shoshone Falls: The Niagara of the West." *Sitelines: The Journal of the Foundation for Landscape Studies* 10 (Spring 2015). www.foundationforlandscapestudies.org/pdf/sitelines_spring15.pdf.

4 Cartographic Representation in the Age of Vernacular Landscape

Pictorial Metaphor in Stephen Long's *Map of the Country Drained by the Mississippi* (1822)

Kenneth Haltman

To the fundamentally fictional nature of maps, their status as social and cultural constructions, we might add the seemingly obvious corollary that such representations, because pictorial, should correspond in meaningful ways to contemporary artistic practices, however non-cartographic or less explicitly cartographic in nature. Certainly, in the case of maps produced literally alongside drawings and paintings commissioned by the same institutional patrons, intended to represent related aspects of the world, such correspondences would seem all but inevitable, differences in technical means and rhetorical strategies notwithstanding. In the case of Major Stephen Harriman Long's two-part *Map of the Country Drained by the Mississippi* (Figure 4.1), based on data gathered in the company of Samuel Seymour and Titian Ramsay Peale, artists under his command on the first federally sponsored scientific exploration of the American West (1818–20), one is less struck by the now conventional insight that the maps themselves served as "a vehicle for the creation and conveying of authority about, and ultimately over, territory" than by their subtle undermining of those claims to authority by pictorial means, registering uncertainty and doubt, a sense of ironic dislocation and anxiety aligned with structural metaphors employed by both Seymour and Peale as landscape painter and assistant naturalist, respectively, in their own expedition images.[1]

The intertextualities governing this ambivalent pictorial poetics are perhaps most apparent in the handful of engravings after field studies by both artists that appeared in late 1822 in an atlas volume accompanying the Philadelphia edition of the expedition's published account immediately following Long's maps that constituted by some measure its culminating achievement.[2] While these maps have long been seen as accomplished examples of period cartography serving to document an arguably overconfident imperial ambition, marking out the literal extent and contours of the national territory with unprecedented accuracy, they offer telling evidence of perceptual and literal confusions regarding that territory, especially when understood as a realm of intercultural interaction and exchange. Just as properly pictorial metaphor in the work of Seymour and Peale arguably serves to suggest the inadequacy of scientific reason to achieve reliable

Figure 4.1 Young and Delleker, after Stephen Long, *Map of the Country Drained by the Mississippi,* 1822, black-and-white engravings, in Edwin James, comp., *Account of an Expedition from Pittsburgh to the Rocky Mountains* (Philadelphia: Carey & Lea, 1822–23), Atlas volume. Yale Collection of Western Americana, Beinecke Rare Book and Manuscript Library.

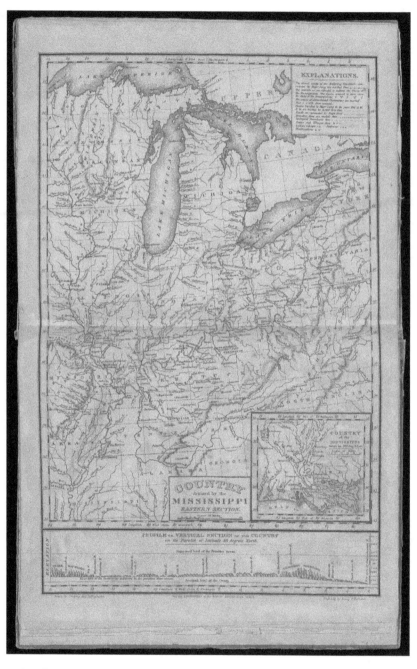

Figure 4.1 Cont.

geological or ethnographic understanding, *Map of the Country Drained by the Mississippi*, attributed to Long but in actual execution produced by a complex team effort, utilizes abstract signs combined with pictographic symbols, wishful narrative inscriptions, and unmarked spaces to express similar uncertainty regarding cognitive and territorial control.

Assessing the map alongside other self-consciously artistic images produced in response to related expeditionary challenges enables us to make properly pictorial sense of its contradictions and peculiarities. Long, who as commanding officer oversaw both artists' work, was enough involved in image making himself to recognize cartographic verisimilitude as a pictorial effect. Balancing mimesis with invention, he combined narrative commentary and figuration with more modern modes of symbolic abstraction in a recognizably aesthetic strategy beholden to those of the artists by whom arguably he was most directly—however unconsciously—influenced.

When in March 1817 President James Monroe had approved Long's proposal to produce "a correct Plan of the country" based on the "Latitudes and Longitudes of all important places," his Secretary of War, John C. Calhoun, who strongly endorsed the project, provided two military assistants, Cadet William H. Swift and Lieutenant James D. Graham, the latter an artillery officer trained at West Point responsible for assisting in making daily observations and carefully recording them, along with funds to acquire the equipment necessary to produce this Plan, this map, from the best suppliers.[3] According to an inventory included in Graham's preface to a description of the expedition's "Astronomical and Meteorological Records," this impressive array of instruments included two sextants, a circle of reflection with a graduated limb 12 inches in diameter, an artificial horizon of mercury with a glass roof, a second such horizon improvised in the field, an achromatic telescope 4 feet in length for observing eclipses of Jupiter's satellites, a box chronometer, a pocket chronometer cased like a common watch, an instrument described as "ingeniously designed" for observing the dip of the magnetic needle (followed by a detailed description of its use), one azimuth compass and one common surveyor's compass, a 50-foot chain, a small theodolite ("for *trigonometrical* purposes"), three mountain barometers (two of which, he notes, malfunctioned), several mercurial and one alcohol thermometers, half a dozen "traveling" and several pocket compasses, a pocket telescope, and on and on.[4]

The expedition set out from Pittsburgh in April 1819 in the *Western Engineer*, an experimental steamboat of Long's own design, and traveled down the Ohio to St. Louis. In June they headed up the Missouri to the vicinity of Fort Lisa where they set up winter camp. The following spring, with a small military escort, Long's team of "scientific gentlemen" set out overland for the Rockies along the Platte. Reaching the Front Range by early July, they found the mountains "impenetrable" and, short on supplies, turned south and shortly thereafter, having split up into two companies, east in the direction of home along the Arkansas and Canadian rivers, respectively—an improvised itinerary clearly, however minimally, marked out on Long's two maps.

The published account compiled from this and other data collected and journals kept by those involved was, after considerable effort and delay, issued in Philadelphia by Carey and Lea in two handsome octavo volumes accompanied by the slender folio atlas previously mentioned containing a total of 11 plates: the two maps, eight engraved illustrations after works by both artists, and a pairing of vertical sections. It measured about one foot in height—a footprint virtually identical to that of the two text volumes laid side by side. Not least in this symbolic fashion, the expedition's differing modes of discourse—narrative, cartographic, and pictorial—were thus conceived, and in fact designed, to fit together.[5]

The expedition's symbolic climax—the arrival at the Rockies in late June 1820—is, for instance, both described at length in the *Account*, represented by Seymour in two images (*View of the Rocky Mountains on the Platte 50 Miles from Their Base* and *View of the Chasm through which the Platte Issues from the Rocky Mountains*), and marked out on the map by a series of small crosses along the Platte accompanied by dates, each representing "a point of encampment" logically spaced at intervals of one day's march. The written narrative composed by expedition geologist, botanist, and journalist Edwin James follows and thus confirms the same orderly movement through time and space marked out on the map, each suggesting purposefulness, steadfastness, and accomplishment. This insistent linearity borrows its sense of order from nature, following the course of various rivers, yet motivated by a desire for cultural control expressed in steady increments of progress graphically superimposed upon the mapped landscape.

Cartographic historian Raymond Craib has described such effects as expressive of a "consuming preoccupation with spatial order, scientific rigor, and visuality," which he attributes to a hegemonic will to impose desired order on the world.[6] In these terms, even the simple lines of the expedition's route as thus inscribed read metaphorically—a "veiled rhetoric" motivated at the very least by Long's desire to secure continued public support for exploration through a display of confident command.[7] His maps were intended to serve similar ends by correcting numerous errors common "even on some of the latest and approved maps" then in circulation concerning the geography of the country west of the Mississippi especially. Discipline was key, and Graham describes the "[c]onsiderable pains" he and Long took to double-check all calculations. Though perhaps not entirely "free from inaccuracies," he felt certain "none of magnitude [would] be found among them."[8]

Long was certainly invested in putting signs of careful measurement on display. The precise location of Engineer Cantonment, for instance, warrants an extended, italicized, extra-cartographic narrative inscription (along the right edge of the Western Section about one-third of the way down from the top) detailing the astronomical observations involved in its calculation, though the field of relative cartographic blankness where this text appears suggests, ironically, that its inclusion meant displacing, perhaps, other data of equal relevance. Indeed, one notes across both sections of the map the vestiges of an even earlier competing mode of visual inscription such as doodled topographic icons representing (labeled) Castle Rock and James' Peak along the left edge of the same section, halfway down, adhering to a different scopic regime altogether in contrast to the more modern cartographic abstraction of the world surrounding them. Suggestive less of scientific mensuration than artful contrivance, such passages derive from the pictorial style of earlier picturesque travel accounts in which the work of the imagination offers a telling contrast to the pictorial rhetoric of "Astronomical Observation," the term Graham and Long prefer in describing their work, subtly undermining the authority of their claims to scientific accuracy.

Yet another extra-scientific version —or vision—of James' Peak appears in the "Profile or Vertical Section" *beneath* the map, stylistically incompatible with the first, in fact by another hand, and so at odds with the prevailing cartographic norm that each mode seems to ironize the other.[9] The doodled pictograph of Castle Rock makes picturesque reference to the European past quite similar to that made later in the atlas by William Hay's engraving after Seymour's far more sophisticated view of the same subject with its meditation on the ruination of a cultural form imitated in a natural formation itself imitated in a work of art.[10] In this sense Seymour, too, was engaged in "mapping" the world, attuned to the interests and ambitions of James in his role as expedition geologist; and yet this juxtaposition of numeric and illusionistic visions of the real ironically weakens the map's scientific authority, calling into question precisely how it should be read.

The map itself does provide some clues. A table of "Explanations" (Figure 4.2) in the upper right corner of the Eastern Section of the map appears just where one presumably is meant to begin to make sense of the world it represents, near Pittsburgh where the expedition began. Here we learn to read the symbols by means of which the world of Nature is inscribed with History, the expedition's route marked out as we have seen with dated points of mere encampment differentiated graphically from those where astronomical observations were also taken. Dotted lines represent somewhat more spectrally the routes of Long's four earlier expeditions. Abstract or geometric symbols represent towns and villages, settlements and fortifications; small, upright isosceles triangles, isomorphic with the real-world structures (teepees) to which they quaintly refer, indicate the presence of seasonal, Indian villages encountered during the summer of 1820.

Just as a stylistically related version of the castle representing Castle Rock appears in Seymour's *View of the Castle Rock*, variants or arguably prototypes of these latter forms appear elsewhere in the atlas as well in the work of both expedition artists. Given the nature of his duties as assistant naturalist, we might expect Peale's approach to delineating Plains Indian dwellings to have been more scientific than picturesque, yet his *Moveable Skin Lodges of the Kaskaias* (Figure 4.3) employs the triangularity of those structures metaphorically to suggest at once mysterious interiority and cultural stability. The single open yet pictorially closed-off entryway teases the viewer with its intimation

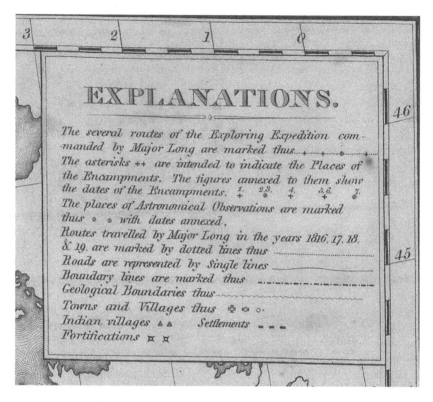

Figure 4.2 Young and Delleker, after Stephen Long, *Map of the Country Drained by the Mississippi*, 1822, Eastern Section, detail: "Explanations." Yale Collection of Western Americana, Beinecke Rare Book and Manuscript Library.

of a hidden ethnologic unknown even as it domesticates that unknown in a vignette featuring familiar mother–child relations, calculated thematic effects here executed by the same engravers, Young and Delleker, responsible for the triangular "signs" identified in the map's legend and distributed across its surface.[11] Peale's skin lodges, in contrast, float within indefinite borders, a vignette at once compositionally centered yet ungrounded, a self-conscious fiction however naturalized as ethnographic reportage.[12]

Immediately following this image, Seymour's *Oto Encampment* (Figure 4.4) represents a line of such teepees closing off the horizon. The image, engraved by Francis Kearney, seems map-like in its own way, but again with symbolic inaccessibility seemingly very much the point. In the left foreground, two barely clad, primitively-armed Indian boys, less Oto than armed Renaissance putti, who mediate between reader-viewers and an unfamiliar world directly derive from the fanciful embellishments of such early modern maps as the *Carte nouvelle de la Louisiane* (1713), available for Seymour to consult in the expedition library.[13] The busyness of Seymour's midground, with Oto riders

Figure 4.3 Young and Delleker, after Titian Ramsay Peale, *Moveable Skin Lodges of the Kaskaias,* 1822, black-and-white engraving, in Edwin James, comp., *Account of an Expedition from Pittsburgh to the Rocky Mountains* (Philadelphia: Carey & Lea, 1822–23), Atlas volume, pl. 5. Yale Collection of Western Americana, Beinecke Rare Book and Manuscript Library.

on horseback racing back and forth and, in the far left distance, very possibly the arrival of a Konza delegation, which in effect *constitutes* the interruption of our view, helps make visible the way in which the map, too, is like a genre painting or engraving filled with incoherent narrative and topographic detail with the expedition's own comings and goings superimposed upon a nominally geographic expanse.

Long's paired maps present, in fact, a barely ordered, awkwardly unchoreographed mass of markings in a range of fonts that in a way humorously run at every angle, recording a diversity of data—topographic, geologic, ethnographic, and historical—in a semiotic confusion, suggesting anxiety at the prospect of inadvertent omission. The product of competing agendas, this density of markings reflects the scope of the expedition's ambitions yet graphically suggests the nature of its failings.[14]

Other among the handful of pictorial engravings in the atlas reinforce this unsettling, arguably governing thematics of disorder; of accumulated, only thinly processed data whose epistemological uncertainty is evident in the art

Figure 4.4 Francis Kearney, after Samuel Seymour, *Oto Encampment,* 1822, black-and-white engraving, in Edwin James, comp., *Account of an Expedition from Pittsburgh to the Rocky Mountains* (Philadelphia: Carey & Lea, 1822–23), Atlas volume, pl. 6. Yale Collection of Western Americana, Beinecke Rare Book and Manuscript Library.

as well. Seymour's *War Dance in the Interior of a Konza Lodge* (Figure 4.5), engraved by Cephas Grier Childs, for instance, represents an action rendered ironically *less* visible by its theatrical lighting, though directly blocked in any case by a dark dividing post at foreground center, precisely in the viewer's line of sight—and, as the atlas itself acknowledges, misidentified, for this "War Dance" was in fact a "Dog Dance." Seymour calls further attention to this drama of *not seeing* by embedding a portrait of three expedition scientists structurally divided from the spectacle that they have come to study, a pictorial figure graphically suggesting the contingency of ethnographic understanding.[15]

View Near the Insulated Tablelands, the final pictorial image in the atlas (a pair of vertical sections follow), suggests the contingency of the expedition's geological and topographic understanding through a similar structural metaphor, its line of march paralleling rather than penetrating the world its "scientific gentlemen" and topographic engineers have come to understand. Such images served to record the scientific data that the expedition gathered, not mimetically in the strictest sense but aesthetically refigured and thematically inflected. A note in the *Account* warns us that even the two vertical sections with which the atlas concludes are in fact calculated fictions: that some "wide and uninteresting plains" have simply been omitted; that the inclinations indicated are "not to be considered applicable to all ... strata"; that certain

Figure 4.5 Cephas Grier Childs, after Samuel Seymour, *War Dance in the Interior of a Konza Lodge,* 1822, black-and-white engraving, in Edwin James, comp., *Account of an Expedition from Pittsburgh to the Rocky Mountains* (Philadelphia: Carey & Lea, 1822–23), Atlas volume, pl. 1. Courtesy Yale Collection of Western Americana, Beinecke Rare Book and Manuscript Library.

other geologic features—for instance Allegheny coal deposits—have not been "particularly represented."[16]

Perhaps it is not too uncharitable to point out that, despite the scientific rigor of which Graham boasts, much else on the face of the map pretends to its accuracy undeservedly because not based on firsthand observation at all, so that, in a sense, the routes traveled by the expedition mark out as much the controlling limits as the extent of its research. Indeed, as we have seen, here and there such non-cartographic spaces are literally overwritten by textual commentary, at times ironically so. The claim that "The Great Desert is frequented by roving bands of Indians who have no fixed places of residence but roam from place to place in quest of game" (printed across the open prairie just east of James' Peak and Castle Rock) calls attention to the very blankness that it otherwise arguably serves to distract one from perceiving.

This inscription does, as Craib nicely puts it, "bring history and geography into mutual dialogue in order to validate or legitimate the position of those in power in relation to those over whom they presume to rule."[17] But it also humorously juxtaposes its non-image of Native hunters with the line of the expedition's route westward, in apparent unawareness or denial of the fact (though well-documented in the expedition *Account*) that

Figure 4.6 Titian Ramsay Peale, untitled sketch of two men crossing the desert, July 25, 1820, graphite with ink on paper. Yale University Art Gallery; gift of Ramsay MacMullen, M.A.H. 1967.

it was ultimately Long and his men, despite the arbitrary linearity of their advance, who were roaming the desert, relatively aimlessly, unsure of their whereabouts as the Native Americans whom they encountered most certainly were not.

A remarkable image in Peale's sketchbook (Figure 4.6) records the actuality of that experience quite poignantly. It takes one a moment, in fact, even to notice the two hapless figures, soldiers or gentlemen, trudging their way across the desert waste, making clear the degree to which Long's Western map in particular rescripts the frictions and the circumstantial blindness of the expeditionary process into signs of "fixity" (Craib's term), so many graphic cartographic claims to cognitive control. And yet the maps *themselves*, as we have seen, resist clear apprehension. Their shifts in pictorial strategy between symbolic abstraction and pictorial illusionism, their incoherence, suggest an inconsistency of purpose; their clutter of data, almost certainly intended as an invitation but in fact overwhelming the gaze, suggests anxiety about as well as the ambition to control.

There are structural issues as well. The atlas, grouping together maps, graphic illustrations, and vertical sections—each relegated, as originally published, to its own tissue-paper-covered sheet—prevents one from considering more than a single image at once, so that each opportunity for vicarious travel becomes interrupted as one turns the page, shifting from subject to subject and, given the number of artistic hands involved, from pictorial style to pictorial style, and among representational modes as well, including, of course, the strictly cartographic. The Long Expedition Atlas is, in fact, unique in its genre. More traditional early nineteenth-century illustrated maps featured inset images relegated to small and in general rectangular "window views" at the margins of cartographic space proper, providing illusionistic glimpses of the world represented more abstractly by the map itself, providing a "visual, historical, and spatial anchor ... to the abstract grid."[18] The decision, essentially without precedent, to decouple expedition maps and illustrations in a separately bound volume must have reflected Long's sense, or perhaps that of his publisher, Mathew Carey, that this pictorial arrangement would have broad appeal, for there were various and differing classes of viewer/readers to be kept in mind: members of the scientific establishment; government officials, including but by no means limited to Long's superiors in the War Department (for his goal was always that of increasing his own opportunities for topographic exploration); and the larger public. Dividing or one might prefer fracturing the continent into paired sections, a decision dramatically reversed in the London edition, would have been part of this same strategy of nationalist hegemonic projection curiously undermined by fragmentation.[19]

The awkwardness and inconsistency of the result—and the fascination the atlas inspires—can perhaps be explained most simply by the overdetermined nature of its production, involving over several years a team of loosely collaborating artists and scientists engaged in surveying not merely physical but cultural space. The maps themselves were of course similarly collaborative efforts, their incoherence arguably the result of, to borrow a useful term from John Pickles, *cartographic bricolage*.[20] Maps, though they pretend to and attempt to achieve a certain seamlessness, are in fact cobbled together out of raw data if possible and fragments of older maps if necessary. We know Long set to work "compiling" his own maps shortly after his return to Philadelphia in late 1820. We know he borrowed cartographic records from the War Department because he complained of their inaccuracy.[21] With Swift's help he set to work laying out what he referred to as "projections," while Graham, with the assistance of a Lieutenant Talcott, "calculated," i.e., translated the vast number of astronomical observations taken over the 18-month course of the expedition into plottable points.[22]

We know that one of the maps Long consulted in Washington was produced during the expedition by Lieutenant Gabriel Field, tracing the route of a military road constructed to supply Camp Missouri, very near Engineer Cantonment.[23] That piece of the puzzle can be clearly discerned on Long's compilation (see Figure 4.1, Western Section), where the straight-as-an-arrow road labeled along its horizon "Field's Trace" transects the more naturally undulating contours of the drainage systems it traverses. This vestige or indeed "trace" of Field's reconnaissance exemplifies the process of *bricolage* that Long and his associates employed. The map, of course, also naturally deconstructs along these selfsame lines. Field's Trace would make an appearance in another period map in a commissioned portrait of Calhoun by Charles Bird King that spring, a further reminder that the expedition was itself but a large piece in a still larger puzzle, informed by competing nationalist and more purely topographic interests.[24]

There are other explanations for the awkwardness and semiotic inconsistency of Long's otherwise quite handsome maps. Art historian Robin Kelsey, previously cited, has attributed such effects to the organizational structure of period expeditionary practice, as a result of which a topographic engineer like Long found himself working alongside and so influenced by professionals in related fields, Seymour and Peale among them, from whom "graphic strategies" could be "borrowed and combined," a "fertile mingling of practices" that "enabled" what Kelsey terms "novel forms of pictorial connotation"[25]—and that we might term modes of pictorial metaphor.

Cartographic historian J.B. Harley, also previously cited, would implicate the map's publisher in this production of pictorial connotation as well. Mathew Carey and successor firms had been the leading producer of maps for the American market for three decades, a success Harley argues owed to entrepreneurial innovation. Rather than himself employing surveyors and a staff of draftsmen, specialist map engravers, colorers, and mounters, Carey subcontracted these tasks out to the many highly trained professionals living and working in Philadelphia, some of whom we have encountered: Cephas Grier Childs, Francis Kearney, Young and Delleker, William Hay. Though the process itself was efficient, its horizontal distribution had visible effects. Fragmentation, linearity, mensuration, illusionism, inaccessibility, and contingency are all in this sense closely related pictorial conditions contributory to and indeed constitutive of these maps' pictorial effects, thus shaping their historical significance.[26] Samuel Lewis, long in charge of Carey's operations, who died just as the atlas plates were being pulled, considered that the better maps that they produced, these certainly included, achieved an elegance that, in effect, made them "pictures."[27] And like many maps, perhaps more than most, complex overdetermined "pictures" they were.

Notes

1 See Denis Wood and John Fels, *The Natures of Maps: Cartographic Constructions of the Natural World* (Chicago, IL: University of Chicago Press, 2008), 7. In the introduction of *The History of Cartography*, vol. 1 (Chicago, IL: University of Chicago Press, 1987), xvi, J.B. Harley and David Woodward more generically define any such map as principally "a graphic representation that facilitates a spatial understanding."

2 See Edwin James, compiler, *Account of An Expedition From Pittsburgh To The Rocky Mountains, Performed In The Years 1819, and '20, By Order of The Hon. J. C. Calhoun, Sec'y of War: Under the Command of Major Stephen H. Long. From the Notes of Major Long, Mr. T. Say, and Other Gentlemen of the Exploring Party,* 2 vols, accompanied by an illustrated atlas (Philadelphia, PA: H.C. Carey and I. Lea, 1822).

3 Herman R. Friis, "Stephen H. Long's Unpublished Manuscript Map of the United States Compiled in 1820–22(?)," *California Geographer* 8 (1967): 77–78. Long amassed a considerable library of over 100 volumes for this purpose as well, many concerned with astronomical and geodetic observation and surveying; see Kenneth Haltman, "Figures in a Western Landscape: Reading the Art of Titian Ramsay Peale from the Long Expedition to the Rocky Mountains, 1819–1820," Ph.D. dissertation, Yale University, 1992, appendix A, 251–262.

4 James D. Graham, "Astronomical and Meteorological Records, and Vocabularies of Indian Languages, Taken on the Expedition for Exploring the Mississippi and Its Western Waters, &c.," in *Account of an Expedition*, 2: iii–v. Measurements of latitude required only an accurate instrument for calculating the height of the sun above the horizon and a reliable set of tables to correct for such factors as "the irregularity of the calendar year, oblique track of the sun across the sky, and the

celestial changes caused by the precession of the equinoxes." Measurements of longitude, the distance of a given place east or west from any other given place, far more complicated, required both a telescope and a chronometer; see Lloyd A. Brown, *The Story of Maps* [1949] (New York: Dover, 1979), 198, 202, 208. Before the end of Aug. 1819 observations to determine latitude were made with the circle of reflection "used as a sextant"; those afterward with the larger sextant itself, except for two occasions when the smaller sextant was preferred. The more precise though more elaborate use of spherical trigonometry to calculate the "true and apparent altitudes of objects," a science in which Graham had been trained by Andrew Ellicott at the Academy, was soon abandoned as impractical in favor of the simpler approach recommended by the Scottish astronomer Andrew Mackay; see Graham, "Astronomical and Meteorological Records," vi, and Andrew Mackay, *The Theory and Practice of Finding the Longitude at Sea or on Land, to Which are Added Various Methods of Determining the Latitude of a Place, &c.*, 2 vols (London: for J. Sewell et al., 1810), a work in the expedition library.

5 Long transmitted to Calhoun a bound copy of the Philadelphia edition of the *Account* on Dec. 21, 1822 and it became available for purchase by the end of the year. A London edition was published by Longman, Hurst, Rees, Orme, & Brown on Feb. 26, 1823; see Neil Woodman, "History and Dating of the Publication of the Philadelphia (1822) and London (1823) Editions of Edwin James's *Account of an Expedition from Pittsburgh to the Rocky Mountains*," *Archives of Natural History* 37 (2010): 28–38. Though the two versions appeared almost simultaneously, and Calhoun subsidized both, they differ. Even the maps in the two editions reveal shifts in the placement of geographic features and variant toponyms; see Herman R. Friis, "Stephen H. Long's Unpublished Manuscript Map of the United States Compiled in 1820–22(?)," *California Geographer* 8 (1967): 85, n. 57, where the Philadelphia version is described as the more cartographically accurate.

6 Raymond B. Craib, *Cartographic Mexico: A History of State Fixations and Fugitive Landscapes* (Durham, NC: Duke University Press, 2004), 8.

7 For the term "veiled rhetoric," see Robin Kelsey, *Archive Style: Photographs and Illustrations for U.S. Surveys, 1850–1890* (Berkeley, CA: University of California Press, 2007), 5.

8 Graham, "Astronomical and Meteorological Records," vii–viii.

9 These doodled features are not just stylistically discordant but impossibly out of scale, occupying "proportionately more space on the map than the features they represent occupy on the ground," the same being true even of the lines representing routes and symbols representing settlements and fortifications. Mark Monmonier, *How to Lie with Maps* (Chicago, IL: University of Chicago Press, 1991), 25 and passim.

10 See Kenneth Haltman, *Looking Close and Seeing Far: Samuel Seymour, Titian Ramsay Peale, and the Art of the Long Expedition, 1818–1823* (State College, PA: Penn State University Press, 2008), 43.

11 Wood and Fels (*The Natures of Maps*, xvii–xviii, n. 3; 32–33, nn. 1–2), following Charles Sanders Peirce, *Philosophical Writings of Peirce*, ed. Justus Buchler (New York: Dover, 1955), 98–119, define this graphic correspondence as *iconic*, as offering some resemblance to a referent while locating its existence in the real world, here a temporary village at such and such a location at a certain moment in time. However, recognizing the reliance of this particular usage on a set of associations shared with artists in the cartographer's circle, indeed employ, we might prefer to see the correspondence as metaphorical, pictorially so, an understanding

more amenable to the thematic insights I pursue here involving less indexical suggestions of dissociation, doubt, and instability.

12 See Haltman, *Looking Close and Seeing Far*, 88. Similar (of course triangular) teepees recur in Peale's expedition sketchbooks.

13 See Haltman, *Looking Close and Seeing Far*, 83–89.

14 The variety of expeditionary data susceptible of cartographic recording is suggested by the *Account* whose table of contents reads like that of an eighteenth-century miscellany. The summary description of vol. 2, ch. 10, which corresponds to the "moment" represented in this detail of the map, crossed by the expedition in late July 1820, reads: "Journey down the Arkansas—Thunderstorm—Some account of the Kiawa, Kaskaia, Arrappaho, and Shienne Indians—New species of toad." Of these topics, the first alone lends itself to (while the others frankly confuse) the cartographic purpose ostensibly at hand.

15 See Haltman, *Looking Close and Seeing Far*, 96–100.

16 *Account*, 2: 442: "Explanation of the Plate."

17 Raymond B. Craib, "A National Metaphysics: State Fixations, National Maps, and the Geo-Historical Imagination in Nineteenth-Century Mexico," *Hispanic American Historical Review* 82 (Feb. 2002): 34, n. 4.

18 Craib, *Cartographic Mexico*, 34.

19 In his original negotiation with Carey (as reported to Calhoun) it was agreed that the atlas would include "a Map or Maps of those parts of the country traversed by the expedition"; Stephen Harriman Long to John C. Calhoun, Nov. 6, 1821, Philadelphia, ALS. The number of maps was left unspecified; the decision to separate Eastern and Western sections thus expressed a particular later intention.

20 See John Pickles, *A History of Spaces: Cartographic Reason, Mapping and the Geo-coded World* (London: Routledge, 2004), passim; and also Magali M. Carrera, *Traveling from New Spain to Mexico: Mapping Practices of Nineteenth-Century Mexico* (Durham, NC: Duke University Press, 2011), 6–9.

21 Friis, "Stephen H. Long's Unpublished Manuscript Map," 85.

22 See Graham, "Astronomical and Meteorological Records," v. Long completed work on his paired maps "of the Country Drained by the Mississippi" (on a scale of 75 miles to an inch) by July 22, 1822, based on (though apparently differing from) a much larger original (on a scale of 36 miles to an inch) measuring 54 ½ × 48 ¾ inches already reported to be "in a state of considerable forwardness" the previous November. A large format, hand-colored version of the map was also included in the first and subsequent editions of Carey and Lea's *A Complete Historical, Chronological, and Geographical American Atlas* (1823); see Friis, "Stephen H. Long's Unpublished Manuscript Map," 86–87; Long to Calhoun, Nov. 3, 1821.

23 Calhoun, in a letter to Samuel Coate Atkinson in early Feb. 1820, acknowledged receipt of a map of the proposed road; see Calhoun to Atkinson, Feb. 7, 1820, in *The Papers of John C. Calhoun*, ed. W. Edwin Hemphill (Columbia: University of South Carolina Press, for South Caroliniana Society, 1967), 4: 646. The original map, preserved in the National Archives, measures 17 × 31 inches.

24 See Haltman, *Looking Close and Seeing Far*, 174–175, nn. 2–3.

25 Kelsey, *Archive Style*, 6. The collaborative nature of the interactions among professionals involved in the production of the atlas is suggested by Long's willingness, at least in theory, to share a percentage of the proceeds from the sale of the *Account*; see Stephen H. Long to John C. Calhoun, Nov. 6, 1821, Philadelphia, ALS, National Archives.

26 J.B. Harley, "Atlas Maker for Independent America," *Geographical Magazine* 49 (Sept. 1977): 766–771. Although this system "made good commercial sense," Harley acknowledges, "for a publisher so under-capitalized as Carey it is doubtful if there was a real alternative. Local engravers could be employed more cheaply than their counterparts in London or Paris, and there was a further advantage of immediate surveillance of the work and speed of production" (771).

27 Cited in Harley, "Atlas Maker for Independent America," 768.

5   Seeing Solitary Deserts Full of People

The Chorographic Commission in Colombia's Eastern Plains, 1856

Nancy P. Appelbaum

How did nineteenth-century cartographers and illustrators envision national territories? In particular, how did they see areas that they only partly glimpsed with their own eyes? How did they represent these regions for others to see? How and why did populations appear and disappear from view? How did such representations vary across different media, shaped by technologies and politics? Such questions are provoked by an 1856 manuscript map and watercolor illustrations depicting Colombia's Eastern Plains (*llanos orientales)* elaborated by the Chorographic Commission (1850–9), a Colombian government-sponsored geographic expedition led by an Italian military engineer, Agustín Codazzi (1793–1859).[1]

I was drawn to this huge map, when I first encountered it in the Colombian national archive, because it provides tantalizing glimpses of what art historian Magali Carrera calls the "fragmented appropriating processes" underlying map production.[2] The map is a hybrid of text and cartography. Boxes full of descriptive text and statistics line each side, as they do on all the provincial manuscript maps drafted by the commission. Unlike most of the provincial maps, however, this one contains over 60 notations that fill the main surface of the map itself. The notations provide details about ethnography, hydrography, and topography while explicitly acknowledging the local Indigenous and black informants who provided much of this information. The notations convey the impression of a diverse and populated region, even as they describe the plains as "vast and deserted savannahs."[3]

This essay examines the 1856 map along with some of the commission's watercolor illustrations and texts to consider how geographers obtained and represented knowledge about a vast swath of territory that the state claimed but did not actually control. In the pages that follow, I argue that the commission depicted grasslands as both solitary and full of people. This paradox, I suggest, reflects differences in how commissioners depicted places and peoples they observed with their own eyes and instruments—however partial or obscured their view might have been—and those they did not personally see, or rather, that they saw through others' eyes. After Codazzi died and the commission ended in 1859, the paradox was resolved by visually emptying out the landscape of its inhabitants. Subsequent published maps based on the 1856

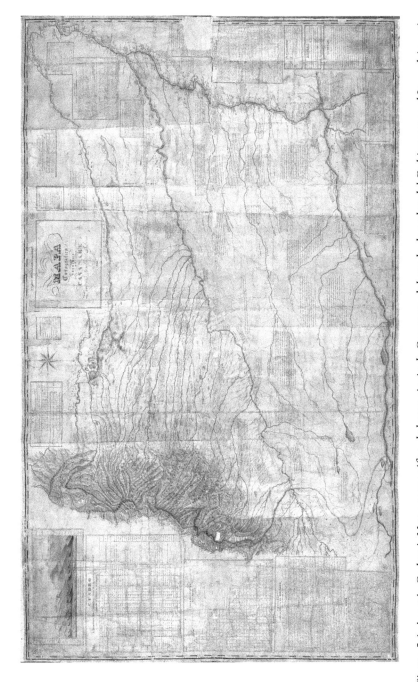

Figure 5.1 Agustín Codazzi. *Mapa corográfico de la provincia de Casanare elaborado de orden del Gobierno por el Jeneral Agustín Codazzi.* 1856. Manuscript. 143 × 240 cm. Courtesy of Archivo General de la Nación de Colombia, Bogotá, Mapoteca 6, Referencia 14.

manuscript elided the contributions of inhabitants of Indigenous and African descent, and indeed, their very existence; the region appeared truly solitary.[4] Thus, in the production of official geographic data for the state, local communities' own knowledge of their environs was appropriated, obscured, and ultimately used to justify their colonization and displacement.

The Chorographic Commission

The Chorographic Commission of New Granada was modeled on a similar project that Codazzi had carried out in Venezuela in the 1830s, in which he drew on the technical training he had received as a young officer in Napoleon's Italian army.[5] After fighting in both the Napoleonic wars and South American independence wars, he became a military officer in the first republic of Colombia (which lasted from 1821 to 1830 and included contemporary Ecuador and Venezuela). He helped found the republic of Venezuela in 1830 and spent much of the subsequent decade mapping it.[6] In 1848 his political faction fell from power and he fled persecution along with his Venezuelan family to neighboring New Granada, as Colombia was then known.[7]

Codazzi signed a contract with the government of New Granada in 1850 to lead a commission to "create a general map of [the] Republic and a chorographic map of each of its provinces."[8] The government intended for the Chorographic Commission to promote capitalist modernization and expand state control over its ill-defined national territory. The commission's mandate was to map, describe, and illustrate the defining features of each province, and so to build, province-by-province, a national map and illustrated text and statistical charts.[9]

Codazzi's commissions in both Venezuela and New Granada thus adapted the seemingly antiquated concept of chorography to the modern imperatives of republican state building.[10] In the early modern world, "chorography" had often referred to highly pictorial maps of local cities or regions, sometimes commissioned by urban elites and often showing cityscapes from an oblique perspective.[11] For Codazzi, chorography depicted "a province with all of its most notable points, such as the position of towns, direction of the mountains, lakes and rivers, borders of the neighboring provinces, and configuration of the land that it describes."[12] He contrasted chorography with topography, by which he alluded to topographic surveys consisting of unbroken networks of triangles plotted across entire national territories and kingdoms, the gold standard for mapping modern states in the nineteenth century. New Granada and Venezuela lacked financial resources and infrastructure to sponsor such comprehensive surveys. Codazzi insisted, in the face of public criticism, that chorography provided a legitimate alternative and the only viable option given local conditions.[13] The "chorographers" (as Codazzi called them) took a holistic approach to each province that integrated descriptive narratives and statistics with illustrations and maps.[14]

The chorographic tradition provided one source of scientific legitimacy for Codazzi's approach; Alexander von Humboldt was another. Humboldt, who had traveled in the same region half a century earlier, employed an integrated and holistic methodology that emphasized the visual "physiognomy" or "aspect" of coherent natural regions, each one unified by its plant life, climate, and physical features. Codazzi quoted Humboldt and cited Humboldt's measurements in both Venezuela and New Granada.

Over the course of the decade, the commission consisted of a shifting group of from two to four official members, including both native-born *granadinos* and foreign-born men like Codazzi. A team of workers accompanied them. Each year the commission would set out at the end of December—the start of the relatively dry season—for a different part of New Granada. The group would spend months mapping and sketching a section of the country. Back in Bogotá for the last few months of the year, Codazzi and several assistants finished up the chorographic maps, while he wrote individual reports on each province and made shorter excursions. An illustrator would finish watercolors based on sketches made in the field.

Among Codazzi's succession of fellow commissioners, the longest lasting was *granadino* artist, cartographer, and military officer Manuel María Paz (1820–1902). Paz started working with the commission in the early 1850s and assisted Codazzi until the latter's death in 1859. The most prolific of the commission's several illustrators, Paz also served as Codazzi's secretary and assistant mapmaker. Paz documented the 1856 trip to the Eastern Plains in pencil, ink, and watercolor and he collaborated on the 1856 map. After the expedition, Paz submitted at least ten small watercolor paintings of the Eastern Plains to the government. They are preserved in the Chorographic Commission's official collection in Colombia's National Library.[15]

The Chorographic Commission was one of most ambitious geographical expeditions in nineteenth-century South America, yet it was technologically limited, minimally staffed, and plagued by obstacles and illness.[16] Scientific instruments repeatedly broke; civil conflicts erupted. Codazzi negotiated constantly with government officials over funding, contract extensions, and control over publications and personnel. The commission tried to cover the whole country, but its reach was limited. The chorographers kept mostly to well-worn trails, inhabited settlements, and known navigable waterways as they made their way through mountain ranges and tropical lowlands.

Codazzi's fieldwork involved extensive personal observations along with trigonometric and astronomic calculations to establish locations and altitudes. Yet even in the Andean regions, where he spent the most time and did his most extensive surveying, he could not measure everything with his own eyes or instruments. He drew heavily on previous expeditions. He sent questions to local officials and intellectuals in advance of his visits, compiled their reports, examined their collections of artifacts, and convened meetings of local notables and guides.[17] Wherever he traveled, he relied on local guides (known in Spanish as *baquianos* or *prácticos*), usually men of humble extraction, who often knew the local terrain and resources "with exactitude."[18] He expressed disdain for them, however, when their beliefs contradicted his own.[19] In the frontier region of the Eastern Plains (and even more so the following year, when he visited the

Amazon Basin), he had little option but to rely heavily on the knowledge of such guides and other residents. Most such informants were never named in the reports or on the maps, but they were often acknowledged anonymously. The acknowledged informants were men, but local women likely contributed as well.

Most of the population of New Granada lived in the three Andean mountain ranges of the country's interior, where higher altitudes lowered the tropical temperatures, and along the Caribbean Coast. Accustomed to the temperate climate of the cordilleras, the commissioners' views of the tropical lowland frontier were filtered through prior assumptions and prejudices. In particular, the commissioners replicated an already well-established dichotomy that pitted the cool highlands, which *granadino* intellectuals tended to associate with civilization, health, and progress, against the hot lowlands, associated with disease and savagery.[20]

Particularly feared were the mosquito-borne diseases endemic to the lowlands (attributed in the nineteenth century not to mosquitos but to "bad airs" caused by rotting organic materials in humid climates). These fears were justified; over the course of the decade, several of the commission's support workers died and everyone on the expeditions took ill at one point or another. Codazzi himself expired on an expedition to the Caribbean Coast in 1859 from unspecified "fevers." The journey through the largely hot, low-lying plains of the Orinoco Basin in 1856 was especially plagued by illness and injury.

Expedition to the Eastern Plains

In December 1855 the Chorographic Commission stood on the slopes of the Andes and looked out at the view of the province of Casanare, which stretched eastward toward Venezuela. Codazzi noted that, from a distance, the far plains of Casanare seemed like an empty ocean, turning a hazy blue as they stretched out toward the limitless horizon.[21] He saw the landscape as monotonous and still, which he found disheartening: "The uniformity of those plains, in which everything appeared immobile, does not refrain from being imposing, although sad."[22] Codazzi repeatedly used the word *soledad* (solitude or loneliness), to describe the region, along with "immense" and "desert." He compared the landscape to a vast ocean that made men feel small and alone. The sparse inhabitants of the plains of Casanare, he wrote, were "drowning in a sea of grass."[23]

Manuel María Paz's watercolor titled *Province of Casanare. General View of "The Plains"* (Figure 5.2) suggests how the commission might first have seen the plains. Painted from the vantage point of higher ground, possibly the foothills of the eastern Andes, the image depicts an infinite expanse dotted with palms. The extent of the landscape diminishes the few heads of cattle in the foreground; smaller still are a lone horse and rider. No human or bovine inhabitants are visible further out on the open plain, but columns of smoke suggest the presence of unseen Indians off in the distance. The cattle and

Figure 5.2 Manuel María Paz, *Provincia de Casanare. Vista jeneral de "Los Llanos,"* c.1856. Watercolor, 23.8 × 30.5 cm. Courtesy of Biblioteca Nacional de Colombia, Bogotá.

horseman might be construed as the future colonizers of this great expanse. The quotation marks in the title suggest the extent to which "the plains" were widely understood as forming a coherent region, distinct from the Andean interior.

As the commission descended down into the foothills and plains, its members and support workers took ill. By the end of January almost all of the laborers were sick. José del Carmen Carrasquel, the indispensable *mayordomo* in charge of the commission's logistics, fractured his arm in an accident involving his mule. Paz, meanwhile, "was at the foot of the tomb."[24] Codazzi suffered from diarrhea and fevers. His letters home chronicled his team's injuries, intestinal worms, dysentery, fevers, abscesses, and diarrhea as well as the various cures he applied, some of which had been obtained from Indians.[25]

They traveled first through villages in and near the foothills. Codazzi then left the sick and injured men in the village of Moreno, the provincial capital, while he, his teenage son Domingo, an unnamed guide, and a cook struck out across the plains by land and water with boatmen and muleteers, who included local inhabitants pressed into service. The group ventured as far north and east as the Arauca River and the Venezuelan border and traveled along the

Meta River, but the travelers still saw only narrow swathes of the plains. The commission returned to Bogotá in early March, exhausted and ill; Codazzi described his team as an "ambulatory hospital," including seven sick men carried in hammocks.[26]

Although the ailing Paz apparently did not accompany them very far into the plains, he did depict Agustín and Domingo Codazzi camped by the side of the Meta River (Figure 5.3).[27] With them was a man of indeterminate ethnicity in a shirt and pants, crouched near the campfire (possibly the cook or guide; he appears in other images that Paz painted of the expedition). Also present were Indigenous men in loincloths and an Indigenous woman in a smock, bearing plantains—a rare bit of evidence of women's many contributions to the commission. A capybara (*chigüiru*), a large rodent native to the plains, roasted over a fire. Two Indigenous men behind them tended the group's thatch-covered boat. Domingo held a gun, suggestive of either the dangers they faced or his prowess as a capybara hunter, while Agustín practiced science with map and compass in hand.[28] Father and son wore boots and jackets, defying the hot temperatures suggested by the scant clothes of their companions. Their clothes and scientific instruments evidenced the Codazzis' ostensibly civilized status amidst putative savagery.

Figure 5.3 Manuel María Paz, *Provincia de Casanare. Ranchería a orillas del Meta,* c.1856. Watercolor. 18.3 × 25.7 cm. Courtesy of Biblioteca Nacional de Colombia, Bogotá.

Depictions of Indians: The Casanare Map and Watercolors

Back up in the high Andean national capital of Bogotá after their arduous journey to the eastern lowlands, Codazzi, Paz, and additional assistants drew on field sketches and notes to elaborate a large map of the plains, alongside textual reports and Paz's watercolor paintings, for submission to the government (Figure 5.1). At just under 5 × 8 ft., it was the largest provincial map that the commission submitted to the government. The title of the map refers only to the specific province of Casanare, which officially corresponded to an area north of the Meta River, yet the map actually depicted a wider section of the Orinoco Basin. It included the jurisdiction of San Martín (or Meta), south of the Meta River and a fair amount of territory claimed by Venezuela. The map thus constituted the Eastern Plains as a coherent region, framed by the Arauca, Orinoco, and Guaviare Rivers, to the north, east, south respectively, and by the Andean cordillera to the west.

Like all of the commission's "chorographic" manuscript maps of individual provinces, the Casanare map constitutes a multi-faceted hybrid of methodologies: it combines text and imagery while simultaneously employing multiple measurement units and scales and cramming descriptive statistics and narratives into boxes along the margins (Figure 5.4). The commission's provincial maps used both the metric system and New Granada measurement units. In the top left corner, an image called a *Perspectiva ideal* compares "the altitude of the hills and mountains of the province to sea level" by depicting hills and mountains jumbled together, towering behind a flat plain. The writing appears to be in Paz's hand, at least in part (Codazzi, whose Spanish was imperfect, relied on his *granadino* collaborators when drafting official texts).[29]

Anna Jagdmann points out that this map conveys an overall impression of two radically differentiated spaces: the Andean and the other.[30] On the far left is a densely plotted mountainous landscape, with relief indicated by shading. Most of the rest of the map appears flat, with barely perceptible elevation other than a few scattered ridges and hills. The Eastern Plains are thus defined in opposition to the Andes by an absence of relief. [31] Their exaggerated flatness reinforces the highland–lowland dichotomy that pervaded most descriptions of nineteenth-century Colombia.

Rather than try and analyze the map in all of its complexity, I focus here on the notations that Paz wrote across the surface of the mapped landscape (Figures 5.4, 5.5). Similar notations cover a subsequent manuscript map of the southern part of the Eastern Plains as well as some rough maps that Codazzi sketched of both the Orinoco and Amazon Basins (the latter were most likely drafted in the field, first in Venezuela in the 1830s and later in New Granada).[32] In this aspect, the manuscript maps of the Amazon and Orinoco frontiers appear quite different from the maps that the commission drafted of the interior Andean provinces, which the commission surveyed in far greater detail. Cartographic conventions that indicate fixed locations of communities, borders, and topographical features fill the Andean provincial maps, leaving space for only occasional notations.[33]

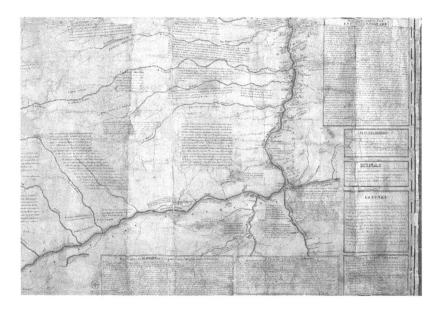

Figure 5.4 Detail of Codazzi, *Mapa corográfico de la provincia de Casanare*, including some of the boxed inserts along the edges of the map and notations on the map. Courtesy of Archivo General de la Nación de Colombia, Bogotá, Mapoteca 6, Referencia 14.

Only the maps of the eastern and southeastern tropical frontiers seem to have room for abundant notations. As scholars have pointed out, the notations provide a practical way to fill otherwise empty uncharted spaces—by substituting text for cartography—and to indicate the location of Indigenous groups in order to facilitate their conquest and subjugation.[34] While undoubtedly correct, these explanations are insufficient. The notations have additional implications that are worth considering.

The appearance of the notations, in relation to the ways in which the map presents other information, provides clues as to how the mapmakers regarded the information contained within them. The notations on the Casanare map look very different than the marginalia along the edges of the map (Figures 5.4 and 5.5). The latter are presented in various formats—tables of statistics, narrative lists, and illustrations of comparative altitude. This information is consistently placed in box inserts with clear borders, under headings written in block print (the descriptive text itself, in both the inserts and the notations, is in cursive). The notations, on the other hand, do not have borders and are located on the map itself, sandwiched between or flowing over rivers and creeks (Figure 5.5). This is not to say that the notations are entirely free form; the edges appear carefully ruled or plotted to fit around topographical features on the map. But the lack of borders nonetheless makes the information contained in the notations seem informal and of a lower order of importance—or certainty—than that

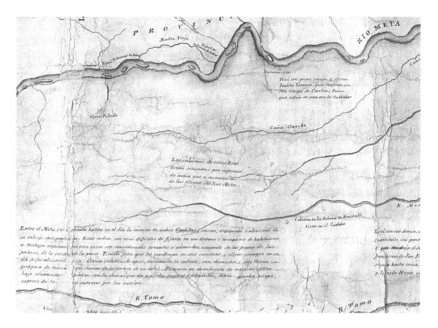

Figure 5.5 Detail of Codazzi, *Mapa corográfico de la provincia de Casanare*: Notations, including one referring to the Guahibos as "dirty, disgusting, and proud of their savage independence." Courtesy of Archivo General de la Nación de Colombia, Bogotá, Mapoteca 6, Referencia 14.

of the boxed data around the edges. Codazzi likely intended that the boxed marginalia would be reproduced in the printed versions of the maps.[35] It is not known if he intended the more informal notations to be printed, or if they were only meant for the eyes of the government officials who received the manuscript maps.

Many of the notations are ethnographic: they describe particular Indigenous ethnic groups, labeled by the mapmakers as Guahibos, Achaguas, and Salivas, among others. These textual descriptions of Indigenous populations contrast with the conventions used to indicate official, non-Indigenous settlements. The ethnographic notations lack the fixity of the towns and villages marked with circular symbols on the map. Different sized circles and dots indicate, in descending order of size (and thus importance) "Provincial Capital," "Circuit Seat," "Parish," "Village or Hamlet," and, finally, "House" (*casita*). The dots fix these communities and homesteads in specific locations on the mapped landscape, while the Indigenous people seem to float across the terrain. Lumped with descriptions of natural topographical features, the Indians appear as natural facets of the landscape and, yet, also nomadic and displaceable. Their lack of fixity implies they will be pushed aside (or perhaps rolled over, like the land itself), as civilization marches forward across the plain in the form of established villages and towns. The map thus acknowledges Indigenous presence while minimizing or even nullifying Indigenous territorial claims, thereby also officially validating claims of recent settlers.[36] Any Indigenous polities or borders that might have existed are ignored. The non-Indigenous communities were officially recognized and located as well-defined places, while the Indians were depicted as hovering in amorphous spaces.

At first glance this representational disparity seems unremarkable. It seems obvious that villages and towns were permanent and that Indians—especially the notoriously mobile and aggressive Guahibos—were nomadic. On the Casanare map Codazzi described "the nation of Guahibo Indians" located between the Meta and Vichada Rivers as

> dirty, disgusting, and proud of their savage independence … more difficult to fix in a terrain and incapable of accustoming themselves to regular work, for this reason they are considered errant or nomads, living off of palm fruits, hunting, and fishing.[37]

More recently, historian Jane Rausch, drawing on Codazzi and other sources, refers to the Guahibos as "true nomads" who "had no dwelling of any kind and never spent more than two or three days in the same place."[38]

Paz's watercolor images reinforce this stereotype of the savage Guahibo, especially *Province of Casanare. Guahibo Indians* (Figure 5.6). This stilted tableau places an Indian group—possibly a family—against a lush backdrop of palms and ferns. The men wear loincloths. They are not entirely untouched by commerce and civilization; one man carries a steel knife and the woman or girl wears the smock typical of Indigenous people living in communities influenced by missionaries (like the woman in Figure 5.3). The composition revolves around a seated, presumably older, man with a taciturn expression; the subjects do not visibly interact but rather stare off into the distance. It is both similar and different to dozens of other images painted by the commission of local inhabitants in their native environments. Throughout New Granada, the commission's illustrators repeatedly depicted local inhabitants of varying complexion and gradations of racial mixture in homes or arrayed in the central plazas and main streets of villages and towns, for example one in a village on the Meta River (Figure 5.7). In each case, the built environment indexed the commission's assessment of the relative progress or backwardness of the specified community, from the rickety mud and thatch houses of lowland Pacific Coastal villages to the white balconies, cobblestones, and tiled roofs of highland Antioquia. The presumably nomadic Guahibos, on the other hand, were not placed in a public square; their plaza was the forest, their homes the palm groves and grasslands of Casanare.

Such scenes were staged to convey particular impressions about local inhabitants, in this case an impression of savagery. Paz assembled *Guahibo Indians* from various elements. His field notebook contains a watercolor study, labeled "Forest on the banks of the Meta River," similar to his family portrait of Guahibos.[39] But it shows only the backdrop: the trees. He added the

Figure 5.6 Manuel María Paz. *Provincia de Casanare. Indios Guahibos,* c.1856. Watercolor. 23.5 × 19.8 cm. Courtesy of Biblioteca Nacional de Colombia, Bogotá.

humans later, based in part on sketches he made of the faces and upper bodies of Guahibo "types" and perhaps on instructions from Codazzi to depict specific clothing and tools. Paz would not have seen the most "savage" Guahibos in their own homes and habitats; rather he would have met only the ones who came to trade in the towns and villages on the western edge of the plains, where he convalesced. Indeed, in both the Orinoco and Amazon expeditions, his sketchbook and official illustrations reflect that he spent time observing the Indigenous and mestizo people who lived in or near official settlements.

Figure 5.7 Manuel María Paz. *Provincia de Casanare. Vista de un pueblo a orillas del rio Meta. Sambo Mestizo Mulato,* c.1856. Watercolor. 26.2 × 20.3 cm. Courtesy of Biblioteca Nacional de Colombia, Bogotá.

Codazzi and Paz clearly accepted and contributed to an enduring and widespread stereotype of the Guahibo Indians as hostile and primitive nomads, but a closer look at Codazzi's comments on the Casanare map and in his accompanying reports yields an unexpectedly nuanced view of Guahibos and other Indians. The local officials' reports compiled by Codazzi recounted that nomadic Indigenous groups circulated through the same lands each year.[40] Some had settled seasonally or even year around along rivers or on mission lands. On the Casanare map, Codazzi located Guahibos and other ethnicities geographically in particular areas. He mentioned some Guahibos who lived near a river and helped travelers pass over a rapid. One of the notations even specifies that the Chorographic Commission visited this group's well-constructed house. The notation describing this friendly and sedentary Guahibo community sits on the map within a few inches of the notation, quoted above, that described Guahibos as filthy and errant.

A possible explanation for this disjuncture is that Codazzi and Paz depicted the people with whom they personally interacted somewhat differently than the ones they learned about secondhand. Thus, Codazzi wrote in 1858, when describing his own interactions in other regions: "How many times have I seen an Indian take one of his tender children in his arms and cuddle and play with him? Does one need more evident proof of the paternal love of these savages?"[41] Yet, in the same report, he quoted Humboldt regarding the putative inscrutability of "the Indian": "the barbarous nations have a physiognomy of tribe rather than individual ... [the Indian] being far from all cultivation ... guided only by his physical wants ... drags on a dull, monotonous life."[42] His personal observation about the "savages" he encountered was condescending but more nuanced than the received racism from Humboldt.

While the plains Indigenous communities were not as mobile as often assumed, the settler communities were not so settled. According to Rausch, such communities "led a precarious existence."[43] Ostensibly permanent settlements were actually quite ephemeral. Most colonial missions had long since disappeared. Several of the mid-century towns and villages had been moved, often more than once, from one location to another, due to epidemics, floods, and "bad airs." Those permanent-looking dots and circles on the map are actually deceptive, reflecting more of an aspiration of permanent settlement and consistent state presence rather than a reality.

The ethnographic notations, for their part, give the impression that a diverse population inhabited every corner of the landscape, a visual impression that both complements and contradicts the content of the textual descriptions on the map itself and in some of the commission's reports and paintings. Visibly inhabiting the Casanare map were the same Indians that Paz's landscape view made invisible. On the map, the Eastern Plains do not appear deserted. In fact, there is very little empty space on the map. The texts—both the notations on the maps and Codazzi's accompanying textual reports—go into ethnographic detail about the history and contemporary state of many groups that made up the Indigenous population, which Codazzi estimated at 22,000.

Codazzi's Eastern Plains thus constituted a solitary desert full of people, topographic features, cultures, and history. The people who inhabited it were portrayed as temporary obstacles to the civilized state's march of progress across the land. Progress would have to transform both land and people. As Codazzi argued in a public report about Casanare: "two great obstacles oppose development: the climate and the Indians. Both can be modified with time."[44] Meanwhile, in order to facilitate such transformation, the existing Indians were differentiated and dissected. They were also located in particular spaces on the map and acknowledged as sources of cartographic and ethnographic knowledge.

Appropriating and Acknowledging Local Knowledge

The use of notations to indicate areas inhabited by Indians had many precedents. Imperial and early-republican manuscript and published maps had often included the putative names of Indigenous groups.[45] Humboldt's 1814 engraved map of the Orinoco River, in particular, might have served as a model for Codazzi.[46] Like the Casanare manuscript map, Humboldt's printed map indicated the location of various Indigenous peoples. Humboldt's notations indicated geographical features and locations, some of which were written in the first person. His notations, moreover, explicitly cited local Indigenous sources of information, for example "the Indians of Javita and of Davipé assured me the sources of the Guainía and Inirida [rivers] are nearby."[47] A recent work by several Colombian historians therefore characterizes Humboldt's map as an "indigenous oral history" that was "dictated" by native informants.[48]

Like Humboldt, Codazzi relied on local guides and drew on local knowledge, both Indigenous and otherwise. Like Humboldt, Codazzi combined Indigenous oral history with information from previous explorers (including Humboldt himself). And like Humboldt, Codazzi acknowledged his informants quite explicitly on the surface of the map itself. One individual referenced repeatedly was a certain *"negro venezolano,"* whom Codazzi encountered on the expedition and recognized as a boatman who had once transported him in Venezuela, long before. The Venezuelan provided a great deal of useful information to the commission. Codazzi prefaced one notation about the Cabres Indians with a caveat: "If credit can be given to the same Venezuelan black ..." Thus, Codazzi explicitly admitted using blacks and Indians as sources of both ethnographic and geographic information, while implying that their information might not be entirely reliable. He might have cited them so scrupulously precisely in order to distance himself from information he was unable to verify personally.[49]

Local informants often remained anonymous. Despite the Venezuelan's importance to the commission and prior connection to Codazzi, the man was never named; he was preserved in the historical record as a generic type rather than an individual. Codazzi also cited anonymous Indigenous sources. For example, some Indigenous residents "indicated" the location of rivers "with their hand."[50] An unnamed "Indian from San Miguel" spoke enough Spanish to provide Codazzi with sufficient information to locate the headwaters and course of a river. A few were given first names on the map, such as an Indian named Simón of a former mission, and a "a rational Indian named Miguel," whose community assisted travelers along a difficult stretch of the Meta River. Meanwhile, Codazzi seemed always to name his European and elite *granadino* informants. Choices made about whether or not to name informants—to fully recognize their individuality, humanity, and "rationality"—reflected Codazzi's and his collaborators' assumptions about race and civilization.

Rationality, which most Indians were assumed to lack, apparently constituted a prerequisite for national belonging. Codazzi expressed great pessimism about their potential for *granadino* citizenship:

> we should not believe that the Indians of Casanare and Meta can be reduced with speeches or learning Christian doctrine, these things will be attained later, when a large population mass will have mixed with them and formed a distinct race, as has already succeeded in other parts of the Republic.[51]

One of the Casanare map's notations said of the Saliva Indians: "little be expected of their limited intellect, which will be modified with time and mixture with other more intelligent persons." Mixture with other peoples was the key to their modification. Codazzi argued that, as a general rule,

> wherever the indigene has crossed with the European or African, he has become enterprising, manifesting clear understanding, activity, and an educable nature. Wherever such mixes have crossed among themselves returning toward Indian origin, the portion of social talents has decreased. Where the indigenous race has been conserved as pure, everything sleeps.[52]

In these racist comments, Codazzi echoed arguments made by several of his prominent *granadino* friends and collaborators, including José María Samper and Manuel Ancízar.[53] The commission's watercolors showing varying degrees of mixture, such as Paz's racially mixed "sambo, mestizo, mulatto" types (Figure 5.7), advanced this same broader argument: mixture was unifying and whitening the diverse population of New Granada. The result, according to the advocates of mixture, would be an enterprising and republican *raza granadina*, of light complexion and democratic disposition.[54]

For Codazzi, the environment (the "climate") would also need to be transformed to facilitate colonization. Blacks and Indians were assumed to better withstand the ravages of tropical humidity and bad airs than whites and mestizos. So black and Indigenous labor would be necessary to drain wetlands and tear down forests. Codazzi envisioned people of African descent playing a key intermediary role in such transformations. He proposed unsuccessfully that the state license "men of color"—blacks and mulattos—to act as entrepreneurial Indian agents or *capitanes pobladores* (populating captains), who would organize and supervise Indigenous agricultural communities.[55] He likely based his proposal on examples and ideas afforded by some local guides of African descent who assisted him in the Amazonian territory of Caquetá.[56] Codazzi also drew on a long colonial legacy of forcibly "reducing" or "concentrating" conquered peoples into sedentary communities.[57]

The Posthumous Maps: Emptied Spaces

Codazzi died in 1859, before the commission's maps and images could be engraved and printed. He had wanted to publish "chorographic maps, in the same scales that they have been presented to the Government of the Republic" to accompany an extensive atlas and illustrated books combining images, maps, and text.[58] Those plans died with him. In the 1860s, the government did sponsor Paz and another of Codazzi's *granadino* collaborators, Manuel Ponce de León, to publish texts and atlases in Paris. The results, however, were far less elaborate than Codazzi had envisioned (Figure 5.8).

Paz and de León published an atlas of state maps. Each map incorporated several former provinces, now combined into states.[59] The map of the new state of Boyacá, to which the former province of Casanare had been appended in 1858, reproduced and accentuated the highland–lowland dichotomy (Figure 5.8). The Boyacá highlands were densely plotted, while the plains portion of the state was presented as a flattened landscape, vacant except for rivers flowing through the plains and a few scattered dots representing official towns and villages. The map (like a similar one for the new state of Cundinamarca to the south) obliterated the Indigenous population that Codazzi and Paz had originally depicted as inhabiting every nook and cranny of the Eastern Plains.

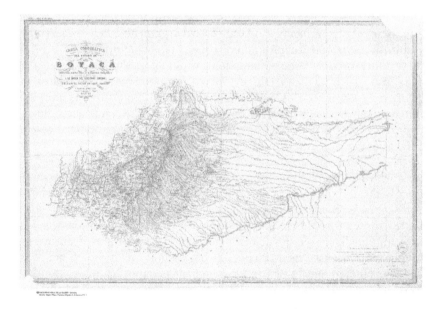

Figure 5.8 Manuel Ponce de León and Manuel María Paz. *Carta corográfica del estado de Boyacá. Construida con los datos de la Comisión Corográfica y del orden del Gobierno General.* 1864. 58 × 90 cm. Courtesy of Archivo General de la Nación de Colombia, Bogotá, Mapoteca 6, Referencia 2.

Indigenous polities, which had not qualified for the commission as legitimate places worthy of formal symbolic representation on the map, were no longer indicated in any manner. Thus, Indigenous inhabitants were simply erased, and any obstacle they may have posed to settlement and capitalist progress was elided.

In eliminating references to the local population and geographical features, moreover, the printed maps obscured the varied local sources of knowledge upon which they were based. Official knowledge assimilated local knowledge while erasing the intellectual contributions of local informants. The underlying "bricolage" inherent to modern cartography was no longer acknowledged; the printed maps appeared as seamless wholes.[60] As a group of scholars recently noted, "in contrast with the manuscript maps, the finished cartography of the commission erased any allusion to the expedition's journey."[61] The local heterogeneity and provincial particularities emphasized by Codazzi's chorographic approach were smoothed out to create more homogeneous spaces. On the printed maps, moreover, the uncertainty of the mapmakers' own knowledge and the incompleteness of their vision was no longer admitted. Without the caveats expressed in the hand-written notations, the printed maps conveyed finality; they imposed an aura of certainty and fixity on highly uncertain and tenuous knowledge.

The elision of local inhabitants, knowledge, and uncertainties can be attributed in part to the simplifying technology of the printing process, reduction in scale, and concerns about cost. At about a quarter of the size of the biggest provincial manuscripts, the printed state maps were necessarily less detailed. The Colombian state, which was poor and unstable at that time, afforded little in the way of subsidies for more elaborate products, such as the chorographic wall maps originally envisioned by Codazzi. These factors, however, do not entirely account for the revision. Earlier nineteenth-century printed maps often did indicate the locations of Indigenous peoples. Humboldt, as noted above, included similar notations and caveats across the surface of his engraved map of the Orinoco.

Politics as well as technology shaped the publications. The printed maps and geographical texts were the subject of power struggles between competing factions that sought to control and shape Codazzi's legacies.[62] One of the major contenders was the powerful military strongman and three-time president Tomás Cipriano de Mosquera (1798–1878). A practitioner of geographic science himself, he had helped create the Chorographic Commission in the late 1840s and subsequently became one of its strongest critics. Among other objections to the commission, Mosquera criticized Codazzi's reliance on local informants: "General Codazzi ... cites in his notes an innumerable list of lakes where he never was, according to the accounts that some Indian or black from around there gave him."[63] As a diplomat stationed in Paris in the mid-1860s, Mosquera supervised the revision, printing, and public presentation of the commission's first atlas. Mosquera probably did not want to be seen by European scientists and investors as uncertain about his nation's geography; much less would he have wanted, in that era of increasingly virulent scientific racism, to admit that much of this knowledge was created by ostensibly inferior races. Moreover, an image of a territory inhabited and controlled by *indígenas* would not have been conducive to the goal of stimulating foreign investment and immigration.[64]

While the initial hand-drawn maps had been intended mainly for the eyes of government officials, the printed maps entered a transatlantic visual economy of circulation and reproduction.[65] Copied several times over the second half of the nineteenth century by Paz and other cartographers, these maps were intended to be seen by numerous and diverse viewers on both sides of the Atlantic, ranging from Colombian schoolchildren to European geographers, immigrants, and investors. After Codazzi's death, the commission's depiction of the Eastern Plains was thus transformed by Colombian mapmakers and statesmen (in collaboration with Parisian engravers and printers) from a complex and diverse space of inter-cultural intellectual exchange to an empty space—what some recent scholars would call a "stage space" for enacting imperialism or, in this case, for republican state building.[66] The Eastern Plains were reconstituted as a blank slate on which the future history of the nation would be written.

The Eastern Plains were open for business—the business of investors who would obtain swathes of public land to develop as cattle ranches, as well as the enterprise of many poor peasants who would follow the rivers down from the mountains to clear land and settle. By the late nineteenth century, investors and settlers from the highlands were flooding into the plains, especially the southern plains south of the Meta River. Violent conflicts over resources ensued (and continue, in various forms, to this day). Although the nineteenth-century Colombian state did not engage in wholesale military campaigns of slaughter and displacement on the scale of, say, the United States or Argentina, the conquest of the plains was nonetheless brutal and catastrophic.[67] Settlers reportedly declared open season on the "savage" Indians; they created the verb *guahibiar* to refer to the hunting down and killing of Guahibo Indians. By the end of the century, missionaries would be contracted by the national government to protect and "civilize" the surviving "savages." Thus, the state once again acknowledged the existence and even the souls of the Indigenous inhabitants of the Eastern Plains, if not their full humanity and legitimacy.

Notes

1 This chapter reworks and expands on material included in Nancy P. Appelbaum, *Mapping the Country of Regions: The Chorographic Commission of Nineteenth-Century Colombia* (Chapel Hill, NC: University of North Carolina Press, 2016), esp. 131–166.

2 Carrera, *Traveling from New Spain to Mexico: Mapping Practices of Nineteenth-Century Mexico* (Durham, NC: Duke University Press, 2011), 8.

3 In addition to the map itself, see also Agustín Codazzi, "Descripción de la Provincia de Casanare: Geografía física y política," in *Territorio de Casanare*, book 1, vol. 3, of *Obras completas de la Comisión Corográfica: Geografía Física y Política de*

la Confederación Granadina, ed. Augusto J. Gómez López, Guido Barona Becerra, and Camilo A. Domínguez Ossa (Bogotá: Fundación Puerto Rastrojo, Fundación Gaia, and Editora Géminis, 2000), esp. 75–76, 88, 105–109.

4   On how native polities, borders, and inhabitants were scrubbed from maps, particularly in North America, see Juliana Barr and Edward Countryman, "Introduction: Maps and Spaces, Paths to Connect, and Lines to Divide," in Juliana Barr and Edward Countryman (eds), *Contested Spaces of Early America* (Philadelphia, PA: University of Pennsylvania Press, 2014), 1–30.

5   Giorgio Antei, *Los heroes errantes: Historia de Agustin Codazzi, 1793–1822* (Bogotá: Planeta Colombiana Editorial, 1993), 41–44; Juan José Pérez Rancel, *Agustín Codazzi, Italia y la construcción del Nuevo Mundo* (Venezuela: Petroglifo Producciones, 2002), esp. 25–72. Of many works on Codazzi's life and the Chorographic Commission, the most complete is Efraín Sánchez, *Gobierno y geografía. Agustín Codazzi y la Comisión Corográfica de la Nueva Granada* (Colombia: Ancora Editores, 1998). The commission's principal co-founder, along with Codazzi, was *granadino* intellectual and official Manuel Ancízar, who traveled with the commission during its first two years.

6   The first republic of Colombia, founded in 1821, split into Venezuela, New Granada (now Colombia), and Ecuador by 1830.

7   The Republic of New Granada lasted from 1830 to 1858.

8   "Contrata para el levantamiento de la carta jeográfica de la Nueva Granada," *Gaceta Oficial* (Bogotá), Mar. 14, 1850, 103.

9   The exact number of provinces varied between 33 and 36 across the decade as they were subdivided, recombined, and finally, in 1858, abolished.

10 On the classical origins of "chorography" versus "geography" see Fred Lukermann, "The Concept of Location in Classical Geography," *Annals of the Association of American Geographers* 51, no. 2 (June 1961): 194–195.

11 Barbara E. Mundy, *The Mapping of New Spain: Indigenous Cartography and the Maps of the Relaciones Geográficas* (Chicago, IL: University of Chicago Press, 1996): 3–5; Richard L. Kagan, "Philip II and the Art of the Cityscape," *Journal of Interdisciplinary History* 17, no. 1 (summer 1986). esp. 126. Some maps of the Viceroyalty of New Granada and the early republic had been labeled "chorographic" as well, seemingly in order to emphasize the smaller sections into which they divided the territory, for example Vicente Tallado y Rivera, *Mapa corográfico del Nuevo Reino de Ganada*, 1808, Archivo General de la Nación, Bogotá (hereafter AGN), Sección Mapas y Planos 6, ref. 136–40.

12 Agustín Codazzi, "Respuesta de la Comisión Corográfica al informe de Mr. May," *El Porvenir*, July 8, 1856, 4.

13 Ibid. See also Sánchez, *Gobierno y geografía*, 479.

14 On the relationship between chorography, federalism, and regionalism, see Appelbaum, *Mapping the Country of Regions*, 31–34, 48–53, 203–214. On the commission's origins within early republican scientific and state-making initiatives in New Granada, see Lina del Castillo, *Crafting a Republic for the World: Scientific, Geographic, and Historiographic Inventions of Colombia* (Lincoln, NE: University of Nebraska Press, 2018).

15 See the meticulous new catalogue provided by Carla Juanita Rodríguez Congote, "Monumentos, curiosidades naturales y paisajes notables en las láminas de la Comisión Corográfica (1850–1859)," MA thesis, Universidad de los Andes, Bogotá, Colombia, 2009. As of 2019, the images can be consulted at www.bibliotecanacional.gov.co.

16 Sánchez, *Gobierno y geografía*; Appelbaum, *Mapping the Country of Regions*.

17 Agustín Codazzi, *Obras escogidas* (Caracas: Dirección de Cultura y Bellas Artes, Ediciones del Ministerio de Educación, 1960), 2: 106–107. For the Eastern Plains, see A. Licciani, "Informe ajeno (prob. debido a A. Licciani) sobre situación física y humana del Casanare," and "Carta de A. Licciani a Codazzi en fecha 10 de enero de 1856," AGN, Colección Guido Cora, rollo 3.

18 Codazzi, *Obras escogidas*, 2: 106–107.

19 Agustín Codazzi, "Informe sobre el oríjen del rio Magdalena y otros particulares," *Gaceta Oficial* (Bogotá), July 18, 1857, 462–464.

20 On late colonial and early republican *granadino* attitudes toward climate, see Alfonso Múnera, *Fronteras imaginadas: La construcción de las razas y de la geografía en el siglo XIX colombiano* (Bogotá: Editorial Planeta Colombiana, 2005), 71–81; Francisco José de Caldas, *Obras completas de Fransisco José de Calda*s (Bogotá: Universidad Nacional de Colombia, 1966), 79–120, 183–211.

21 Codazzi, "Descripción de la Provincia de Casanare," 99.

22 Ibid., 111. He echoed Alexander von Humboldt's comment that "the monotony of these steppes is imposing, sad, and oppressive," *Personal Narrative of a Journey to the Equinoctial Regions of the New Continent*, abridged and trans. Jason Wilson, historical introduction by Malcom Nicolson (New York: Penguin Books, 1995), 162.

23 Codazzi, "Provincia de Casanare," 119.

24 Agustín Codazzi, "Trabajos relativos al Estado de Cundinamarca," *Gaceta Oficial* (Bogotá), Dec. 13, 1858, 565.

25 For example: Agustín Codazzi to Araceli Codazzi, Feb. 7, May 2 and 10, 1856, folios 77–82, carpeta 2, Archivo de la Sociedad Geográfica, Bogotá, Colombia.

26 Agustín Codazzi to Secretario de Estado del Despacho de Gobierno, July 30, 1858, AGN, Colección Enrique Ortega Ricaurte, Comisión Corográfica, no. 587, folios 89–92.

27 Paz's sketchbook from the excursion did not include this image, which makes me wonder if Paz witnessed the scene or was instructed to paint it this way, Manuel María Paz, *Libreta de apuntes de Manuel María Paz* (Medellín: Universidad de Caldas and Fondo Editorial Universidad Eafit, 2011), n.p.

28 On the importance of instruments for the scientific identity of Humboldt-influenced explorers, see Burnett, *Masters of All They Surveyed: Exploration, Geography, and a British El Dorado* (Chicago, IL: University of Chicago Press, 2000), 91. The two other watercolor illustrations of the commission that depict Codazzi also show him using scientific instruments: Carmelo Fernández, *Soto. Campamento de la Comision corográfica in Yarumito*, ca.1851; Henry Price, *Córdova. Mesa de Herveo. Ruiz. Tolima. Santa Isabel*, 1852.

29 Paz, like the painter Carmelo Fernández before him, was at times authorized to draft final maps, based on maps sketched in the field, and submit them to the government, Agustín Codazzi to Araceli Codazzi, Oct. 12, 1857, folios 139–140, Archivo de la Sociedad Geográfica, Bogotá.

30 Anna Jadgmann, *Del poder y la geografía: la cartografía como fuente de legitimación en Colombia*. Ph.D. dissertation, Freie Universitat Berlin, 2006, 53–54.

31 Ibid., 56–57.

32 For example: Agustín Codazzi, "Mapa corográfico del Estado de Cundinamarca, perteneciente a la Confederación Granadina. Levantado de orden del gobierno por el general Agustín Codazzi, una parte en los años de 1856 y 1857 y concluido

en 1858," AGN, Sección Mapas y Planos 6, ref. 18; "Rio Orinoco, original por Agustín Codazzi," n.d., Archivo Central e Histórico de la Universidad Nacional de Colombia, Bogotá, unclassified; Agustín Codazzi, "Borrador de un mapa de la región comprendida entre Caballaro y Arauca, provincia de Casanare," Biblioteca Nazionale Universitaria di Torino, Italy, 1856; image available at www.codazzi. mitreum.net/es/medida/cartografiacolombia.php, as of July 2015.

33 Lina del Castillo, "Interior Designs," in Jordana Dym, and Karl Offen (eds), *Mapping Latin America: A Cartographic Reader* (Chicago, IL: University of Chicago Press, 2011), 148–152; Appelbaum, *Mapping the Country of Regions*, esp. 48–53.

34 Augusto J. Gómez López, Guido Barona Becerra, and Camilo A. Domínguez Ossa (eds), *Territorio de Casanare*, book 1, vol. 3 of *Obras completas de la Comisión Corográfica: Geografía Física y Política de la Confederación Granadina* (Bogotá: Fundación Puerto Rastrojo, Fundación Gaia, and Editora Géminis, 2000), 70; Arias Vanegas, *Nación y diferencia en el siglo XIX colombiano*, 59.

35 For examples of contemporaneous printed maps with similar boxed inserts, see Antonio García Cubas's printed 1857 state maps discussed in Carrera, *Traveling from New Spain to Mexico*, 149–154.

36 Such nullification had potential legal consequences, Germán A. Palacio Catañeda, *Fiebre de tierra caliente: Una historia ambiental de Colombia, 1850–1930* (Bogotá: Instituto Latinoamericano para una Sociedad y un Derecho Alternativos, 2006), 41, 102.

37 In referring to the Guahibos or to other groups as "nations" Codazzi did not seem to confer any legitimacy on their autonomy, which he sought to curtail. Rather, he used "nation" interchangeably with "race" or "tribe."

38 Jane Rausch, *A Tropical Plains Frontier: The Llanos of Colombia, 1531–1831* (Albuquerque, NM: University of New Mexico Press, 1984), 17–19.

39 Paz, *Libreta de apuntes*, n.p.

40 José M. Quintero, "Informe sobre el territorio del Caquetá," in *Territorio del Caquetá*, book 1, vol. 1 of *Obras completas de la Comisión Corográfica: Geografía física y política de la Confederación Granadina*, ed. Domínguez Ossa, Camilo A., Augusto J. Gómez López, and Guido Barona Becerra (Bogotá: COAMA, Fondo José Celestino Mútis, Fondo Fen Colombia, Instituto Geográfico "Agustín Codazzi," 1996), 133; Pedro Mosquera, "Relacion historiada que hace Pedro Mosquera, correjidor de la barbara tribu de Mesaya, al presidente Jeneral Mosquera en la marcha que hizo de San Francisco de Solano, hasta el territorio de San Martin, i de ahi a esta capital," *La Discusion* (Bogotá), Oct. 2, 1852, 3–4.

41 Codazzi, "Descripción del Territorio del Caquetá," in *Territorio del Caquetá*, 188.

42 Ibid.

43 The capital was changed a dozen times and only two of the *llanos* towns founded in the nineteenth century (Villavicencio and Orocué) "achieved an enduring vitality." Jane Rausch, *The Llanos Frontier in Colombian History 1830–1930* (Albuquerque, NM: University of New Mexico Press, 1993), 330.

44 Codazzi, "Informe sobre la provincia de Casanare," *Gaceta Oficial* (Bogotá), Apr. 16, 1856, 299.

45 Several Colombian examples are reproduced in Sebastián Díaz Angel, Santiago Muñoz Arbeláez, and Mauricio Nieto Olarte, *Ensamblando la nación: Cartografía y política en historia de Colombia* (Bogotá: Facultad de Artes y Humanidades, Facultad de Ciencias Sociales, Departamento de Historia, CESO, Ediciones Uniandes, 2010), 82–87.

46   Alexander von Humboldt, *Carte intineraire du cours de l'orenique de l'atabapo, du cesifuiere et du Rio Negro*," in *Relation historique. Atlas geographique et physique du nouveau continent* (Paris: Chez Schoell, 1814).

47   Ibid.

48   Díaz Angel et al., *Ensamblando la nación*, 25.

49   Historian Fa-ti Fan writes that when British naturalists in nineteenth-century China were unsure about scientific information provided by Chinese informants, they would distance themselves from the data by using qualifiers, such as "I was told by the natives," *British Naturalists in Qing China: Science, Empire, and Cultural Encounter* (Cambridge, MA: Harvard University Press, 2004), 150–151.

50   Unfortunately, we lack information about actual face-to-face interactions with the local informants. Did they indicate "with their hand" in the air or by drawing maps? Did they have maps? How did they delineate the space in which they lived? What gifts or payments were exchanged for knowledge? Scholars have explored such questions elsewhere, for example Malcolm G. Lewis (ed.), *Cartographic Encounters: Perspectives on Native American Mapmaking and Map Use* (Chicago, IL: University of Chicago Press, 1998).

51   Codazzi, "Descripción de la provincia de Casanare," 89.

52   Agustín Codazzi, "Antigüedades indígenas. Ruinas de San Agustín, descritas y explicadas por Agustín Codazzi," in *Estado de Cundinamarca y Bogotá—Antiguas Provincias de Bogotá, Mariquita, Neiva y San Martín*, vol. 2 of *Obras completas de la Comisión Corográfica: Geografía física y política de la Confederación Granadina*, ed. Augusto J. Gómez López et al. (Bogotá: Alcaldía de Bogotá, Instituto Distrital de Cultura y Turismo, Gobernación de Cundinamarca, 2003), 282.

53   Appelbaum, *Mapping the Country of Regions*; Frank Safford, "Race, Integration, and Progress: Elite Attitudes and the Indian in Colombia, 1750–1870," *Hispanic American Historical Review* 71, no. 1 (Feb. 1991), esp. 22–26; Brooke Larson, *Trials of Nation Making: Liberalism, Race and Ethnicity in the Andes, 1810–1910* (Cambridge: Cambridge University Press, 2004), esp. 71–102.

54   Manuel Ancízar, *Peregrinación de Alpha* (Bogotá: Imprenta Banco Popular, 2004), 1: 121; 2: 252.

55   Codazzi, "Descripción de la Provincia de Casanare," 89.

56   In his 1857 expedition to Caquetá, Codazzi relied heavily on brothers Pedro and Miguel Mosquera, local officials and traders variously described as black or mulatto. Pedro Mosquera had written a report about an expedition he led in 1847–8 through the Amazon and Meta, which Codazzi read before venturing to the Eastern Plains. Miguel Mosquera later served as Codazzi's guide in the Amazon. They seem to have earned his respect and might have softened some of his racist views. See Codazzi, *Mapa corográfico del Estado de Cundinamarca*; Codazzi, "Descripción del Territorio del Caquetá," 154, 187, 195; Agustín Codazzi to Araceli Codazzi, Dec. 28 and 30, 1856, Feb. 5, 1857, Archivo de la Sociedad Geográfica, Bogotá, carpeta 2, folios 100–107. See also Manuel María Paz, *Territorio del Caquetá. Indio reducido de la Nacion Andaquí. Miguel Mosquera, nacido en el Caquetá, práctico e intérprete que acompañó a la Comision Corográfica en 1857*, ca. 1857, watercolor, Biblioteca Nacional, Bogotá.

57   While in New Granada's heavily Indigenous eastern borderlands, the commission depicted mulattos and blacks as "rational" and civilized, in the Pacific Coast, the growing majority black population was depicted as lazy, dissolute, and requiring harsh labor discipline, Appelbaum, *Mapping the Country of Regions*, 81–105.

58 Agustín Codazzi, "Esposición del plan de la obra de la jeografía general de la República i particular de los Estados," *Gaceta Oficial,* Dec. 11, 1857, 606–611.

59 In the late 1850s, the 30-plus provinces of New Granada were combined into eight larger states. The newly created state of Boyacá included the old Province of Casanare. The southern *llanos* (San Martín or Meta), meanwhile, were appended to the state of Cundinamarca. In 1858, the country became known as the Granadine Confederation. Then, in 1863, a new constitution created the United States of Colombia, which lasted until 1886 and was replaced with the Republic of Colombia, which replaced states with departments. Today, after various subsequent reconfigurations, the former Casanare Province corresponds roughly to the departments of Casanare and Arauca, while San Martín corresponds to what are now Meta, Vichada, and Guainía. Both of the provinces ostensibly included territories now governed by neighboring countries.

60 On the "bricolage" see John Pickles, *A History of Spaces: Cartographic Reason, Mapping, and the Geo-coded World* (New York: Routledge, 2004), esp. 86–89.

61 Díaz Angel et al., *Ensamblando la nación,* 51.

62 Sánchez, *Gobierno y geografía,* 443–453; Appelbaum, *Mapping the Country of Regions,* 184–202.

63 Tomás Cipriano de Mosquera, "Informe sobre la jeografía jeneral de Colombia, escrito por Felipe Pérez," *Diario Oficial,* June 22, 1866, 604.

64 Mosquera stressed the need to promulgate a positive image of Colombia abroad for this purpose, ibid.

65 On visual economy, see Deborah Poole, *Vision, Race, and Modernity: A Visual Economy of the Andean Image World* (Princeton, NJ: Princeton University Press, 1997). On the commission's broader influence, see Appelbaum, *Mapping the Country of Regions,* 203–213.

66 They argue that the perspectives of on-the-ground explorers were often quite different than those of their government sponsors. Explorers on the ground saw and grappled with the local complexities of place while their patrons preferred to see a broader "stage" on which imperial expansion or nation-state-building would be acted out, Burnett, *Masters of All They Surveyed,* esp. 10–12; Raymond Craib, *Cartographic Mexico: A History of State Fixations and Fugitive Landscapes* (Durham, NC: Duke University Press, 2004); both draw on Paul Carter, *The Road to Botany Bay: An Essay in Spatial History* (Boston, MA: Faber & Faber, 1987).

67 Augusto J. Gómez López, *Indios, colonos y conflictos: Una historia regional de los llanos orientales 1870–1970* (Bogotá: Siglo XXI Editores, Pontificia Universidad Javeriana, and Instituto Colombiano de Antropología, 1991); Julio Arias Vanegas, "En los márgenes de la nación: indígenas nómadas y colonialismo en los llanos orientales colombianos en la segunda mitad del siglo XIX," in Antonio Escobar Ohmstede, Raúl Mandrini, and Sara Ortelli (eds), *Sociedades en Movimiento. Los Pueblos Indígenas de América Latina en el siglo XIX* (Buenos Aires: Instituto de Estudios Histórico-Sociales, 2008).

Part II
Lines and Tracings

6   Intervisible Border

Photographs and Monuments along the US-Mexico Boundary

Katherine G. Morrissey

Writing from Chiapas in November 1886, Mexican assistant topographical engineer Luis R. Servín described the impact of his labors on his body. Dysentery wracked his intestines and the tropical heat exhausted his energy; an undefined stomach ailment had laid him low. A member of the fraught Mexico-Guatemala boundary survey team, Servín had been in the field for more than three years, crisscrossing the riverine and jungle environments, coping with disgruntled crews, landowners, and villagers, and measuring the landscape with mathematical calculations, reports, and maps. Now, he needed to recover. His letter requested a two-month leave of absence, which would enable him to return to Mexico City to consult physicians and recuperate. By January 1887, his request denied, the young topographical engineer had resigned his position.[1]

Nineteenth-century international boundary survey work in the Americas was undeniably taxing. For those engineers, astronomers, surveyors, and other team members engaged in their nations' efforts to fix territorial claims in the landscape, the fieldwork involved physical labor, exposure to the elements, and ventures into the unfamiliar. Such factors contributed to interruptions and restructured plans for the work itself. On Servín's survey, for another example, its entire Mexican military escort also succumbed to disease, necessitating an emergency medical intervention. Detailed to the region by the Secretary of Agriculture and Development, Dr Marial Vargas administered medicines and care in a specially set up hospital camp.[2]

I begin with Luis Servín's body to remind us of the physicality of boundary surveying, as well as to consider those unintended disruptions. The physical processes of boundary making—its impact on bodies and borderlands environments, its creation of maps, reports, monuments, and images, its movement of instruments, medicines, peoples, and letters through space, all these and more—link the material with the abstract. As visualization projects, international boundary surveys constructed borders through a combination of cartographic, scientific, physical and photographic means. The survey teams strove to make abstract lines visible, marking national boundaries with obelisk-shaped monuments, astronomical calculations, two-dimensional maps, sketches, and images.[3] At times such efforts occurred concurrently. Alongside the laborers who erected monuments on the Guatemala-Mexico and US-Mexico borders in the 1880s and 1890s, for example, photographers created glass plate negatives of the structures. After the survey's completion, the developed photographs and the monuments themselves simultaneously reinforced, and made visible, the line.

Visual processes, products, and intents shaped boundary making. Not surprisingly, therefore, their cartographic, topographic, and photographic languages are replete with visual terms. For boundary surveying, in particular, intervisibility—establishing two objects that are in sight of each other—was a critical concept. To construct a line across the landscape required surveyors to see from one point to another. Utilizing a direct line of sight, as mediated through instruments, surveying teams measured, rechecked, and marked the physical locations of international border markers and monuments. Human eyesight confirmed that points along the line were mutually visible, that is, intervisible.

Beyond its literal definition, the term is useful here for conveying other interpretive meanings. It might refer to that combination of cartographic, scientific, physical, and photographic ways in which international boundary commission teams marked the border. These multiple genres—largely reliant on human vision—inscribed and reinscribed the borderline in an effort to fix the line in place. In a diplomatic sense, intervisibility could also apply to these bi-national efforts to collaborate in boundary making, for the two sides to see things in the same way, to come to agreement. It might also refer, more abstractly, to the cross-border intents of boundary making itself, to clarify and focus attention on particular points.

And yet, intervisibility has its limits. Imbedded within the term and its meanings—as topographic concept, as processes of production, as bi-national agreements, as clarification efforts—are ellipses and interruptions. When sighting from one mountaintop to another, for example, portions of the intervening landscape remain obscured from view. Interior valleys, hills, and other obstructions prevent a comprehensive survey. In the service of nation-states and guided by professional scientific methods, the late nineteenth-century boundary fieldwork did not always follow national and scientific scripts. Physical experiences, especially in border spaces, influenced the visual products (Figure 6.1). The overlapping aesthetic objects—especially maps, photographs, and monuments—that resulted from their labors led to multiple readings and interpretations. Maps and photographs, despite the popular nineteenth-century beliefs in their mimetic qualities, are products of specific historical cultural constructions and representations.[4]

Topography and Photography

Luis Servín is a useful guide in exploring such issues. He served on both his nation's Guatemala and US border survey teams. While his responsibilities along the southern boundary rested in his cartographic work, he was pressed into photographic service for the 1891–96 International Boundary

Figure 6.1 Physical evidence of the survey crews' work includes the survey pole, flag, and water canteen, along with the monument and the photograph itself. "Monumento Numero 128 (Hierro), Vista al Noroeste. En una Arista de la Sierra de Pajaritos," *Vistas de los monumentos á lo largo de la línea divisorial entre México y los Estados Unidos de El Paso al Pacífico / tomadas, por parte de México, bajo la dirección del ingeniero Jacobo Blanco* (New York: Impr. de J. Polhemus & Co., 1901). Newberry Library, Chicago, F 83047.44, vol. 3, pl. 128.

Commission resurvey of the US-Mexico border. As topographer and photographer, he participated in crafting maps and images that circulated well beyond the two borders. Working in these overlapping scientific arts of representing landscapes, Servín bridged distinct genres and resulting products of expression. His experiences, alongside those of his compatriots, offer an opportunity to consider the ways maps and photographs intersected, both as part of the border surveys and as visual markers unmoored from border spaces and reassembled in albums and archives. Trained as a topographical and mining engineer at the Escuela Nacional de Ingenieros (formerly known as Colegio de Minería), as were most members of the late nineteenth-century Mexican border survey teams, Servín was accustomed to viewing the landscape through instruments and translating the variegated visual scene into measurable, and presumed stable, forms, using science and mathematics.[5] During his three years (1878–81) at the Escuela Nacional, his specialized courses included applied mathematics, geometry, topography, hydrology, geodesy, and astronomy. He initially pursued a degree in mining engineering, before switching his emphasis to topography. Under Mexico's late nineteenth-century politicized educational reforms, it was a curriculum filled with pragmatic professional forms of knowledge, and embedded in a broader nationalist agenda.[6]

Servín came to his border assignments with an awareness of the distinctions among international surveying and astronomical methods, gained in large part from his coursework. He had learned from Francisco Diaz Covarrubias, *Tratado de topografía y de geodesia con los primeros elementos de astronomía pràactica,* the similarities and differences among surveying systems and instruments used in France, Germany, the United States, and Mexico.[7] Some of the topographical iconography for mapmaking—such as the specific marks used to indicate hill elevations—varied in form and intensity, whether designated as continuous wavy lines or short strokes of the pen. In addition to these national distinctions among the visual vocabularies of mapmaking, Covarrubias discusses the use of specific Mexican geographical terms—taken from Mayan language—to refer to landforms and human alterations of the environment. In lieu of the German term *thalweg* or "valley road," that was in international use, for example, some Mexican engineers intentionally wrote *becan* or "snake road" to more accurately describe a serpentine path.[8] This was practical and environmental knowledge, to be sure, of use to a Mexican engineer-in-training, but it also carried cultural and national intents. The distinctions, while relatively minor from a scientific perspective, underscored national identity. Pointing out such variants in linguistic and cartographic practices, Covarrubias emphasized partisan expertise, naming specific *Mexican* engineers and noting the strengths of the *Mexican* practices.[9]

Still, for Servín and other students, knowing about the different styles would also enable communication among engineers in the field, whether from Mexico, Guatemala, Germany, or the United States. And, for the men at work, accuracy and scientific advancements could trump national pride. On the 1890s Mexico-US boundary resurvey, the Americans brought along an updated zenith telescope that the Mexican astronomer Jose Salazar was pleased to use (Figure 6.2). In doing so he followed the North American Talcott method and gained extraordinary precision in his measurements.[10] Sharing space, results, and methodologies in both formal and informal ways, the 1880s and 1890s Guatemalan, Mexican, and US survey teams operated in tandem and influenced each other's work in the field.[11]

The 1880s Mexico-Guatemala border survey was one of Luis Servín's first official duties as a young topographical engineer.[12] The joint survey, instituted by an 1882 agreement, which settled a long-standing dispute over competing claims to the state of Chiapas and the Soconusco coastal district, began its work the following year. A Mexico City meeting established the detailed plan of operation "para trazar la línea divisoria con la precisión debida en mapas fehacientes, y establecer sobre el terreno monumentos que pongan a la vista los límites de ambas repúblicas."[13] Despite agreements over the composition of the survey teams, construction of monuments, and general direction of the

Figure 6.2 The Mexican section's field astronomical observatory in Tijuana. "Observatorio Astronomico de la Seccion Mexicana en Tijuana," *Memoria de la Sección Mexicana de la Comisión Internacional de Límites entre México y los Estados Unidos que restableció los monumentos de El Paso al Pacífico / bajo la dirección por parte de México del ingeniero Jacobo Blanco, jefe de la Comisión Mexicana* (New York: J. Polhemus, 1901), between pp. 42 and 43. Newberry Library, Chicago, F 83047.44, vol. 1, pl. 38.

line, the troubled survey soon disagreed over the specifics, especially as teams began to work in the field. Part of the troubles rested in the description of the line, which utilized both "scientific" and "natural" language and methods to designate its intended location. Servín's responsibilities, for example, included running a portion of the line from the Rio Lagartero to Cerro Ixbul. In doing so he employed triangulated astronomical calculations from one landform to another. Problems arose in sections where the "natural" landmarks, especially rivers, were not as stable as supposed. The multi-branched Usumacinta River, a major river designated as part of the boundary line, became the focal point of the disputes. These troubles and other delays, due to a combination of political, diplomatic, and medical reasons, meant that the survey would take more than 12 years to complete.[14] Rivers were not the only causes for variances from a straight line; local interests also played a role. The topographical work occasionally veered two or three leagues away from the scientific line, for example, in order to accommodate Guatemalan villages that might have otherwise straddled the boundary or been located in Mexico. As historian Casey Marina

Lurtz has observed more generally, "local experience and knowledge of the border formed the basis for negotiating its settlement."[15]

Issues over border line placement also plagued Mexico's northern boundary. The Mexico-US border, dictated by the Treaties of Guadalupe Hidalgo and Mesilla, had been established by US and Mexican field survey teams between 1849 and 1855. Artists, scientists, and cartographers—but not photographers—had accompanied the initial US-Mexico surveys and crafted visual representations of the border region, ones that worked to make the desert, mountain, and river landscapes comprehensible to their US and Mexican audiences. As art historian Gray Sweeney has noted, their maps, watercolors, engravings, and paintings constructed "a visual order" that defined and shaped understandings of the new border as a national boundary and an environmental place.[16] Still, the 1,969 mile-long border, marked by only 52 monuments, was not as orderly as it might have appeared on the maps. By the 1880s, the frequency of local disputes over exactly where this boundary existed on the ground, especially in the Arizona-Sonora region, drew the attention of US and Mexican governments. After a reconnaissance of the border confirmed the disorder and inconsistencies, the nations agreed that the temporary joint International Boundary Commission would resurvey the borderline. Two engineers-in-chief, Lieutenant Colonel John Whitney Barlow, US Army Corps of Engineers, and Señor Jacobo Blanco, led the joint survey teams for their respective countries from El Paso to the Pacific Ocean, aiming to locate and repair existing monuments as well as to add new monuments.[17]

Blanco, who had been early involved in planning the Mexico-Guatemala border survey, assembled the Mexican section of the Mexico-US International Boundary Survey from the well-seasoned surveyors and astronomers who had been at work along the southern border. United through personal connections, their educational training, and their fieldwork, the team brought a specific set of experiences that shaped their new enterprise. Although not part of the original assemblage, Luis Servín joined the group in February 1892 as an assistant engineer. His skills as an amateur photographer may have made him a desired addition.[18] Barlow and Blanco, who had recently established their detailed plan of operations during a meeting at El Paso, Texas, and Ciudad Juarez, Chihuahua, included photography as one of their interlocking methods for reinscribing the border.[19] Along with astronomical and geodetic work, they each agreed to map the boundary area, in a two-and-a-half mile swath along their respective sides of the border.[20] "The topography thus obtained," the plan went on to describe, "should be supplemented by sketches and photographs, especially in the vicinity of the monuments, for the purpose of more exactly defining their positions."[21] This cartographic responsibility, similar to that assigned to artists in the earlier original 1850s survey, linked the tangible results—maps, monuments, and photographs—to more abstract ones—the legal, political, and imaginative boundary between the countries.[22] While perhaps intended as parallel representations, it is worth noting the somewhat different meanings

MONUMENTO NÚMERO 138 (HIERRO), VISTA AL OESTE—EN UNA LOMA BAJA.

Figure 6.3 Along with the map (No. 9, see Figure 6.6) this photograph shows the location of border monument 138 on a low hill near Sasabe, Arizona. "Monumento Numero 138 (Hierro), Vista al Este. En una Loma Baja," *Vistas de los monumentos á lo largo de la línea divisoria entre México y los Estados Unidos de El Paso al Pacífico / tomadas, por parte de México, bajo la dirección del ingeniero Jacobo Blanco* (New York: Impr. de J. Polhemus & Co., 1901). Newberry Library, Chicago, F 83047.44, vol. 3, pl. 138.

assigned the maps, monuments, and photographs (Figure 6.3). The monuments visually mark the border line, and the maps represent the border line, while both the maps and photographs identify the more precise locations of the monuments.[23]

Blanco sent to St. Louis, Missouri, for the necessary camera equipment and assigned Servín his new role. After the materials arrived in late August, Servín began photographing.[24] Although relatively new to the craft, he had likely watched photographers at work during his time on the Mexico-Guatemala border survey; Antonio W. Rieke and Mansueto Cristiani each took official photographs as part of that earlier survey.[25] Their work, intended to illustrate Mexican governmental reports and document the progress of the surveys, captured vignettes that told those stories: the survey images invariably included national flags, work teams, and equipment; completed border monuments were centered in the frames, all proud evidence of the nation-state.

As European-born photographers, Rieke and Cristiani also held interests that ranged beyond Mexican national concerns. Cristiani, for example, eagerly turned his lens on other monumental structures—Mayan ruins recently visited and photographed in the region by the competing foreign travelers and archaeologists Alfred P. Maudslay and Désiré Charnay. Following in their footsteps, Cristiani took shots of Palenque that reflected the dominant romantic genre for such subjects, mixed with scientific observation. Devoid of overt human presence, the ruins appear as lost remnants of an ancient past emerging out of the jungle wilderness.[26]

Servín also drew on the expertise of his American counterpart, commercial photographer Daniel R. Payne.[27] Blanco initiated their introduction in the summer of 1892, suggesting that Servín could benefit from meeting with the American artist.[28] Based on Servín's improving photographic skills, he likely gained some professional tips. The photographers at times operated in tandem; images of each other show up in their monument shots. While Payne's and Servín's official responsibilities were to document the position of each of the 258 monuments that the field commissions either built or restored, they also pointed their cameras in other directions. Servín, for example, took group portraits at local rancheros and snapped young girls bathing in streams, capturing borderlands life and peoples.[29]

Although the two national teams mainly worked independently, their leaders held frequent meetings to compare findings and their work parties passed each other in the field and, occasionally, camped together.[30] During the two years of fieldwork each section relied on multiple parties—including those working in supply camps, as well as astronomical and tangent workers, biological collectors, topographers, and monument builders in a series of more mobile camps.[31] Local ranchers, freighters, and merchants provided contracted supplies, horses, transportation, and other support services. Given the varied necessities and dispersed nature of the teams, the photographers both operated independently and also contributed other collaborative labors—Servín continued his duties as an assistant engineer, and Payne became an essential member of the monument building crew.

The photographers and their photographs were well integrated into the commission. The likeable and useful Servín and Payne gained the appreciation of other survey members. And their images, when printed, became the record not only of the official placement of monuments but also of the workers' lives in the borderlands. Some of their photographs—especially those related to topographical questions—were immediately consumed. While in the field, both Barlow and Blanco selected and sent small image collections back to their respective capitals. Availing themselves of the equipment and skills of El Paso photographic shops, they had specific images developed and printed. Photographs sent to the Secretaría de Fomento, for example, illustrated the desert conditions, marked national interests, and helped clarify surveying problems, especially along the north 31° 47' line.[32] They joined other photographic images from government surveys and

Figure 6.4 The individual next to the camera is likely US section photographer Daniel Payne. "Monumento Numero 222 (Hierro), Vista al Nordeste. En el Valle del Rio Nuevo," *Vistas de los monumentos á lo largo de la línea divisoria entre México y los Estados Unidos de El Paso al Pacífico / tomadas, por parte de México, bajo la dirección del ingeniero Jacobo Blanco* (New York: Impr. de J. Polhemus & Co., 1901). Newberry Library, Chicago, F 83047.44, vol. 3, pl. 222.

projects—such as those of the Mexico-Guatemala border survey, archeological ruins in the Yucatan, railways and public works—helping to shape the Ministry of Development's visual vocabulary and to document Porfirian modernization.[33]

At the completion of the survey fieldwork in 1894, photographers Payne and Servín also worked separately and simultaneously in San Diego to develop their negatives and to organize their photographs into albums for their respective governments (Figure 6.4). In the process they shared some of their negatives with each other, to enable each group to have a complete photographic set of the 258 monuments. Servín enlisted the services of a San Diego landscape photographer, Chauncey William Judd, to help with his darkroom work, especially in retouching damaged or underexposed negatives.[34] In the end, Servín completed three identical albums of his set of photographs, which he presented to the Secretaría de Fomento in Mexico City, and Payne made four identical albums of his set of more than 600 photographs, which he sent to Washington, DC.[35]

While both photographers were in the service of the state, Servín's position as a topographical engineer embedded him firmly into government service and placed his photographic work as a side task. As an artist and essentially an independent subcontractor, Payne was only a temporary government employee. Comparisons between the two photographers' work also identify significant differences. Commercial photographer Payne exhibits greater technological skills; almost two-thirds of the images selected by Barlow and Blanco as the "best negatives" for their final report are his. His artistic sensibility, especially his awareness of perspective and his familiarity with the landscape genre, shapes his work. Accustomed to wielding his craft in the service of his clients, Payne frames his images in a more consistent style. When he takes his photograph directly from the west, he shows the monument's number clearly, and excludes any other evidence of the survey teams' work. In contrast, Servín incorporates numerous survey personnel in his photographs, often arranged in narrative vignettes—whether demonstrating the work processes, striking a heroic pose, or documenting their presence. Debris and team supplies, such as empty barrels of Portland cement or surveying equipment, are scattered across the viewscape around the base of the monuments. Servín more often aims his camera at an angle to the monument, so that both the number and one of the plaques are visible.

For the topographer-turned-photographer, there were some obvious links between the two forms of labor. Servín brought an eye trained to focal points, hands accustomed to manipulating technological instruments, and a mind honed to translate three-dimensional environments into two-dimensional visual products. His photographic assignment, like his more familiar mapping efforts, placed him in the same relationship to his subjects, in a basic physical sense. His body, triangulated through his camera, enabled him to calculate new angles of vision. Servín's personal choices of photographic subjects—the vignettes, the borderlands peoples—are, however, more human than scientific. As he captures the process of mapping the border, his images reveal its unruly aspects.

Monuments and Maps

The fieldwork required for the construction of maps, and monuments, involved bodily engagement with instruments and environment in ways that left traces in the final products. The responsibilities of US section photographer Payne, for example, significantly expanded as the survey progressed. In addition to constructing views, he lent his hands and muscles to constructing the monuments themselves. Son of a blacksmith, Payne had worked as a teamster and held other manual jobs as a young man in southern California, so his skill set readily extended beyond his camera work.[36] Conscientious about maintaining any preexisting monuments, Payne and his crew rebuilt the few remaining edifices—an irregular lot, made of dressed stone, rock, and masonry—left by the 1850s Emory-Salazar survey. The teams added descriptive and admonitory bilingual texts to their replacement efforts: "Repaired by the Boundary Commission created by treaties of 1882–1889" and "The destruction or displacement of this monument is a misdemeanor, punishable by the United States or Mexico." Finding all of the original markers proved to be quite difficult. Over the past 40 years, many had been moved, at times intentionally, obscured, or improperly marked. In Nogales, the survey team found old boundary maker 26 relegated to a rock pile, now holding up part of John Brickwood's saloon. Situating the new monument in the old location, the survey building team nestled the now renumbered 122 inside an exterior nook.[37]

Most of the 258 monuments were new, and uniform. Fabricated in an El Paso foundry, these obelisks—cardinally oriented, four-sided iron columns, topped with a pyramidal cap—were transported in sections to their sites. Although the selection of the obelisk as the form for the physical boundary markers themselves occasioned no special comment, it held cultural significance. As a universal symbol of political power, albeit ascribed with diverse meanings and associations, the form had already been appropriated for other national boundaries, including the Mexico-Guatemala border, and memorial monuments in both the United States and Mexico. Plaques on their north and south faces of the US-Mexico boundary monuments identify their purpose and authority—"Boundary of the United States, treaty of 1853, reestablished by the treaties of 1882-1880" and "Límite de la Republica Mexicana, tratado de 1853, restablecido por tratados de 1882-1880" (Figure 6.5). Attachments for mounting a flagpole, on the west side, and the monument numerals, on the east, adorn the other faces.[38]

Spaced no more than five miles apart, the monuments were numbered sequentially from El Paso to the Pacific Ocean. As the International Boundary Commission secretary L. Seward Terry explained the reason for the variable locations to *The New York Times*, "conspicuous positions were chosen for placing the new monuments, with the intent of making them intervisible."[39] The monuments' implied transparency, as a function of their geographical locations, worked two ways, both dependent on human interactions with the structure. First, in making one monument visible from the next, the placements essentially strung an immaterial border line, one brought into being through human eyesight. When the bilingual texts, viewed from the north or the south, were read, the marker's meanings were translated across the line. The linkage among words, bodies, and monument did not end there. Inside the final monument, no. 258, located along the Pacific Ocean at the mouth of the Tijuana River, both commissions deposited written documents—in English and in Spanish—signed by commission members, which identified official treaties and governmental authorities as well as enumerated the commissions' physical achievements. Embedded for future generations to uncover, the documents reveal a historical and archival sensibility.[40]

Monumento Número 185 (hierro), Vista al Noroeste.—En un Pico Alto y Escarpado de la Sierra del Tule.

Figure 6.5 Border monument 185, one of the new obelisks with its Spanish-language plaque visible, situated on a high steep peak of Sierra del Tule. "Monumento Numero 185, (Hierro), Vista al Noroeste. En un Pico Alto y Escarpado de la Sierra del Tule," *Vistas de los monumentos á lo largo de la línea divisoria entre México y los Estados Unidos de El Paso al Pacífico / tomadas, por parte de México, bajo la dirección del ingeniero Jacobo Blanco* (New York: Impr. de J. Polhemus & Co., 1901). Newberry Library, Chicago, F 83047.44, vol. 3, pl. 185.

Indeed, the original establishment of the sequential line of boundary monuments constituted a form of archives (Figure 6.6). In its modern sense, an *archive* might refer to an organized physical collection of artifacts, open for interpretation and analysis; a repository for stored memories; a general system that both formulates and transforms bodies of knowledge.[41] As signifiers, the monuments as well as the photographs and maps of those monuments, have taken on diverse and changing meanings, power and authority.[42] Produced, reproduced and consumed, the physical monuments, maps, and photographic albums link the tangible and the abstract. What happens in the transformations of monument to document?[43]

Tethering monuments to text, the production of border maps was a multi-step process, involving many different hands, and relied, for the most part, on painstaking work on the ground. Consider the common process as

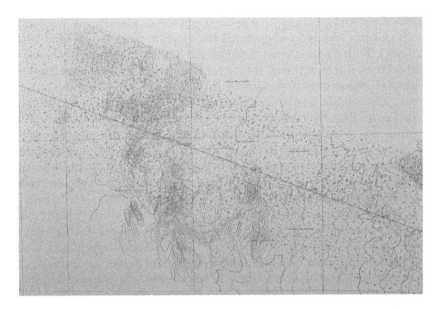

Figure 6.6 This map section, demarcating a portion of the Sonora-Arizona boundary line and new border monuments 138 through 142, also shows the placement of the "old monuments" and Sonoran ranches. Map No. 9, *Línea divisoria entre México y los Estados Unidos al oeste del Río Grande levantada y marcada / bajo la dirección, por parte de México, del ingeniero Jacobo Blanco, por la Comisión Internacional de Límites creada por la convención de julio 29 de 1882, renovada por la de febrero 18 de 1889* (New York: Impr. de J. Polhemus & Co., 1901). Newberry Library, Chicago, F 83047.44, vol. 2, map 9.

employed by the 1890s US section: operating from separate mobile camps, topographical teams walked the landscape and drew sketch maps, made observation notes, and provided calculations in notebooks. After some experimentation with different methodologies, the commission relied largely on stadia measurements.[44] One observer sighted through a telescope across the distance to the stadia, or graduated rod, held vertically by another transit man. The system, which provided horizontal and vertical angles as well as the distance, consumed significantly less time than triangulation. The field teams performed multiple sightings—US transit men took an average of 44 sights per day, for example—in their quest to achieve accuracy. In calculating the borderline length from one monument to the next, for another example, topographical engineers and their assistants made double measurements, "first as a foresight and then as a backsight," in the field.[45] These measurements, sketches, and calculations were then reconciled into larger sectional sheets, usually by a different cartographer working at the commission's urban base office, which moved through time from El Paso to Tucson to Yuma to San Diego.

In the field, the topographers dealt with physical, technological, and eco-logical constraints. Struggling with the rough terrain and soaring temperatures, numerous laborers and rod men quit the survey rather than contend with the extremes. With daytime highs well into the 90s and frequently sustained over 100 degrees, it was, reported the US field workers, "always hot and hideously repulsive." Water tanks transported by wagon helped sustain the sweltering crews. The intense heat of the Sonoran Desert during the summer months boiled more than their blood. Bubble tube liquids inside the survey's delicate instruments, as well as metals exposed differentially to the sun, felt the envir-onmental effects, limiting the accuracy of the tools. The rising heat, which exacerbated the vibration of the atmosphere, especially on the plains, also played havoc with lens sightings. Pinpoint light signals, when seen through the heliotrope under these conditions, flamed out to the sides; transit rods received a "sinuous appearance and a wave-like movement." These "particu-larly unfavorable" conditions prevented instrument work for five hours or more each day. Survey engineers undertook multiple experiments to study the "boiling" of the air, as they termed it. The atmospheric refraction, which increased with the rapid variation in air density, also produced mirages— "illusions of distant lakes, with images of waving trees mirrored in their clear, cool depths, were most common."[46]

As they contended with tricks of the eye, the desire for cartographic certainty bedeviled the field workers and permeated the correspondence between the Mexican section and the Secretaría de Fomento.[47] A goal of the commission, after all, was to correct the preexisting maps, and to create a new one that would more permanently affix national meanings to the borderline. The final bilingual version—initially aggregated and drawn in San Diego with data and information from both the Mexican and US sections—was published by a New York firm as part of the International Boundary Commission's offi-cial report, each page signed and attested to by the leadership of the US and Mexican sections.

With its clearly designated five-mile swath of land, the joint map simul-taneously defined the border line and the borderlands. As a shared space of rancheros, towns, trails, rivers, mountain ranges, mines, and water sources, the mapped borderlands made visible that "fugitive landscape" where personal, economic and environmental connections, at times more than national iden-tities, defined allegiances to place.[48] Individual names identified local know-ledge, landmarks and owners: Ranchería de Pozo Verde, San Rafael Ranch (Cameron), for a few examples. Still, there were long stretches without such personalized designations, where fewer individual properties marked the landscape. While such absences might have been read by early twentieth-century viewers as signs of an empty desert, for those who knew the region these ellipses might have been surprising since they essentially erased existing habitations and land uses, especially on the US side of the border. The cause for this omission lay partially in the original topographers' work—pressed to complete the survey, and loath to overexpose their bodies to the desert heat, the US section relied on general reports rather than field sketches for a long

150-mile stretch. Reconciling differences between the American and Mexican cartographic symbology also reduced the level of details.[49]

Another, more visible, interpretive difference showed up on the joint map where the border wended along the Colorado River between monument 206 and 209. The continuous shifting of channels, river banks and bars made efforts to map and mark the designated borderline in the middle of the river especially taxing (Figure 6.7).[50] The US section based its map on fieldwork in March 1893, while the Mexican drawings relied on the following year's efforts of engineers Jose Gonzalez-Moreno and Manuel Alvarado (February to March 1894). Unable to reconcile the multiple variations, the commissioners dedicated a separate map sheet to the Colorado River section, using color to distinguish the differences between the two sections' topographies and to make both versions visible on the same sheet.[51]

On each atlas page, the boundary line runs straight across the mapped borderlands. Small black squares, interrupting the broken line of the border, designate the monuments on the joint map. Although the chosen symbol suggests each monument's actual footprint, the square's exaggerated size and adjacent sequential numbers are representations of their significance and not intended as exact replicas. Smaller dots carefully mark the former locations of old monuments, especially along the Sonora-Arizona border where they had been erroneously placed by the 1850s survey. These abstractions—common to the cartographic practice—depict traces of markers no longer visible in the landscape.

Despite all these efforts at depicting the monuments, and photographically recording their locations, the representations contained hidden imperfections. Intervisibility has its limits. A few monuments went missing from the commission's photographic record. Only through some darkroom sleight of hand—etching the negative with a small line in distant mountains—did Monument 153, for example, come into view. The physical monuments also faced erasure. An 1895 winter storm, for example, destroyed the Tijuana River monument early (255).[52] The force of nature overpowered the work of "Uncle Sam and the Mexicans," according to the *Los Angeles Times*; "the merciless flood did not even respect the combined dignity of the two republics." Now buried "out of sight beneath the mud," the monument needed to be replaced and located out of harm's way. [53] In the landscape, on the maps, and in the albums not all of the monuments were intervisible.

The bi-national efforts to collaborate in boundary making, like its related processes, faced limits. Both the US and Mexican individual written reports praise effective international collaborations in the field.[54] There were, however, moments of strife not necessarily emphasized in the official public documents. Speaking about negotiations between the US and Mexican commissioners over the final collaborative report, Blanco characterized the process as "difficult and delicate," one that gave rise to "sometimes quite heated" discussions; "La formación de ese informe fue difícil y delicada. Dio lugar a muchas discusiones, algunas veces bastante acaloradas."[55] Hidden from public view, these negotiations echo other disruptions that rippled below the surface of

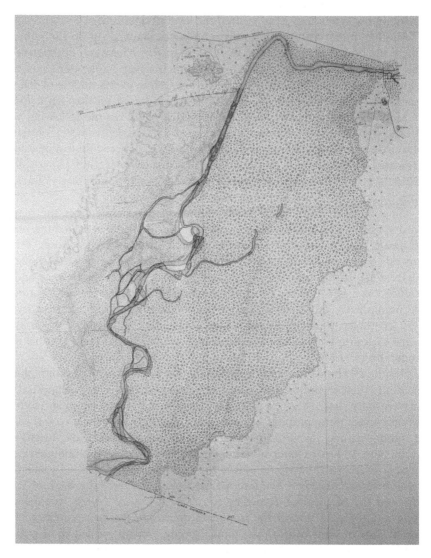

Figure 6.7 The challenges of mapping the Colorado River as border are clear on this
map. It includes two overlapping depictions of the channelized river—one
based on US fieldwork, the other on Mexican fieldwork. Map No. 19,
Línea divisoria entre México y los Estados Unidos al oeste del Río Grande
levantada y marcada / bajo la dirección, por parte de México, del ingeniero
Jacobo Blanco, por la Comisión Internacional de Límites creada por la
convención de julio 29 de 1882, renovada por la de febrero 18 de 1889
(New York: Impr. de J. Polhemus & Co., 1901). Newberry Library, Chicago,
F 83047.44, vol. 2, map 19.

nineteenth-century international boundary surveys in the Americas. Beyond the diplomatic realm, such factors as the physical interactions in the unfamiliar borderlands environments, the instability of nature as a fixed marker, the decisions and practices of survey personnel, and the interventions of local interests, all these physical experiences and more influenced the border-creation process and its resultant aesthetic products.

Bodies, in particular, were largely obscured in the aesthetic results. Consider the labor and presence of borderlands residents—from local merchants in Nogales, Sonora, and Bisbee, Arizona, who supplied survey camps, to the Guatemalan villagers, whose presence redirected the surveyor's lines—as well as that of the semi-anonymous topographers and photographers, including Luis Servín. Although traces of both can be seen in the complete photographic record and original commission papers, the intentions of the photographic albums, official reports, and maps worked to hide their impacts.

In many ways these modernist efforts to create permanent meanings and scientific lines belied the centrality of human intervention. The visualization projects relied on eyesight to bring the border line into focus, after all, and it was that necessary emphasis on human physiological intervention that opened them up to multiple discernments. Each form of archive—border photographs, maps, monuments—offered spatial ruptures, resurveying and redefining the borderline for specific purposes. As the maps and monuments strove to create visual order, they also marked signs of disorder and offer unruly interpretations: distinctions between US and Mexican photographic views, the visibility and invisibility of human actors, as essential components of the construction and definition of the borderline, and the emphases on public display. While the surveys and their visual artifacts may have been intended as national acts, the creation, selection, and circulation of the aesthetic objects migrated beyond those intents.

Acknowledgments

My thanks to the University of Arizona Press for publication permission. A somewhat different version of this chapter appears in Katherine G. Morrissey and John Michael Warner (eds), *Border Spaces: Visualizing the U.S.-Mexico Frontera* (Tucson, AZ: University of Arizona Press, 2018).

Notes

1 Luis R. Servín to [], Nov. 1886, Expediente 1, Legajo 2, Caja 1, Limites con Guatemala, Limites con Estados Unidos y Guatemala, No. 176, Secretaría de Agricultura y Fomento, Galería 5, Archivo General Nación, México City. [Hereafter Límites con Guatemala, 176, AGN].

2 Expediente 105, Legajo 5, Caja 4, Limites con Guatemala, 176 AGN.

3 I borrow the term "visualization projects" from Daniela Bleichmar, *Visible Empire: Botanical Expeditions and Visual Culture in the Hispanic Enlightenment* (Chicago, IL: University of Chicago Press, 2012), 7.

4   I appreciate Matthew Edney's reminder on this point. J.B. Harley, *The New Nature of Maps: Essays in the History of Cartography* (Baltimore, MD: Johns Hopkins University Press, 2001).

5   Escuela Nacional de Ingenieros, *Libro de Inscripciones, 1868–1879*, ML32a, Archivo Histórico del Colegio de Minería, UNAM Facultad de Ingeniería, Acervo Histórico del Palacio de Minería, Mexico City [hereafter cited as AHPM]; Escuela Nacional de Ingenieros, *Registro de títulos expedidos*, ML301a, AHPM; Francisco Diaz Covarrubias, *Tratado de Topografía y de Geodesia con los Primeros Elementos de Astronomía Práctica*, 2 vols (México: Imprenta del Gobierno, en Palacio, 1868).

6   José Omar Moncada Maya, Irma Escamilla Herrera, Gabriela Guerrero Cisneros, and Marcela Mezza Cisneros, *Bibliografía Geográfica Mexicana La Obra de los Ingenieros Geógrafos*, Serie Libros Num. 1 (México: Instituto de Geografía, UNAM, 1999), 9–14.

7   Covarrubias, *Tratado de Topografía*. This standard text went through several editions. Servín was likely also familiar with the 2nd ed., retitled Francisco Diaz Covarrubias, *Tratado Elemental de Topografía, Geodesia y Astronomía Practica*, 2nd ed., 2 vols (Paris: A.H. Bécus, 1884). Its title-page boasted, "Esta obra es la adoptada como texto en los Colegios de la República Mexicana, y fue premiada en la Exposición de Filadelfia en 1876."

8   Covarrubias, *Tratado de Topografía*, 1: 484.

9   Covarrubias' text and practices reached beyond Mexico. On "the Covarrubias method," see John F. Hayford, *A Textbook of Geodetic Astronomy* (New York: John Wiley & Sons, 1904), 93. Hayford, on loan from the US Coast and Geodetic Survey, served as an assistant US astronomer for the International Boundary Commission. William H. Burger, "Biographical Memoir of John Fillmore Hayford, 1868–1925," *National Academy of Sciences of the United States of America Biographical Memoirs*, vol. 16, 5th memoir (1931): 159–292.

10   Covarrubias, *Tratado Elemental*, 2: 444–445.

11   While the survey business had become increasingly professionalized, centralized, and scientific by the late nineteenth century, these modernization efforts were certainly not uniformly applied, especially at the local level. The unruly processes involved in boundary surveying challenged even the most scientific and rational individuals. See William H. Goetzmann, *Exploration and Empire: The Explorer and the Scientist in the Winning of the American West* (New York: W.W. Norton, 1966); Robin Kelsey, *Archive Style: Photographs and Illustrations for U.S. Surveys, 1850–1890* (Berkeley, CA: University of California Press, 2007), 143–145; and Raymond B. Craib, *Cartographic Mexico: A History of State Fixations and Fugitive Landscapes* (Durham, NC: Duke University Press, 2004).

12   Luis G. Zorrilla, *Relaciones de México con la Republica de Centro América y con Guatemala* (México: Editorial Porrúa, 1984), 441–462; Manuel Angel Castillo, Monica Toussaint Ribot, and Mario Vazquez Olivera, *Espacios Diversos, Historia en Común: México, Guatemala y Belice: La Construcción de una Frontera* (México: SRE, 2006); Jan de Vos, *Las Fronteras de la Frontera Sur: Reseña de los Proyectos de Expansión que Figuraron la Frontera entre México y Centroamérica* (Villahermosa, Tabasco, México, Universidad Juárez Autónoma de Tabasco/ Centro de Investigaciones y Estudios Superiores en Antropología Social, 1993).; Alberto Amador, *Memoria de la Cuestión de Límites entre México y Guatemala* ... (México: SRE, 1931). For a nineteenth-century Guatemala-centered perspective, see *La Cuestión de Límites entre México y Guatemala (por un centroamericano) y Cuestiones entre Guatemala y México*, Colección de artículos del Mensajero de

Centro-América (Guatemala: Centro Editorial "José de Pineda Ibarra," Ministerio de Educación Pública, 1964).

13 *Memoria de la Secretaría de Fomento;* "to draw the dividing line with due precision in authoritative maps, and to establish monuments on the ground that will put in view/sight the borders of both republics."

14 The history of the Mexico-Guatemala border controversies has been recounted and analyzed by a range of scholars. In addition to the works cited above see, for the US involvement in the matter, David Healy, *James G. Blaine and Latin America* (Columbia: University of Missouri Press, 2001), 17–39; Matías Romero, "Mr. Blaine and the Boundary Question between Mexico and Guatemala," *Journal of the American Geographical Society of New York* 29, no. 3 (1897): 281–330.

15 "Informe del Jefe de la Comision de Limites Mexicana sobre los Trabajos Científicos Concluidos Hasta la Fecha," *Memoria de la Secretaría de Fomento*, vol. 1 (México: Oficina Tip. de la Secretaría de Fomento, 1887), 30; Casey Marina Lurtz, *From the Grounds Up: Building an Export Economy in Southern Mexico* (Stanford, CA: Stanford University Press, 2019), 46.

16 Gray Sweeney, "Drawing Borders: Art and Cultural Politics of the U.S. Mexico Boundary Survey, 1850–1853," in Dawn Hall (ed.), *Drawing the Borderline: Artist-Explorers of the U.S.-Mexico Boundary Survey* (Albuquerque, NM: Albuquerque Museum, 1996), 23–77.

17 For the history of the Mexico-US border surveys see Leon C. Metz, *Border: The U.S. Mexico Line* (El Paso: Mangan Books, 1989); Joseph Richard Werne, "Redrawing the Southwestern Boundary, 1891–1896," *Southwestern Historical Quarterly* 104 (July 2000): 1–20; Joseph Richard Werne, *The Imaginary Line: A History of the United States and Mexican Boundary Survey, 1848–1857* (Fort Worth, TX: Texas Christian University Press, 2007); Luz María Oralia Tamayo P. de Ham, *La geografía: Arma científica para la defensa del territorio* (México: Plaza y Valdes Editores, 2001); Luz María Oralia Tamayo Pérez, "Jose Salazar Ilarregui, personaje central de la Comisión de Limites Mexico, 1849–1857, y Dos de Sus Colaboradores: Francisco Jiménez y Agustín Díaz," in María Luisa Rodríquez-Sala (ed.), *De estamento ocupacional a la comunidad científica: Astrónomos-astrólogos e ingenieros, siglo XVII al XIX* (México: Universidad Nacional Autónoma de México, 2004), 215–242; Paula Rebert, *La Gran Línea: Mapping the United States-Mexico Boundary, 1849–1857* (Austin, TX: University of Texas Press, 2001).

18 Expediente 89, Legajo 3, Caja 2, Límite con Estados Unidos, Límites con Estados Unidos y Guatemala No. 176, Secretaría de Agricultura y Fomento, Galería 5, Archivo General Nación, México [hereafter Límite con Estados Unidos, 176, AGN]. After recovering from his stomach troubles, Servín's work as a topographical engineer sent him back in the field for surveys of central Mexico mining regions before he joined the northern survey. Luis R. Servín, "Informe que presenta a la Secretaría de Fomento como resultado de la exploración de la zona minera en el Mineral de Pregones, Municipalidad de Tetipac, Distrito de Alarcón, Estado de Guerrero," *Boletín de Agricultura Minería é Industrias publicado por la Secretaría de Fomento, Colonización e Industria de la Republica Mexicana* (Oct. 1892): 289–332; Rafael Aguilar y Santillán, *Bibliografía Geológica y Minera de la República Mexicana* (Mexico: Oficina Tipográfica de la Secretaría de Fomento, 1898), 111.

19 Expediente 39, Legajo 1a, Caja 4, Límite con Estados Unidos, 176, AGN.

20 The joint map was published as *Boundary between the United States and Mexico, as Surveyed and Marked by the International Boundary Commission, under the Convention of July 29th, 1882, Revived February 18th, 1889, Línea Divisoria entre*

México y Los Estados Unidos trazada y demarcada por la Comisión Internacional de Límites, según la convención de 29 Julio de 1882 Renovada en Febrero 18 de 1889.

21 US Senate, 55th Congress, 2d sess. Senate Doc. 247, *Report of the Boundary Commission upon the Survey and Remarking of the Boundary between the United States and Mexico west of the Rio Grande, 1891 to 1896, Part I: Report of the International Commission; Part II: Report of the U.S. Section* (Washington, DC: GPO, 1898) [hereafter Report of the Boundary Commission], 17.

22 US House, 34th Congress, 1st sess., House Ex. Doc. 135, William H. Emory, *Report of the United States and Mexican Boundary Survey, made under the Direction of the Secretary of the Interior*, vol. 1 (Washington, DC: Cornelius Wendell, 1857), 96 [hereafter Emory, *Report*]. On the visual work of the 1850s survey team, see Kelsey, "Arthur Schott: Marking the Mexican Boundary," *Archive Style*, 19–72; Robert V. Hine, *Bartlett's West: Drawing the Mexican Boundary* (New Haven, CT: Yale University Press, 1968); William H. Goetzmann and William N. Goetzmann, *The West of the Imagination*, 2nd ed. (Norman, OK: University of Oklahoma Press, 2009), 161–166; *Drawing the Borderline*. On the social and political processes imbedded in mapping and surveying see Craib, *Cartographic Mexico*. Also useful in thinking through the issues surrounding surveying, mapmaking, and nation-states have been: Matthew H. Edney, *Mapping an Empire: The Geographical Construction of British India, 1765–1843* (Chicago, IL: University of Chicago Press, 1997); Peter Sahlins, *Boundaries: The Making of France and Spain in the Pyrenees* (Berkeley, CA: University of California Press, 1989); Catherine Tatiana Dunlop, *Cartophilia: Maps and the Search for Identity in the French-German Borderland* (Chicago, IL: University of Chicago Press, 2015); Thongchai Winichakul, *Siam Mapped: The History of the Geo-Body of a Nation* (Honolulu: University of Hawaii Press, 1994).

23 In comparison, the earlier 1850s US-Mexico international boundary survey teams agreed to discount the monuments as official markers, since their stones were so easily moved; they relied on the combination of maps and images to define the borderline. Emory, *Report* 1 (Part 1): 38. See Paula Rebert's assessment in "Views of the Borderlands: The *Report on the United States and Mexican Boundary Survey, 1857–1859*," *Terrae Incognitae: The Journal for the History of Discoveries,* 37 (2005): 75–90.

24 Blanco to Secretaría de Fomento, Aug. 24, 1892, 78, Libro 2, Legajo 2, Caja 9, Límite con Estados Unidos, 176, AGN. "En nuestra Comisión teníamos al Ingeniero Ayudante Luis R. Servín, que, aunque no era fotógrafo de profesión, teis conocimientos y practica en el arte, y lo hizo muy bien, según se vio después por los resultados." *Memoria de la Sección Mexicana de la Comisión Internacional de Límites entre México y los Estados Unidos que restableció los monumentos de El Paso al Pacifico; bajo la dirección de México del ingeniero Jacobo Blanco, jefe de la Comisión Mexicana* (New York: Impr. De J. Polhemus y Compania, 1901), 15.

25 For Servín's role on the Mexico-Guatemala survey, see Expediente 37, Legajo 2, Caja 1, Límites con Guatemala, 176, AGN. On the photographers who accompanied the Mexico-Guatemala survey see Límites con Guatemala, 176, AGN. See also Límites entre México y Guatemala, L-E-2019, L-E-2020, L-E-2003, Serie Legajos Encuardarnados, Archivo Histórico "Genaro Estrada," Secretaría de Relaciones Exteriores, México [hereafter cited as SRE, AH].

26 Olivier Debroise, *Fuga Mexicana: Un Recorrido por la Fotografía en México* (México: Consejo Nacional para la Cultura y las Artes, 1994), 78–93, esp. 78, 85–86; Roberto Garcia Moll and Daniel Juarez Cossio (eds), *Yaxchila: Antología de su*

Descubrimiento y Estudios (México: Instituto Nacional de Antropología e Historia, 1986); Ian Graham, *Alfred Maudslay and the Maya: A Biography* (London: British Museum Press, 2002).

27 By all accounts, the 45-year-old Daniel Payne had more experience in photography than his Mexican counterpart. Daniel's older brother Harry, an artist, writer, and journalist, had likely introduced him to photography some 15 years before. The two brothers both worked as commercial photographers and painters in the greater Los Angeles area during the late 1870s and 1880s. The peripatetic Daniel, however, never made a career in the arts or photography. In fact, he was likely seeking mining opportunities in northern Mexico when he was hired onto the American survey team. US Federal Manuscript Census, 1880, Los Angeles, Ancestry.com; See reference in H.T. Payne, *Game Birds and Game Fishes of the Pacific Coast* (Los Angeles, CA: News Publishing Co., 1913).

28 Blanco to J.W. Barlow, Feb. 1892, 92, Libro 1, Legajo 1, Caja 29, Límite con Estados Unidos, 176, AGN.

29 As discussed below, a selected collection of photographs was published as US Senate, 55th Congress, 2d sess. Senate Doc. 247, *Report of the Boundary Commission upon the Survey and Re-marking of the Boundary between the United States and Mexico west of the Rio Grande, 1891 to 1896, Album* (Washington, DC: GPO, 1899) [hereafter Report of the Boundary Commission Album]. Unpublished photographs can also be found in the manuscript and photographic collections at AGN and NARA. Payne's original glass plate negatives are located at Still Pictures, NARA, College Park, MD. Although AGN archival documents indicate that Servín's glass plate negatives were sent to Mexico City along with the Mexican section's other records, they are not currently found with these materials in the AGN's 176 collections in either Galería 5 or Fototeca.

30 The official reports of the Mexico-US survey were published as: US Senate, 55th Congress, 2d sess. Senate Doc. 247, *Report of the Boundary Commission upon the Survey and Remarking of the Boundary between the United States and Mexico west of the Rio Grande, 1891 to 1896, Part I: Report of the International Commission; Part II: Report of the U.S. Section* (Washington, DC: GPO, 1898); Report of the Boundary Commission Album; *Memoria de la Sección Mexicana de la Comisión Internacional de Límites entre México y los Estados Unidos que restableció los monumentos de El Paso al Pacífico; bajo la dirección de México del ingeniero Jacobo Blanco, jefe de la Comisión Mexicana* (New York: Impr. De J. Polhemus y Compania, 1901). See also Charles A. Timm, *The International Boundary Commission* (Austin, TX: University of Texas Press, 1941). The manuscript collections at the respective national archives offer more complete records of the commissions' work: US Section, International Boundary Commission, United States and Mexico, Records of International Boundary Commissions Concerned with the Southern Boundary of the United States 1796–1937, RG 76, Records of Boundary and Claims Commissions and Arbitrations, 1716–1994, National Archives, College Park, MD; Límite con Estados Unidos, Límites con Estados Unidos y Guatemala, No. 176, Secretaría de Agricultura y Fomento, Galería 5, Archivo General Nación, Mexico.

31 Individual published accounts by survey workers include: Edgar Alexander Mearns, *Mammals of the Mexican Boundary of the United States*, Smithsonian Institution, United States National Museum, Bulletin 56 (Washington, DC: GPO, 1907); D.D. Gaillard, "The Perils and Wonders of a True Desert," *Cosmopolitan* (Oct. 1896): 592–605; William Healey Dall, "Report on the Mollusks Collected by

the International Boundary Commission of the United States and Mexico, 1892–1894," *Proceedings of the U.S. National Museum* 19, no. 1111 (1897): 333–379.

32 See discussion of 18 photographs sent in spring 1893, Blanco to Secretaría de Fomento, Apr. 28, 1893, 481, Libro 2, Legajo 2, Caja 30, and Manuel Fernández Leal, Secretaría de Fomento to Ingeniero en Jefe Blanco, Sept. 24, 1892, 203, and May 6, 1893, 290, Exp. 546, Legajo 36, Caja 21, Límite con Estados Unidos, 176, AGN. These 18 images are likely those included in Caja 19, Coleccíon Fotográfica "Límites entre México, Estados Unidos y Guatemala," No. 176, Fototeca, AGN. Some of Payne's and Servín's prints may have remained in the borderlands. It seems likely that Sonoran family group shots taken by Servín, for example, were produced for the families. I do not, however, have any textual confirmation of this supposition.

33 See Exp. 103, Legajo 5, Caja 4, Límite con Guatemala, 176, AGN, on Senior Engineer Prospero Goyzueto's practice of sending photographs to the Secretary of Development. Photography had been employed by the Mexican Ministry of Development since the 1870s. In 1876 it began using photographs in its annual reports, and established its own photographic studio. See Debroise, *Fuga Mexicana*, 70. John Mraz, *Looking for Mexico: Modern Visual Culture and National Identity* (Durham, NC: Duke University Press, 2009); Rosa Casanoa and Adriana Konzevik, *Mexico: A Photographic History* (Mexico City: Consejo Nacional para la Cultura y las Artes/Instituto Nacional de Antropología e Historia. 2007); Roberto Tejada, *National Camera: Photography and Mexico's Image Environment* (Minneapolis, MN: University of Minnesota Press, 2009); Leonard Folgarait, *Seeing Mexico Photographed: The Work of Horne, Casasola, Modotti and Álvarez Bravo* (New Haven, CT: Yale University Press, 2008).

34 Jacobo Blanco to Manuel Fernandez Leal, Sr Ing, Nov. 2, 1894, 178–181, Libro 5, Legajo 5, Caja 33, Límite con Estados Unidos, 176, AGN; *Memoria de la Sección Mexicana*, 40; *Directory of San Diego City and County, 1897* (San Diego: Tine Olmsted Printers, 1897), 142, 302.

35 I have been unable to locate the Servín-Judd San Diego-created albums. Although the transmissions of the Luis Servín's San Diego-created albums as well as his specific prints and negatives are referenced in the Mexican commission papers, the 15 albums now at the AGN Fototeca are those based on the later plates. The 612 glass plate negatives by Daniel Payne, now at the Still Pictures Division, National Archives, RG 76.3, are likely the basis of Payne's San Diego-created albums.

36 California State Library, California History Section, *Great Registers, 1866–1898*, Collection Number: 4 - 2A, CSL Roll Number: 16, FHL Roll Number: 976466, Ancestry.com, *California, Voter Registers, 1866–1898;* US Federal Manuscript Census, 1870, Los Angeles, Ancestry.com.

37 The story of monument 122 has been retold by several scholars, see Metz, *Border*, 110–112; Rachel St John, *Line in the Sand: A History of the Western U.S.-Mexico Border* (Princeton, NJ: Princeton University Press, 2010), 90–96; and Charles R. Ames, "Along the Mexican Border, Then and Now," *Journal of Arizona History* 18 (Winter 1977): 444.

38 Plans for the monuments date to the 1880s. Although those plans were altered a bit for the final versions used in the 1890s, they all used the obelisk form. For copies of the plans—both 1880s and 1890s—see Legajo 1, Caja 37, Límite con Estados Unidos, 176, AGN. Brian A. Curran, Anthony Grafton, Pamela O. Long, and Benjamin Weiss, *Obelisk: A History* (Cambridge, MA: MIT Press, 2009); Kirk Savage, "The Self-Made Monument: George Washington and the Fight to Erect a

National Memorial," in Harriet F. Senie and Sally Webster (eds), *Critical Issues in Public Art: Content, Context and Controversy* (New York: Harper Collins, 1992), 5–32. With the relatively recent completion of extenuated construction of the visually striking Washington Monument, for example, the symbol held specific contemporary resonances within the United States.

39 "The Mexican Boundary Line," *The New York Times,* Dec. 29, 1894. L. Seward Terry was employed by the US section in the Commission's San Diego office as secretary and disbursement clerk.

40 Oct. 3, 1894, Legajo 47, Caja 26, Límite con Estados Unidos, 176, AGN. Blanco to J.W. Barlow, Jan. 22, 1895, 305, Mar. 8, 1895, 375, and Mar. 23, 1895, 397, Libro 5, Legajo 5, Caja 33, Límite con Estados Unidos, 176, AGN.

41 The latter definition draws on Michel Foucault's influential analyses of discourse and power in modern thought. There is an extensive interdisciplinary literature on archives, including the theoretical approaches by Michel Foucault, esp. *L'archéologie du savoir* (Paris: Gallimard, 1969), *The Archaeology of Knowledge and the Discourse on Language,* trans. A.M. Sheridan Smith (New York: Pantheon, 1972), and Jacques Derrida, *Mal d'archive: Une impression freudienne* (Paris: Galilée, 1995), *Archive Fever: A Freudian Impression,* trans. Eric Prenowitz (Chicago, IL: University of Chicago Press, 1998).

42 In thinking about the relations among photographs, monuments, landscapes, and maps, I have found useful Martha A. Sandweiss, *Print the Legend: Photography and the American West* (New Haven, CT: Yale University Press, 2002), 155–206, esp. 180–204; Joan M. Schwartz and James R. Ryan (eds), *Picturing Place: Photography and the Geographical Imagination* (London: I.B. Tauris, 2003), esp. 117–140, 226–242; James R. Ryan, *Picturing Empire: Photography and the Visualization of the British Empire* (Chicago, IL: University of Chicago Press, 1997).

43 I am playing here with the Foucauldian notions of "monument" and "document," esp. in reference to the practice of history. Foucault, *Archaeology of Knowledge*, 6–11. See also Rosalind Krauss, "Sculpture in the Expanded Field," *October* 8 (Spring 1979): 33–44.

44 For their discussion and employment of these various measurement systems, see Report of the Boundary Commission, 153–155, 165.

45 Report of the Boundary Commission, 168.

46 "The Mexican Boundary Line," *The New York Times,* Dec. 29, 1894; Report of the Boundary Commission, 160, 161, 166, 159.

47 The long-drawn-out Mexico-Guatemala border survey had pointed to the deficiencies of the region's current maps and spatial knowledge and, for the Ministry of Development, reinforced the desire for cartographic certainty along the northern border. See, for example, #8, Legajo 1, Caja 37, Límite con Estados Unidos, 176, AGN.

48 I borrow the term "fugitive landscape" from Samuel Truett, *Fugitive Landscapes: The Forgotten History of the U.S.-Mexico Borderlands* (New Haven, CT: Yale University Press, 2008). In thinking about local knowledge and mapmaking I have found useful, in addition to histories of cartography noted above, D. Graham Burnett, *Masters of All They Surveyed: Exploration, Geography, and a British El Dorado* (Chicago, IL: University of Chicago Press, 2000).

49 As US topographer P. D. Cunningham noted in his California-Arizona field book:

"The sketches in the remaining part of this book were not made in the field but compiled from the sketches in Books containing Lines 'C' U.S. Topog. and from memory. The purpose is to give a somewhat connected representation of topog. without regard to minutiae. There being no time for field sketching, this proved to be the only alternative."

See field notebooks in Entry 460, Box 25, International Boundaries, US-Mexico Border, Records of Boundary and Claims Commissions and Arbitrations, RG76, NARA, College Park, MD. Jacobo Blanco, "Reseña de los Trabajos Topográficos," *Memoria de la Sección Mexicana,* appendix 11, p. 259.

50 As the Mexican engineers' report described the process: "La exuberante vegetación de las márgenes de rio, así como el gran número de esteros, bajos y pequeñas hondonadas que se encuentran en sus riberas, cuyo suelo, en lo general, presenta poca resistencia, pues la arena de que están formadas, es removida y aumentada por el acarreo que anualmente recibe en la época de las crecientes." *Memoria de la Sección Mexicana,* 319.

51 Sheet 5, *Boundary between the United States and Mexico* map; see *Memoria de la Sección Mexicana,* appendix 25, pp. 315–352, for the comparative astronomical and mathematical calculations and a visual representation of the triangulations.

52 Blanco to J.W. Barlow, Jan. 22, 1895, 305, Mar. 8, 1895, 375, and Mar. 23, 1895, 397, Libro 5, Legajo 5, Caja 33, Límite con Estados Unidos, 176, AGN.

53 "The Late Storm, Damage Done on the Mexican Border. The Boundary Monument," *Los Angeles Times,* Jan. 28, 1895.

54 These written reports are organized differently, a reflection perhaps of cultural preferences as well as field management decisions. Blanco organized his five chapters chronologically and, as perhaps befits a topographical engineer, geographically by location (Paso del Norte, Nogales, Yuma, San Diego, Washington). He relegated special reports, calculations, and other matters to appendices. Barlow organized the chapters by task and incorporated written reports and key correspondence within his ten-chapter report.

55 *Memoria de la Sección Mexicana,* 47. Blanco goes on to credit the harmonious team-work established in the field for enabling successful settling of these disagreements.

7 "Visual Expeditions" Supporting Geopolitical Vindications

Maps, Photographs, and Other Visual Devices in the Diplomatic Dispute over the Andes as a Natural Border (1900)

Carla Lois

Introduction: The Andes as a Border

Towards the end of the nineteenth century, during negotiations to resolve a boundary dispute between Argentina and Chile, official Argentine bureaus collected materials to build a geographical argument based on the general principle of natural borders (in the sense coined by Friedrich Ratzel), taking the Andes mountains as their preferred reference.[1] Argentine negotiators used pictures, maps, diagrams, gravures, and panoramic photos to demonstrate their claims of the existence of a "visible" border, in effect offering a topographical criterion. This chapter examines a document (*Argentine Evidence*, 1900) presented to the British crown, which had been chosen to arbitrate the conflict.[2] This 1,091-page, four-volume report included 71 maps, 182 photographs, 175 fold-out panoramic photos, 12 engravings, and 15 sketches. These images are in dialogue with each other: the photographs underwent a cartographic treatment (inscriptions, toponyms, etc.), while the maps are linked with the photographic record by red arcs that show the photographed locations (Figures 7.1a and 7.1b).[3] Focusing on the interplay among image, map, and topography, this essay reveals the relations between geographic arguments and the use of visual devices in processes of claiming territory.

Several treaties and agreements reached between the Argentine and Chilean governments in the 1880s and 1890s proved only partially successful in establishing the international border on the Andes. There remained some discrepancies about how to draw the line in poorly explored areas, for example. Moreover, the two countries intended to apply different criteria to solve the problem.

Paradoxically, the starting point of all disagreements between Argentina and Chile was an assumption shared by both: namely that Argentine and Chilean territories were inherited following the dissolution of the Spanish Empire in the New World, and that both states had agreed that the Andes Mountains separated their dominions as had been previously established by the colonial administration. In fact, that consensus depended upon the mutual recognition

Figure 7.1 a–b. *Preliminary Map of the South-Western Region of the Argentine Republic. Showing the different points from which Photographs, reproduced in the "Argentine Evidence" have been taken.* Drawn on stone and lithographed by W. & A. K. Johnston, Limited, Edinburgh and London, 1901. American Geographical Society Library, University of Wisconsin-Milwaukee Libraries.

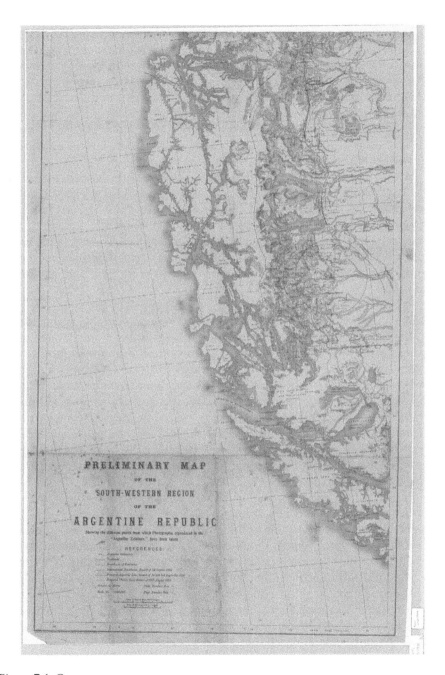

Figure 7.1 Cont.

of all documents—the old and the modern, the public and the private[4]—which had referred unvaryingly to the mountain range as the eastern border of Chile.[5]

However, by the end of nineteenth century, two concomitant processes turned this consensus into a weak and (especially) ineffective criterion. First, modern ways of organizing territorial sovereignty required more precision concerning what "cordillera" meant in order to establish the rights and duties of people (citizens) settled there and to claim ownership of local resources. Second, the very idea of territorial boundary was progressively reconceptualized; initially understood as a more general zone, it increasingly came to be seen as a discrete and mappable line.[6]

In that context, after Argentine and Chilean experts had stipulated that the Andes worked as a border, the critical point was how to draw a dividing line along the mountain chain. But while the Argentine experts suggested drawing a line following the highest summits (topographic criterion), their Chilean counterparts suggested a line that divided the Atlantic and the Pacific drainage basins (hydrographic criterion). Each country maintained a criterion whose application would result in a gain of territory for itself and in a loss for the other.

In order to present their arguments, the Argentinians prepared *Argentine Evidence*, a document aimed to support and develop the topographic criteria on the basis both of the theory of natural borders and a plethora of visual materials (pictures, maps, diagrams, gravures, and panoramic photos). It is worth stressing that majority of photographs focus on landscapes and panoramic views. In that respect, photographs are closer to the pictorial tradition than to the then-recent development of photogrammetric mapping techniques. The clear predominance of photographs over engravings, sketches, and the other kind of graphic materials reinforce the idea that "visual experience" was overvalued as a way to "get a sense of real geography." This epistemological assumption seems to explain the heavy priority of the photographs in the book over other graphic material.

Francisco Pascasio Moreno[7] led the organization of the comprehensive work and noted that he "sought to get together all the data which permit the appreciation of the exactness and fitness of the line traced by the Argentine Expert."[8] Though in general terms, the work is presented as anonymous, it is possible to follow some traces to identify Moreno's responsibility as a director of this diplomatic document. On the other hand, there is no explicit or implicit information about graphic materials, their production process, their dates, or their makers. Although some historical maps have been visibly redrawn from their originals, they are largely made up of coherent and intertwined materials that seem to have been produced for this work.

It is not my intention to dwell on the legitimacy of the arguments in support of either of these systems, which in my view have been rebutted successfully elsewhere. Rather than inquiring into the diplomatic affair,[9] I will address the strategies of argumentation used to support a diplomatic position set forth in one particular document presented when Argentina and Chile submitted the conflict to British arbitration.

The Argentine Position: "The Mountain Range Is a Natural Border"

The document *Argentine Evidence* developed the idea of mountains as a boundary rooted in the concept of "natural borders." As such, it echoes what at the time was an influential treatise, *Politische Geographie* (1897) by Friedrich Ratzel. In a long chapter devoted to the idea of natural borders,[10] the German geographer explained that a natural frontier seemed to clearly define "coherent" human settlements, naturally determined.[11] Ratzel assumed that a natural element would "naturally" produce clear social differences on both sides of the border, and emphasized that such a natural element should be easy to see. Similar statements accompanied the photographs included in *Argentine Evidence* as can be seen in Figures 7.2a and 7.2b.

However, the greatest elevation and the watershed do not coincide over the Andes. In a certain sense, it was an unexpected problem: it was assumed that the line of high summits and the ridge of high land dividing two areas that are drained by different river systems would match: Ratzel had even contemplated the case in which in the "architecture of the relief, the direction of the partition

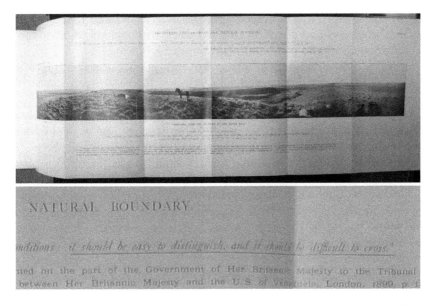

Figure 7.2 (a) "Panorama from the Sources of the River Pico." *Argentine Evidence,* pl. VII. "A natural feature, to make an efficient frontier boundary between States, should fulfill the following two main conditions: *it should be easy to distinguish and it should be difficult to cross.*" (b) *Argentine Evidence,* pl. VII (detail) "Easy to distinguish" in this context meant that "the arcifinious boundary should be (...) in the line of *greatest elevation* shall be sought the watershed."* American Geographical Society Library, University of Wisconsin-Milwaukee Libraries.

*Argentine Evidence, 465, italic in the original.

is not sufficiently clear," then "the watershed comes to one's aid, and the international right admits, in cases of doubt, that the border on mountainous chains must be defined of that way."[12] Such cases of doubt, however, supposed that a line of high summits would neither be visible nor recognizable.

The Argentine document affirmed that all the clauses of the Treaty of 1881 (which are cited later in the Protocol of 1893 and the Agreement of 1896) had implicitly ratified the topographic criterion because when they affirmed the status of the Andes Mountains as a natural barrier, they necessarily alluded to the line of highest summits: *Argentine Evidence* affirms, not without irony, that by "Andes" all those texts meant "mountains" and not "water":

> The examination already made of the rules of International Law governing this subject has demonstrated that, according to the unanimous opinion of writers—before and after the Treaty of 1881—those countries which are separated by mountains extend their rights of property along the entire slope facing them, as far as the culminating line; that when those writers referred to the watershed, they have done so in the sense of locating, within the crest, the precise points through which the line crosses; that no one, absolutely no one, has spoken even incidentally of the continental divide; that still less have they insinuated that the orographic boundary could be transformed into a hydrographic boundary, and that it is the contrary to their views and doctrines, when dealing with a chain, to abandon that chain and descend to distant plains in search of sources.
>
> It is not necessary to revert to this point, although the Chilian Representative insists upon it.[13]

Taking for granted that all diplomatic antecedents had referred to topography, *Argentine Evidence* held that the criterion for demarcation was not under discussion because "such limit will remain at all events 'immovable' between the two Republics," and that the only answer would be the material practice of demarcation and the line on the map which would result.[14]

Finally, the document suggests that the hydrographic criterion proposed by the Chileans was relatively recent and capricious, considering that "during the whole course of the negotiations which preceded the Treaty of 1881, the advisability of a hydrographic limit was never mentioned."[15] It added: "a divortium aquarum is not a permanent line," whereas "geographical facts entirely support the Argentine line."[16] If that is the case, how do those geographical facts work?

The Maps and the Facts

The "natural barrier" had to be an object of demarcation rather than negotiation. A mountain range was understood as a "geographic fact" that could not be contradicted by any map. The opposition between geographic fact (or reality) and document (or map) was clear: a natural barrier is a reality, and the maps—which are not the reality—are good only if they show that reality.

Neither Argentina nor Chile, when agreeing to the boundary on the edge of the Cordillera de los Andes, have looked on maps: the frontier was imposed itself. The limit along the mountain range was not arrived at as a consequence of cartographical work: the law of nations and the patrimony of the two countries pointed to it, as no other better division of the inheritance from Spain could be sought for. Maps were used only as helps to appreciate certain features of the range, but never have the indications contained in them preponderated over the traditional natural boundary.[17]

Therefore, *Argentine Evidence* argued that it would be completely useless for the Chileans to keep "looking for maps that prove something that is contrary to the geographical facts."[18] This argument actually admitted that there were many maps representing different positions. That was one of the reasons to doubt that maps offered unquestionable proof. Moreover, the map is shown as a manipulatable device that has in fact been manipulated (by the Chileans, naturally):

Recently, owing to the active propaganda on the part of the Chilian geographers in favour of the boundary line in the continental divide, some cartographic publications have modified the traditional boundary, although not always in complete agreement with the Chilian ideas.[19]

Part of the Argentine argument consisted in refuting the opponents' evidence, that is, in demonstrating that their arguments relied on "inaccurate maps." At first glance, the existence of a chapter ("8. Inutility of inaccurate maps") devoted to "the uselessness of vague maps" would suggest that the reliability of maps was bound up in their accuracy or—to use their contemporary words—in their capacity to represent facts.

Although a whole chapter was dedicated to "inaccurate maps," no epistemological or methodological criteria were given for judging accuracy in cartography. Finally, the *Evidence* concluded with the claim that the only valid maps were those that had been previously recognized as official.

In this process, somehow a "good map" had shifted from being something that reflects geographical fact into something that has been previously declared as official:

These words which are strictly applicable to the present question, deprive erroneous maps of any value, where dealing with the geographical lines proposed by the two Experts. Of what avail are the maps commented upon in this and the previous chapters—the map of Napp, those attributed to Burmeister, and Siemiradzky, the map of Brackebusch, quoted in the Chilian statement in support of the theory maintained by Señor Barros Arana, etc.? Further, what force can maps have for that purpose, which do not bear an official character? The maps have no reliable geographical basis, and neither the Argentine nor the Chilian Government have accepted them as evidence to define the common boundary. The only ones that bear that character are the official maps published in reference to this question.[20]

A similar criterion is applied in order to evaluate the cartographer's job: only when their maps supported the Argentine position were cartographers accepted as competent professionals:

> This coincidence only proves the complete unacquaintance of the cartographers who drew those maps with the true physical character of the range, while other maps showing the water-gaps in the same reveal that their draughtsman had more knowledge of the ground.[21]

How then could cartographers get to that "true physical character of the range"? One possibility identified in *Argentine Evidence* was through appropriate visualizing strategies.

The Visible as Evidence: Creating Visions (through Photographs)

The Argentinians claimed that mountains were a "geographical fact," with a tangible and visible reality. Therefore they consistently rejected the Chilean hydrographic arguments on the basis of their comparative intangibility and invisibility.[22] Such visual devices, by impressing audiences and their educated sensibilities, made the Argentine position appear realistic, material, and apprehensible through the senses.

Any reflection on the use of these graphic materials must be contextualized as, at the time, jurisprudence held that "words are enough." In legal disputes, it was assumed that "written opinions have an aura of dignity, and offer an opportunity for explication and reflection."[23] However, many official "memoirs" of the protracted border conflict included both "written documents" and "graphic documents."[24] Such graphic documents were indeed used in this case. This begs the question: what were the properties or values that made such documents worthy of supporting these high-stakes diplomatic arguments?

First, when we consider the difficulties involved in exploring the upper Andes (mainly because of its vastness and uneven terrain), photographs worked as a guarantee that a particular area was in fact accessible. The photograph, understood as a mechanical image necessarily taken by someone that was there, certified at least some visual accessibility. This point was seen as crucial when historical and present accessibility to the disputed area formed part of the arguments to vindicate territorial sovereignty. Indeed, *Argentine Evidence* explicitly notes:

> Besides this possible strategical point of view, those lands, as in the case with many others, are, must be repeated, valueless and useless to Chile, as they cannot have easy communication with the actual territory of Chile, viz. that of the western slope of the Andes; but on the other hand, they are useful and continuation of her dominions, and a portion of the eastern

slope of the Cordillera, all of them being at all times within easy reach of the Argentine centers of commerce and activity. Manufactories, railways, roads, ports—every Argentine channel of life and progress can easily reach them, or can be reached by them, whilst they are entirely cut off from all the Chilian channels of life and progress, for Nature has interposed between them the snowy range.[25]

It is also important to note that such photographs were reproduced in order to be understood as traces of a physical experience. Given that that historical settlements would be taken into account in determining the border, proving visual control of the area thus would reinforce Argentine claims. Additionally, the mimetic essence between a photo and sensible "reality" reaffirmed its effectiveness in two ways.[26] On the one hand, the "resemblance" was used to reproduce the argument: many travelers and Spanish administrators had seen *this* object (peak, summit, etc.) when they affirmed the extent of the border. On the other, it placed the reader into the role of an observer in the field. That is to say, photographs proposed a visual experience as if the observer were *in situ*.

Second, in this context, photos as mechanical images can suppose a certain objectivity, understood here as a prudent distance between the represented object and the observing subject. Thus this kind of visual device would guarantee not only a physical distance between the photographer and the photographed object but also an intellectual distance that could place the argument beyond subjective opinions expressed by words or texts, as well as beyond any deliberate or unintentional inaccuracies attributable to the cartographer. Susan Sontag expressed this idea:

> photography has powers that no other image-system has ever enjoyed because, unlike the earlier ones, it is not dependent on an image maker. However carefully the photographer intervenes in setting up and guiding the image-making process, the process itself remains an optical-chemical or electronic one, the workings of which are automatic, the machinery for which will inevitably be modified to provide still more detailed and, therefore, more useful maps of the real.[27]

According to *Argentine Evidence*, whereas "maps have no reliable geographical basis, [... the] illustrations that accompany this chapter are sufficient to show."[28]

Third, our way of thinking about knowledge itself has long privileged the faculty of sight.[29] If this way of conceiving knowledge is valid in diverse subject areas, it was particularly significant to the representation of terrain: topography was understood as an exploration experience founded on seeing (catching something with the sight), understanding (appropriating the seen thing through reason), and organizing (representing the thing on a map).[30] In this sense, the certification of an *in situ* experience, even from the distance implied in photographic shoots, can demonstrate a knowledge of the terrain that can be invoked as a key argument in order to claim possession of said territory. If "to photograph a thing is to appropriate the thing photographed," this visual framework implicitly suggests a historical appropriation to uphold the vindication of sovereignty.[31]

Photographs in this context presupposed an expedition, and invited others to explore an area through a book. Rather than landscapes, they created visions—images but also illusory experiences. They thus worked together with maps to create evidence from the visible.

The Evidence and the Evident: Visual Devices

Argentine Evidence contained not only an atlas but also a considerable number of maps distributed along its volumes, inserted within the text as well as folded in between pages. Nevertheless, in many passages it was emphatically remarked that the maps would neither give nor would clear rights by themselves. The role of old maps in supporting an argument concerning territorial rights requires more attention. Like photographs or other graphic materials, Hyung K. Lee has demonstrated that old books and maps, although they were not completely excluded, were generally only considered as long as they did not contradict other verbal testimonies (not only written, also oral testimony of a living witness).[32]

Whether the Argentine delegation purposely downplayed these maps because they were too obviously slanted is something that requires further examination (something beyond the scope of this chapter).[33] However, regardless of their motivation, the Argentine strategy consisted in moving the negotiation away from the cartographic arena and situating the debate in the field itself.

Knowing that the task of the British arbitrators would necessarily result in a physical demarcation and a cartographic image, Argentina developed and published a map articulating their claims (Figures 7.1a and 7.1b). Predictably, as noted in the legend, the map represents elements that would demonstrate the effective administration of those territories by the Argentine State (infrastructure, settlements, and highways), as well as several borders: the border proposed by Argentina according to records dated from September 1–3, 1898, the border proposed by Chile according to the record dated August 29, 1898, and the international border established in October 1898 (Figure 7.3).

However, the map is not only used to trace the border. Among its most visible elements are red lines, dots, and numbers, which refer to photographs. Indeed, the map's title explicitly refers to these photographs: *Preliminary Map of the South-Western Region of the Argentine Republic / showing the different points from which Photographs reproduced in the "Argentine Evidence" have been taken.* (See Figure 7.7.)

The red arcs included in the full map, as can be seen in the detail in Figure 7.4, represent the visual field covered by each photograph (each identified by numbers). These photographs in turn appear inserted in the text and, if their great size required it, were folded between the pages of the volumes. Photographs are cited on the map with references to the page number (arabic) where the photograph is reproduced (in the cases of the smaller photographs,

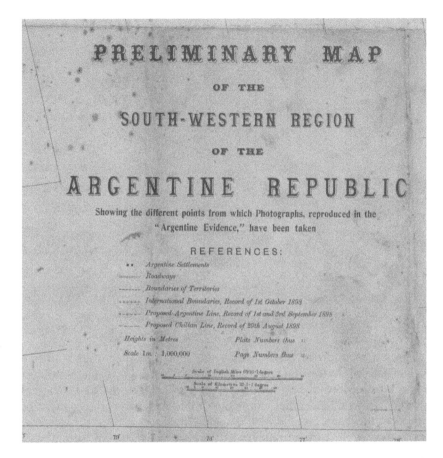

Figure 7.3 Preliminary Map of the South-Western Region of the Argentine Republic,
   1901. Detail. American Geographical Society Library, University of
   Wisconsin-Milwaukee Libraries.

e.g. Figure 7.5) or plate number (roman) for the larger photographs that are
folded and lack a page number (e.g., Figure 7.6).

In fact, those photographs suggest how "Argentinian eyes" would, in theory,
be able to examine the entire border from various locations. The arcs displayed
on the map suggest a visual exploration, a visual experience of the territory,
but they do not represent any physical or material exploration, for the arcs
represent landscapes seen from hundreds of meters away. Somehow, these arcs
themselves create a borderline: on the map, beyond the arcs, one can see blank
areas designed as "unexplored" territories (see Figure 7.4). By suggesting that
beyond the photographs there were "unexplored" territories beyond the scope
of vision from distant points, the authors seem to demonstrate that the Andes
blocked any view beyond themselves, and thus that the Andes constitute a kind
of visual natural border.

Figure 7.4 Preliminary Map of the South-Western Region of the Argentine Republic,
1901. Detail. American Geographical Society Library, University of
Wisconsin-Milwaukee Libraries.

The correspondence between map and photograph is thus reaffirmed in
both registries. On the other hand, many photographs have quasi-cartographic
elements added to them, such as toponymic references and geographical
coordinates, as well as other marks that invite the viewer to recognize specific
aspects of the image (see Figures 7.8a and 7.8b), appealing to the viewer's own
ability to read the cartographic record, to show what must be seen.

Like other "annotated drawings" this cartographic treatment modifies the
original photograph: a) it invites us to read particular features; b) it selects
certain elements of this landscape; c) it suggests that those selected elements
maintain a privileged relationship among themselves; d) it explains what the
observer is seeing. Similar to the "didactic program" that Bender and Marrinan
observe in other kinds of diagrams (which combine scale, references, names,
realistic aesthetics, and measurements), this cartographic treatment produces
new forms of knowledge and understanding.[34]

Nevertheless, even to the trained eye, it is not always simple to recognize the
supposed "evidence" offered by the photographs. A closer examination reveals
that, if the ultimate objective of all the photographs is to show a line of high
summits as a self-evident border, they do not consistently achieve that objective,
sometimes because of the low quality of the images, sometimes due to the lack
of clear reference points, and at other times because of a lack of correspondence between the accompanying text (titles which proclaim general rights or
principles) and what is observable in the image itself. Nevertheless, the images
operate as an endorsement of the Argentine argument. The very suggestion
that the evidence in favor of Argentine claims is supported by physical realities

746   *Divergences in the Cordillera de los Andes.*

To the south of the pass, the lofty snow-covered chain follows, always in a southerly direction. Its lowest pass is covered with snow only in winter, according to the statements of the last Chilian explorers, while others are permanently covered, and it may, therefore, be stated without rashness that the mean height of the ridge cannot be under 2000 metres (6562 feet). It suddenly becomes lower to give passage to the upper part of the river Manso which, in comparatively recent times, has received the waters of the eastern slope of the main chain of the Cordillera, which originally flowed into the old branches of the Lake

BARILOCHE GAP FROM SOUTH-WEST TO NORTH-EAST, AND LAKE CHRISTIE.

Nahuel-Huapi which empty eastwards. The line of the Argentine Expert passes along the crest of the said ridge, and bears number 285 at the narrow gorge of the river Manso, where the said line cuts that river.

The illustrations which accompany this chapter are sufficient to show the general features of the Cordillera in its eastern slope, and also the parallel ridges of the Pre-Cordillera which bound it to the east. Lake Nahuel-Huapi (Plate LX.) is a typical example of the great lakes to be met with in these latitudes. To the west rise the high mountains into which it penetrates through deep fjords, which are secondary lakes, and which have become isolated branches

Figure 7.5 "Bariloche Gap from South-west to North-East, and Lake Christie," *Argentine Evidence*, photo, p. 746. American Geographical Society Library, University of Wisconsin-Milwaukee Libraries.

Figure 7.6 "The Alluvial Fan Between Lakes Gutierrez and Mascardi." *Argentine Evidence*, pl. LXII. American Geographical Society Library, University of Wisconsin-Milwaukee Libraries.

Figure 7.7 Preliminary Map of the South-Western Region of the Argentine Republic, 1901. Detail, with references to photo, p. 746 (Figure 7.5) and pl. LXII (Figure 7.6). American Geographical Society Library, University of Wisconsin-Milwaukee Libraries.

that can be documented and presented in photographs intended to work as a powerful visual proof or evidence for supporting the general argument, seeming to offer a greater objectivity than maps could alone. The photos that accompany the maps are thus designed to increase the trustworthiness of the maps that illustrate the *Evidence*.

Many photographs are underpinned by quasi-cartographic elements that express toponymic references, geographic coordinates, and other marks that invite to recognize specific aspects of the image, to show what to see, appealing to skills of own reading of the cartographic record.

Figure 7.8 (a) "Panorama of Lake Nahuel-Huapi from Peninsula de San Tadeo." *Argentine Evidence*, pl. LX. (b) Detail. American Geographical Society Library, University of Wisconsin-Milwaukee Libraries.

Toward the end of the nineteenth century, after several piecemeal diplomatic agreements failed to achieve a definitive and integral solution, texts, maps and photographs, when put together, made the following argument: the Argentine border can be seen on the ground, and since it is visible, it is plausible and even self-evident.

Final Remarks: Making Evidences from the Visible

Some authors have suggested that "in its historical origin the frontier was not a legal concept and not, or at least not essentially, a political or intellectual concept. It was rather a phenomenon of the 'facts of life'—a manifestation of the spontaneous tendency for growth of the ecumene."[35] By the end of nineteenth century, the idea of the border had been redefined in light of scientific theories that, within the framework of the processes of territorial formation of modern states and also of the diffusion—or vulgarization, in Raffestin's words—of cartography, made it translatable into graphic language in the form of lines on a map.[36]

Rather than intending to analyze how the line drawn between Argentina and Chile had developed over time or to compare the arguments put forward by the two countries in supporting the borders they had proposed, this chapter has explored the role played by visuality and visual devices in producing and legitimating geographical knowledge applicable to international territorial disputes. My goal has been to determine, by examining the composition of the document *Argentine Evidence*, a) what were the theoretical, historical, and factual arguments used to claim a specific border? b) What were the resources used to develop the vindication? and c) How have textual and visual resources been combined in order to support those claims?

By adopting the term "evidence" in the title of their tract, Argentine diplomats made rich and powerful use of the connotations of this word. First, the word has a legal connotation that suggests conclusive proof in favor of a proposal. Second, the power of the physical and material existence of an object, in this case the Andes, the fact that the mountains existed, could be seen in photographs, and plotted on maps, made the Argentine proposal seem more substantial and real, in contrast to the visual intangibility of the Chilean proposal of watersheds. Third, the connotation of rationality implied in the common use of "evidence" builds on a long philosophical tradition according to which the concept "evidence" plays a key role in our acquisition of knowledge and exercise of rationality: the validity of knowledge depends on the nature and solidity of the evidence, but also on its adjustment to a system of judgments. Our senses are a primary source of evidence (as well as our memory, the testimony of others, and reason). Since the Enlightenment, sight has been held in the highest regard among the senses in terms of modern scientific knowledge production.

The title also activates the common meaning of the word: according to the *Real Academia Española* dictionary, evidence is "certeza clara y patente de la que no se puede dudar" (a clear certainty that is not possible to doubt).

In order to make the "topographic criterion" for the border prevail, Argentine diplomats tried to state their position in terms of an "evident argument" based on "visible evidence." That strategy of argumentation is made possible not only by the verbal text that threads the images together but also by the scale model or the map used to situate the images and by the references that act like a prosthesis for what one cannot see in the photograph.

That seemingly inconsistent accumulation of maps, photographs, and texts worked, in fact, as a network. At that time, the map was a material that could only be taken into account as a legal document in certain cases. Exactly because of its written character, the map was not free from subjective "contamination," unless other reliable documents accompanied it. There was nothing in its own nature to make it solid legal evidence. Nevertheless, the map was a useful device to transfer the diplomatic conflict to a different theater of operations, a theater of exhibition and visual evidence. Photography, on the other hand, relied on its mechanical and mimetic nature for trustworthiness. But just in case the photographic images were not entirely convincing by themselves, the photographs were given titles, epigraphs, quotations, and numbers that link them to their locations, toponyms, and other topographical information. Photos seem to have been more useful as evidence when treated cartographically to make the theory visible. The inexorable restriction of the field of vision that is offered by a single isolated photograph is solved by the combination of several photographs that, placed in a cartographic context, generate a comprehensive (even impossible) scene to make the evidence visible.

Notes

1 Friedrich Ratzel, *Géographie politique*, trans. Pierre Rusch with Carhles Hussy (Lausanne and Geneva: Editions Régionales Européenes, 1897 [1988 reprint]).

2 The entire title is *Argentine-Chilian Boundary. Report presented to the Tribunal appointed by her Britannic Majesty's "to consider and report upon the differences which have arisen with regard to the frontier between the Argentine and Chilian Republics" to justify the Argentine claims for the Boundary in the summit of the Cordillera de Los Andes, according to the Treaties of 1881 & 1893." Printed in compliance with the request of the Tribunal, dated December 21, 1899* (London: Printed for the Government of the Argentine Republic by William Clowes & Sons, Ltd, Stamford Street and Charing Cross. 1900). Two years later, a new edition in Spanish was released in London, in 2 vols: *Frontera argentino-chilena. Memoria presentada al Tribunal nombrado por el gobierno de Su Majestad británica "para considerar é informar sobre las diferencias suscitadas respecto á la frontera entre las Repúblicas Argentina y Chilena" á fín de justificar la demanda argentina de que el límite se trace en la cumbre de la cordillera de los Andes de acuerdo con los tratados de 1881 y 1893. Impresa para satisfacer la indicación hecha por el Tribunal en diciembre 21 de 1899* (London: Impresa para el gobierno de la República Argentina por W. Clowes e hijos, 1902).

3 The Chilean counterpart also produced a set of documents to be printed in English in London. Colonel Harold Holdrich selected for publication: "Un informe narrativo" by Sir T. Holdrich, two general reports by Captain B. Dickson; an "Informe Geográfico" by Sir T. Holdrich; a geographical report (incomplete) by Captain C. Robertson; a memorandum for a borderline proposal by Sir. T. Holdrich. In a letter addressed to Villiers, Holdrich also expressed his wish to add maps and photographs that were not yet ready in order to complete that set of official documents. The final presentation included a topographical large-scale map in six sheets. See Octavio Errázuriz Guilisasti and Germán Carrasco Domínguez, *Historia de las Relaciones Internacionales de Chile. Las relaciones chileno–argentinas*

durante la presidencia de Riesco. 1901–1906: El arbitraje británico de 1899 a 1903. Sus aspectos procesales (Santiago De Chile: Ediciones Andrés Bello, 1968).

4 On the methodological difficulties involved in validating the legitimacy of historical documents in diplomacy between Argentina and Chile, see Pablo Lacoste, *La imagen del otro en las relaciones de la Argentina y Chile (1534–2000)* (Buenos Aires: Fondo de Cultura Económica, 2003), 32–33.

5 "Without considering the exceptional jurisdiction over the provinces of Cuyo until the erection of the Virreinato del Río de la Plata, to which that province was incorporated, no Chilian authority ever existed to the east of the high Andean crest, until the occupation of the Strait of Magellan in 1843." *Argentine Evidence*, 532.

6 "El término límite deviene del latín *limes-itis*, concepto empleado para denominar la línea fortificada que separaba a los romanos de los pueblos bárbaros. Contrariamente a lo que se suele afirmar, el *limes* no era una línea delgada y recta. Tal como ha señalado Duroselle, el *limes* era una franja ancha, un espacio articulado por puestos avanzados, fortificaciones principales y secundarias, y calzadas de retaguardia para casos de frontera" (Lacoste, *La imagen*, 10). Claude Raffestin, *Pour une géographie du pouvoir* (París: Libraires Techniques (LITEC), Colección Géographie Economique et Sociale, 1980), also affirmed that linearity as a property of the concept of limit is connected to the modern organization on states, though he added that the effectiveness of such semantic connection required "l'apparition et la vulgarisation d'un instrument de représentation: la carte. La carte est l'instrument privilégié pour définir, délimiter la frontière. (...) C'est, au fond, le passage d'une représentation 'floue' à une représentation 'nette' inscrite dans le territoire. La ligne frontière n'est véritablement établie que lorsque la démarcation a eu lieu. 'Véritablement établie' signifie n'étant plus sujette à contestation de la part de l'un des Etats ayant cette frontière en commun. Par la démarcation, on élimine, non pas un conflit général, mais en tout cas un conflit dont la frontière pourrait être le prétexte." Raffestin *Pour une géographie*, 150–151).

7 Francisco Pascasio Moreno (1852–1919), an Argentine naturalist devoted to exploration and fossil collecting. Some of his works are:

> *Records of the proceedings of the Argentine and Chilian experts concerning the demarcation of the boundary-line between the Argentine Republic and Chili,* in collaboration with Diego Barros Arana (Buenos Aires: M. Biedma é hijo, 1898).

> *Reconnaissance de la région Andine, de la République Argentine. Notes préliminaires sur une excursion aux territoires du Neuquén, Rio Negro, Chubut et Santa Cruz, effectuée par les sections topographique et géologique* (La Plata: Museo de La Plata, 1897).

8 *Argentine Evidence*, xvi.

9 On Nov. 20, 1902 the arbitration award of British King Edward VII set a limit ad hoc, a line that sometimes coincided with the line of high peaks and sometimes coincided with the watershed (with the intention of respecting existing settlements). More than 400 measured points on the field would be established on the ground. The area in dispute (about 90,000 km^2) was distributed in such a way that, at the end of accounts, each country received nearly equivalent areas.

10 "Les barrières dressées par la naturre sont l'amorce de frontières naturelles. (...) Le fait de tracer une frontière politique sur la crête [des Alpes] n'est que la mise en valeur d'un rupture naturelle, présente de toute manière." Ratzel, *Politische Geographie*, 349.

11 Ratzel, *Politische Geographie,* 349–350.
12 Ratzel, *Géographie politique,* 356.
13 *Argentine Evidence,* 464–465.
14 Ibid., 475.
15 Ibid., 476.
16 Ibid., 490, 529.
17 Ibid., 556.
18 Ibid., 556.
19 Ibid., 558.
20 Ibid., 562.
21 Ibid., 556.
22 "Such a survey would have been totally unnecessary for studying the question in the form in which it has been placed before the Tribunal by the Representative of Chile, since the Chilian Expert himself has affirmed that the line which he proposed to the Argentine Expert is wholly independent of the exactness on the maps. If a mere principle of delimitation—viz. the orographic (that of the summit line of the Cordillera), or the hydrographic (that of the Continental divide)—should have been submitted to Arbitration, the decision could have been arrived without any particular knowledge of the ground." (Ibid., xi.)
23 Hampton Dellinger, "Words Are Enough: The Troublesome Use of Photographs, Maps, and Other Images in Supreme Court Opinions," *Harvard Law Review,* 110, no. 8 (1997): 1704.
24 For instance, in *La frontera Argentino-Chilena. Demarcación General, 1894–1906,* Oficina de Límites Internacionales, vols 1 and 2 (Buenos Aires: Talleres Gráficos de la Penitenciaría Nacional, 1908), 1, those kinds of materials are presented as follows:

> La *documentación escrita* comprende todas las actas que levantaron y firmaron los Jefes de las Subcomisiones Mixtas que han intervenido en aquella operación, las actas aprobatorias de las mismas subscriptas por los Peritos y las que se refieren a resoluciones importantes adoptadas por estos en cumplimiento de su cometido.
>
> La *documentación gráfica,* en la que se cuentan once mapas generales de las secciones demarcadas, varios diagramas, croquis, etc., informa sobre la situación relativa de los hitos y el consiguiente emplazamiento de la línea divisoria, y se reduce en cuanto a la frontera respecta, a la representación de una extensión limitada de terreno a uno y otro lado del límite, abarcando, además de las zonas en que actuaron las Comisiones arriba mencionadas, todas aquellas en que la Comisión especial enviada por el Gobierno Británico ha materializado la línea definitivamente establecida en el Laudo de 20 de noviembre de 1902.

25 *Argentine Evidence,* 528–529.
26 Philippe Dubois, *El acto fotográfico. De la representación a la recepción* (Barcelona: Paidós Comunicación, 1986 [1983]), 20.
27 Susan Sontag, *On Photography* (London: Penguin Books, 1979), 169–170.
28 *Argentine Evidence,* 562, 746.
29 The bounds between sight and knowledge in scientific practices has been predominantly focused on instruments that modified natural seeing as noted by Jutta Schickore, *The Microscope and the Eye: A History of Reflections, 1740–1870* (Chicago, IL:

University of Chicago Press, 2007). Several scholars have also underscored that images/representations allow the potential to see/access/possess new objects. See, for example, Michael Lynch and Steve Woolgar (eds.), *Representation in Scientific Practice* (Cambridge, MA: MIT Press, 1990); Bruno Latour, "Les 'vues' de l'esprit. Une introduction à l'anthropologie des sciences et des techniques," in Madeleine Akrich and Michel Callon (eds.), *Sociologie de la traduction. Textes fondateurs* (Paris: Presses de l'Ecole des Mines de Paris, 2006), 33–70; and Anne Sauvageot, *Voir et savoirs. Esquisse d'une sociologie du regard* (Paris: Presses Universitaires de France, 1994). Specifically, the historical relationship between photography and the geographical imagination has been increasingly discussed; see Joan Schwartz and James Ryan (eds.), *Picturing Place: Photography and the Geographical Imagination* (London and New York: I.B. Tauris, 2003). On visuality, knowledge, and political control in South America, see Marta Penhos, *Ver, conocer, dominar. Imágenes de Sudamérica a fines del siglo XVIII* (Buenos Aires: Siglo XXI, 2005).

30 "Représenter la topographie avait toujours été fondé sur trois actions: voir (appréhender par la vue, aussi bien que découvrir, c'est-à-dire prendre connaissance), comprendre (s'approprier par le raisonnement la chose vue) et organiser (reporter sur la carte un schéma correspondant à la réalité du terrain). La pensée intelligente et scientifique assimila et transcrit la connaissance perceptive (et les mesures), pour organiser l'espace fictif de la carte." See Catherine Bousquet-Bressolier (ed.), *L'œil du cartographe et la représentation géographique du Moyen Age à nos jours* (Paris: Comité des Travaux Historiques et Scientifiques, 1995), 9.

31 Sontag, *On Photography*, 2.

32 "International law, however, has a very distinctive rule that limits the evidentiary value of maps. Traditionally, international tribunals were more restrictive in evaluating maps than almost any other kind of evidence. In most instances, they regarded maps as secondary evidence at best, and frequently as hearsay in character. Consequently, the evidentiary value of maps often becomes one of the most contentious issues in international boundary or territory disputes. Further complicating the matter, not all courts and tribunals accord the same value to map evidences." Hyung K. Lee, "Mapping the Law of Legalizing Maps: The Implications of the Emerging Rule on Map Evidence in International Law," in *Pacific Rim Law and Policy Journal* 14 (2005): 159–188.

33 Sanz explains that most of the documents used by Chile to support their claims were books and maps published within Argentina. In order to deny any kind of official legitimacy for those materials, the Minister of Foreign Affairs affirmed that those documents had been produced by foreign professionals. See L.S. Sanz, *Zeballos. El tratado de 1881. Guerra del Pacífico. Un discurso académico y seis estudios de historia diplomática* (Buenos Aires: Ed. Pleamar, 1985). However, he neglects to mention that these foreign professionals had been hired and paid by Argentine national governments. See Carla Lois, "Técnica, política y 'deseo territorial' en la cartografía oficial de la Argentina (1852–1941)," *Scripta Nova. Revista Electrónica de Geografía y Ciencias Sociales* 10: (Aug. 1, 2006): 218–252.

34 John Bender and Michael Marrinan, *The Culture of Diagram* (Palo Alto, CA: Stanford University Press, 2010), 31.

35 Ladis K. D. Kristof, "The Nature of Frontiers and Boundaries," in *Annals of the Association of American Geographers* 49, no. 3–1 (Sept. 1959): 270.

36 See Raffestin, *Pour une géographie du pouvoir*.

8 Female Eyes on South America
Maria Graham in Brazil

Katherine Manthorne

In 1819 Maria Graham (née Dundas, 1785–1842; later Maria, Lady Callcott) sat for her portrait by Thomas Lawrence, then London's most fashionable painter (Figure 8.1). In his typical manner he created a flattering image of this controversial, talented woman gazing dreamily off into the distance, wearing a turban-like headpiece that references her earlier travels and publications on India, and—more practically—hides a childhood injury. Perhaps they conversed about art, given that she was a skilled graphic artist, wrote books on artists including her *Memoirs of the Life of Nicolas Poussin* (1820), and counted among mutual friends the painter Charles Eastlake.[1] Lawrence depicted her head in a three-quarters view against a dark, loosely painted background, and left the lower portion of the canvas covered only in cream-colored under-paint, as though she was too hurried for anything but a quick sketch. Its spirit is fitting for a female life conducted over several continents and dedicated to art and travel writing.

Two years after the portrait sitting, in August 1821 she was in Falmouth boarding the frigate HMS *Doris* commanded by her husband Captain Thomas Graham, bound for South America. His task was to protect British commercial interests in the southern cone, including support for Brazilian independence. They touched down in Recife in the state of Pernambuco, Brazil, in September 1821, but shortly thereafter Captain Graham became ill. They then traveled from Brazil around Cape Horn to Chile, but he passed away aboard ship before he was ever able to step on shore. When the ship reached Valparaiso, Chile, his 37-year-old widow refused offers of passage back to Europe and resolved to remain there on her own in what was a politically unstable region in the throes of the Wars of Independence. From 1821 to 1825 she resided for a time in Chile and then Brazil, keeping a diary and making drawings that provided material for two publications: *Journal of a Residence in Chile* (1824) and *Journal of a Voyage to Brazil* (1824).[2]

Maria Graham authored her *Journal of a Voyage to Brazil and Residence there, during part of the years 1821, 1822, 1823* (1824) as equal parts adventure story, political reportage, naturalist's day-book, and social exposé. As an early travel narrative of Brazil, it helped shape Anglo-American concepts of that country. Equally important, it demonstrates how an independently minded and self-educated woman found a way to carve out a professional

Figure 8.1 Sir Thomas Lawrence, *Maria, Lady Callcott,* 1819, oil on canvas, 23½ ×
19½". Ref. no. 954. © National Portrait Gallery, London.

life for herself in Brazil, while ironically back in Britain the public eagerly
devoured her written accounts, including that of a devastating earthquake, but
she was barred as a female from presenting her paper on the event before the
Royal Geological Society.

Long neglected, Graham has recently begun to receive scholarly attention
including publications by Regina Akel and Jennifer Hayward, both of whom
focus on the theme of feminine self-fashioning.[3] She also appears in collective
studies of female travelers in Latin America by Alicia Lubowki-Jahn and
Adriana Méndez Rodenas.[4]

Complementing their scholarship, I perform a close reading of the pictorial
imagery in *Journal of a Voyage to Brazil* and situate it within the broader context

of South American travel art. Graham sketched in pencil and watercolors wherever she went and, judging from those drawings that have been preserved in public collections, she was working in portable sketchbooks ranging in size from about 5 × 9" to 7¼ × 11". This scale allowed her to make the preliminary sketch on site, even if she elaborated detail back home. Picture making was therefore central to her travel practice. When the time came to publish her book on Brazil she turned her drawings over to an engraver, identifying each one as "Drawn by Maria Graham/ Engraved by Edwd Finden." A London-based line engraver, Edward Finden (1791–1857) was so popular that he and his brother William employed many assistants to fill their numerous commissions. Comparison between Finden's engraving and her original drawings—when possible—indicates that the prints remain true to Graham's original drawings.

Gender unquestionably played a role in shaping Graham's vision of Brazil. No matter how deeply she immersed herself in the travel accounts of her (male) predecessors and reimagined the heritage established by Alexander von Humboldt, Johann Baptist Spix, and Carl Friedrich von Martius, and others, she was hindered by the limited geographical range and scientific training to which she had access. Casting her female eyes on Brazil, I posit that Graham adapted their expeditionary methods to locales close to her temporary home in Rio de Janeiro that were available to her as a woman in the 1820s. Domesticating the masculine expeditionary mode, she engaged her readers with four major themes: (1) Setting the historical stage, she established herself as key witness to revolutionary events. (2) Collecting botanical specimens, she engaged in an activity associated with both naturalists and female amateurs and synthesized those dual perspectives. (3) Being confined to the city, she was able to expand the canonical views of Rio de Janeiro. (4) Combining her on-site drawings with text facilitated her accommodation of Brazilian scenery to the aesthetic category of the Picturesque.

Domesticating Expeditionary Literature

From the outset of Graham's transatlantic journey she kept a diary that helped her to make sense of her experiences and provided the raw material for books that would establish her as a pioneering travel writer—regardless of gender— in the newly independent empire. Her *Journal of a Voyage to Brazil* had few antecedents.[5] She cited one major inspiration and influence: the pioneering work of Alexander von Humboldt, Prussian explorer of Spanish America. His journey across northwest South America, Mexico, and Cuba (1799–1804) and his numerous subsequent publications—especially *Vues des Cordillères et monuments des peuples indigènes de l'Amérique* (1810–13)— established the itinerary of requisite landscape sites for New World nature, equiva-lent to the Grand Tour for the Old World.[6] Those who trod in Humboldt's footsteps maintained a running dialogue between their own experiences and his observations, while those who chose an alternative route to his were at pains to explain their departures. Although Humboldt never visited Brazil, his work set the standards for expeditionary literature on South America. To establish her own credentials on the southern continent, Graham had to demonstrate her familiarity with his work. Defining a visible link between herself and her distinguished predecessor, she devoted the second of her eleven illustrations to "the Great Dragon Tree of Oratava, of which Humboldt has given so interesting an account" (Figure 8.2). She was referencing a passage in his *Personal Narrative* when on Tenerife Humboldt described a dragon tree "of enormous magnitude," and called it "one of the oldest inhabitants on our globe" and the final plate illustrating his *Vues des Cordillères.*[7] Mindful that her sketch of the arboreal ruin was but a faint echo of Humboldt's evocations, she added to her illustration caption: "He saw it in all its greatest; I drew it after it had lost half its top." Given that this natural landmark is located in Tenerife—one of Spain's Canary Islands off the coast of North Africa—it was hardly essential to her narrative of Brazil, and was featured primarily to reinforce her kinship with Humboldt.

Her most eminent predecessors within Brazil were the German zoologist Johann Baptist Spix and botanist Carl Friedrich von Martius who in 1817 accompanied Maria Leopoldina of Austria to Rio de Janeiro, where she was to marry Emperor Dom Pedro. Once there, the naturalists traversed the country in search of botanical and zoological specimens to bring back to Europe. For part of their journey they had as their companion the Austrian painter Thomas Ender, who produced hundreds of watercolors of the environs of Rio during

Figure 8.2 Edward Finden after Maria Graham, *Great Dragon Tree of Oratava.* Her plate II, to face p. 85. British Museum no. 1871,1111.613. © The Trustees of the British Museum.

his ten-month stay. Sadly he failed to exhibit or reproduce them and therefore they remained little known.[8] Spix and Martius by contrast published various scientific treatises along with an account intended for the general public titled *Reise in Brasilien ... in 1817–1820*, printed in three volumes in 1823, 1828, and 1831 and translated into English (first volume only, in 1824) and Portuguese. Graham would have known of their presence in the country and possibly consulted their 1823 volume as she finalized her book.

Setting the Historical Stage

As travel literature evolved into an increasingly popular genre in the nineteenth century, certain conventions became firmly entrenched. The narrative followed a set chronology, opening with the individual's touch down in the target country and following day by day until the journey's end and departure for home. The writer's physical movement through the landscape provided the "plot," while her attitudes and state of mind provided the point of view in a land presented as a tabula rasa, lacking any significant history prior to the arrival of the foreigner. Graham broke with these conventions. The first mention of her presence in Brazil appears only on p. 76, after an extended lesson on the country's politics and history.[9] With this deft move, she accomplished two things: she demonstrated her command of a field of knowledge rarely considered the domain of the female narrator, and she underscored that her arrival coincided with a major transition in the history of the country.

In March 1823 she sailed from Chile to Brazil, then also undergoing something of a revolution. It had only recently been declared independent from Portugal with Pedro I crowned as Emperor. By the time of Graham's final farewell to Brazil in 1825, she had witnessed momentous changes in its passage from Portuguese colony to independent empire,[10] which provides a significant backdrop for her experiences. Without some historic background, as she put it, "the journal of what passed while I was in Brazil would scarcely be intelligible" (p. 75). Her narrative transcends "mere" travel literature to become a witness to the making of history. Mary Louise Pratt applied her "imperial eyes" model to Graham, whom she portrayed as an agent of European capitalism.[11] It is true that her engraved illustrations of Rio de Janeiro portrayed the city as attractive to foreign eyes and to possible future investment or settlement. As I attempt to demonstrate, however, a dual reading of text and image reveals her more nuanced attitude toward Brazil's geography and history than that Eurocentric reading might allow.

Travel narratives are understood as an intricate network of texts in which one traveler conducts an internal conversation with his predecessor or successor: Humboldt quoted La Condamine, Darwin quoted Humboldt, Louis Agassiz quoted Spix and Martius. Travel art is similarly in dialogue with prior imagery, and opens the door to future efforts. In this spirit Maria Graham referenced and at times inserted the work of another hand into her volume. A case in point is the oeuvre of independent traveler artist Augustus Earle (1793–1838), represented in her *Journal of a Voyage to Brazil* by three works. In March 1818

Earle left England on an around-the-world sojourn and spent over six years in the Americas. From about 1820 to 1824 he was in Brazil, where he produced a significant body of drawings of landscapes, portraits, and scenes dealing with slavery.[12] Since his residence in Rio overlapped with Graham's, and given their mutual interests and the interconnectedness of the British community there, the two certainly met. The fact that drawings by Earle were given to the British Museum by Maria's second husband August us W. Callcott indicates that the artist presumably gave them to her for use in her book.[13] These included Earle's *Portrait of Dona Maria de Jesus*, who fought in the revolution. Graham's text records her meeting with the brave woman, when she could have done her portrait. But perhaps her lack of experience with figure painting prompted her to use Earle's more than competent image of Dona Maria in uniform. She also featured two of his images of slave markets, *Gate and Slave Market at Pernambuco* and *Slave Market at Rio de Janeiro* (Figure 8.3), showing the street where the buyers examine the slaves, including a group of African children at the center of the composition. She had in fact observed the slave market on her first landing in 1821 in Recife, a major Brazilian port and capital of the state of Pernambuco. But to judge from the written account she penned, her shock and physical disgust at what she saw prevented her from taking out her sketchbook and rendering it on site. Earle's images therefore filled that important gap.

Figure 8.3 Edward Finden after Augustus Earle, *Val Longo, or Slave Market at Rio*, her plate I, to front the title-page. British Museum no. 1871,1111.614. © The Trustees of the British Museum.

During her residence she gained increasing facility with Portuguese, which enabled her to plumb material contained in local libraries. "I have begun to read diligently every scrap of Brazilian history I can find," she tells her readers (p. 302):

I have commenced by a collection of pamphlets, newspapers, some MS. Letters and proclamations, from the year 1576 to 1757, bound up together; some of these tracts Mr. Southey mentions, others he probably had not seen, but they contain nothing very material that he has not in his history. The morning's study of Brazilian history in the original language is one great advantage I derive from my removal into town.

The source she cited is Robert Southey's *History of Brazil* (3 vols, 1819), a copy of which she owned. This compilation by the British lake poet provided an indispensable background, which she supplemented with her own research and observations. Going against the stereotype of women travel writers as apolitical, Graham shared her political views on many topics, from debates in the Assembly to which she was privy to discussions about the proposed Constitution. She defends the emancipation of Brazil from Portuguese rule, and at various points expressed indignation over slavery, in which the British at that date were still trafficking. She made no pretense at complete objectivity but mixed fact and her own clearly identified opinion throughout her project.

She distinguished herself from most travelers not only by her command of the language but also by her unprecedented access to the imperial court. She enjoyed friendship with the Empress Maria Leopoldina, who as a recent arrival from Austria perhaps shared some of the feelings of the transplanted British writer in this strange land. And for a short time Graham was governess to the imperial princess Doña Maria de Gloria (daughter of Dom Pedro I), who would later become Doña Maria II of Portugal. Towards the end of her narrative she wrote (p. 317):

October 12th—This is the Emperor's birth-day, and the first anniversary of the coronation. I was curious to see the court of Brazil, so I rose early and dressed myself, and went to the royal chapel, where the Emperor and Empress, and the Imperial Princess, were to be with the court before the drawing-room.

Witness to the birth of a new nation, she intertwines her own story with that of its emerging independence.

Botanizing

No visitor to Brazil could remain indifferent to its vegetal world. Graham describes herself as botanically ignorant, but her knowledge certainly grew over the course of her residency. At various points she writes like a layman seduced by the plant life she encounters: "Brazil is particularly rich in splendid creeping flowers and shrubs; and these are mingled with orange and lemon blossoms, and the jasmine and rose from the East, till the whole is one thicket of beauty and fragrance" (p. 162). At other times, such as when she visited Rio's Botanical Gardens, she refers to plants by their scientific names and indicates their utility.[14]

Private correspondence and unpublished sketches further corroborate her expanding facility with botany.[15] She offered assistance to William Hooker, director of Kew Gardens back in London, and later wrote: "I do not habitually draw flowers but I could do that—and also any peculiar form of seed & c— Only let me know how I can be useful & I will try to be so."[16] Graham assured Hooker that not only would she be diligent in her search for plants, but she would also engage others in their collecting efforts. "I am very fond of plants," she insisted, "& scruple neither muddy feet nor torn clothes for their sake."[17] Growing between her cottage and the top of Corcovado were such a wide variety of ferns that she was able to collect twenty-two different species, which she dried and shipped to Hooker on the ship *Aurora*. In situations when she could not provide a dried specimen, she substituted a careful drawing. Between 1824 and 1825 she made over hundred drawings of Brazilian flora that were collected in a portfolio and now preserved in the Archives at Kew Gardens. When the portfolio was received on loan in 1933 the then director made a note on the front page: "The drawings are certainly of value. Mrs. Graham evidently possessed enough botanical knowledge to enable her to make what appear to be accurate illustrations of plants, and clearly she had considerable artistic skill."

The British Museum holds one of her sketchbooks of Rio that includes a colored pencil drawing of *Helioconia* that contrasts a close-up study of the plant with a distant view of the waters of the bay at Rio and Corcovado Mountain.[18] She depicted the plant from a low vantage point, allowing it to stand out against the landscape background while simultaneously indicating its habitat. The manipulation of visual strategies to achieve this positive result evidences a skillful hand and knowledge of a broad repertoire of floral imagery. Why, then, did she not illustrate them in her own travel account? Women, if they were acknowledged at all in the field of art and travel, tended to be stereotyped as lady flower painters. Having worked so hard to gain respect as a female intellectual, she resisted inserting pictures in her book that might induce such a branding. Instead she chose to work behind the scenes, making drawings and collecting specimens to share not only with Hooker but also with David Douglas, John Sims, and Carl Von Martius, all of whom acknowledged her in their publications.[19] By these means she functioned as an important link in the global network on which Kew and ultimately British natural science depended in its efforts to categorize the world's plant population. Collecting botanical specimens, she engaged in an activity associated with both naturalists and female amateurs and synthesized those dual positions to create an individual perspective.

Picturing the City: Iconic Subjects and Sites of Personal Discovery

After leaving England, the HMS *Doris* made a stop on the island of Madeira, off the African coast, then proceeded across the Atlantic. Their first landfall in Brazil occurred on September 22, 1821 at the port of Recife in the state of Pernambuco (p. 97). After spending some time there, they set off on October 14 and "coasted along within sight of the shores of Brazil" until they "anchored in the bay of All Saints, opposite to the town of St. Salvador, commonly called Bahia." There "my eyes opened on one of the finest scenes they ever beheld: A city, magnificent in appearance from the sea" (p. 132). On December 9 they were again underway and six days later arrived at Rio de Janeiro, where Graham—like so many travelers before and after her—struggled for words to describe it (p. 159):

> Nothing that I have ever seen is comparable in beauty to this bay. Naples, the Firth of Forth, Bombay harbour, Trincomalee, each of which I thought perfect in their beauty, all must yield to this, which surpasses each in its different way. Lofty mountains, rocks of clustered columns, luxuriant wood, bright flowery islands, green banks, all mixed with white buildings, each little eminence crowned with its church or fort; ships at anchor or in motion; and innumerable boats flitting about in such a delicious climate,—combine to render Rio de Janeiro the most enchanting scene that imagination can conceive.

No wonder then that she set up residence in its suburb of Catete, which became the base camp for her exploration of the city and its immediate environs. We have to remind ourselves that Brazil encompassed a vast territory, even as it was consolidating its holdings during Graham's visit. To give some idea, present-day Brazil is larger than the contiguous United States (excluding Hawaii and Alaska). It encompasses a wide range of tropical and subtropical landscapes, from the Amazonian rain forest in the north to the Iguassu Falls on the Argentine border, with the largest remnant of primitive Atlantic forest. The title of Graham's book *Journal of a Voyage to Brazil and Residence there, during part of the years 1821, 1822, 1823* (1824) would lead us to believe that she covered a significant part of the country. Aside from brief stops in the ports of Recife and Bahia, however, she remained on the central coast. She never saw the Amazon or visited the interior. Her primary focus was Rio de Janeiro. This fact alone requires consideration.

However strong-willed or independent-minded she was, a solitary woman was prevented from extensive travel in the sparsely populated, poorly mapped, and dangerous territories by physical barriers as well as social norms. Graham chafed against these constraints, and complained of her inability to travel freely about the countryside. To compensate for that, she focused on the city of Rio and its environs as her objective and adopted expeditionary practices of journal keeping, mapping, and drawing to study it and make it comprehensible to her readers. This she does for the better part of 175 written pages and a series of illustrations. Corcovado or Hunchback Mountain—which looms over Rio de Janeiro— is a major landmark with a long history in the visual arts. The 710 m (2,300 ft.) high peak provided a natural belvedere from which to take in the city and its breathtaking bays, so that sketches and photographs abound from this site. Depicted by innumerable travelers, the vista of Corcovado from across the bay—where its distinctive form is most evident—became the canonical view.

Graham, by contrast, positions herself on a garden terrace, so that we see the peak's profile between the forms of a house at right and left and framed below by the fence that bisects the space into the cultivated zone in the immediate foreground and the wilder or more sublime nature beyond (Figure 8.4). Art historian Ana Maria Belluzzo reinforces this idea of Graham viewing the mountain from an enclosed garden:

> She devotes herself to the distant view of the peaks while inhabiting the intimate space of the garden. In the drawing *The View of Corcovado,* the garden, abounding in varieties of life, functions as a repoussoir from where one can see the edge of the irregular peak. The *hortus conclusus* is a place for retreat and contemplation.[20]

Her composition anticipates that adopted by British artist Marianne North (1830–90) who traversed the globe to delineate plants. Upon the death of her parents she sold the family home and in 1871 commenced her life of travel that eventually embraced North and South America, Japan, India, Ceylon, Australia, New Zealand, and South Africa. She eventually completed over 800 paintings that she bequeathed to Great Britain's Royal Botanic Gardens at Kew, along with the funds to build a gallery to house them (where they can still be seen today). Significantly, one of her formative experiences was her eight-month residence in Brazil in 1872–3, where she kept a written journal (edited and published posthumously by her sister) that complemented her pictorial record. She took an unconventional approach to the delineation of botanical specimens, eschewing the usual practice of focusing on an individual plant and preferring to depict the broader landscape that provided its natural habitat. Among the more than 100 panels she painted in Brazil was her *View of the Corcovado Mountain, near Rio de Janeiro,* for which she positioned herself on the edge of a fenced garden looking over the low-lying shrubs and trees—especially the royal palms—so that the famous peak seems to emerge from the womb of tropical nature. Positioning themselves in this outdoor domestic space, both women reference the tradition of depicting the Virgin Mary as *hortus conclusus* or Mary of the Enclosed Garden. The image of Mary seated in a bounded outdoor space surrounded by flowers arose about 1330 and continued into the Renaissance, linking her practically and symbolically with cultivated nature.[21] While final assessment awaits identification of further imagery by female hands, this preliminary evidence demonstrates a departure

Figure 8.4 Edward Finden after Maria Graham, *Corcovado from Botofogo*, her plate VIII, to face p. 220. British Museum no. 1871,1111.615. © The Trustees of the British Museum.

from the canonical view on the part of these women, pointing to a distinctly feminine perspective on this mountain icon.

At times Graham strayed from such iconic scenes to feature sites she "discovered" and described. Wandering the area south of the city she came upon Laranjeiras in valley of the Carioca River. Founded in the seventeenth century, it constitutes one of the oldest residential neighborhoods (p. 161):

I walked ... up one of the little valleys at the foot of the Corcorado [sic]: it is called the Laranjeiros [sic], from the numerous orange trees which grow on each side of the little stream that beautifies and fertilizes it. Just at the entrance of that valley, a little green plain stretches itself on either hand, through which the rivulet runs over its stony bed, and affords a tempting spot to groups of washerwomen of all hues, though the greater number are black; and they add not a little to the picturesque effect of the scene ... Round the washerwoman's plain, hedges of acacia and mimosa fence the gardens of plantains, oranges, and other fruits which surround every villa ...

Surveying her picture (Figure 8.5) punctuated by vibrant trees and shrubs that complements this written description, we can almost sniff their pleasant fragrance permeating the atmosphere. Beyond these pleasures Graham's attention to Laranjeiras signals a key feature of her enterprise: she alternated between major landmarks seen through her feminine lens and modest sites that she found personally enjoyable or meaningful.

Forging the Picturesque through Text and Image

From the late eighteenth century through the mid-nineteenth century, debates about landscape centered on three aesthetic ideals: the sublime, the beautiful,

Figure 8.5 Edward Finden after Maria Graham, *Larangeiras, Brazil*, her plate V, facing
p. 163. British Museum no. 1871,1111.610. © The Trustees of the British
Museum.

and the picturesque. When artists first confronted the incomprehensible vegetation, waterways, and landforms of Latin America, these modes provided a
system of analyzing empirical as well as emotional reactions, thereby guiding
their pictorial responses. The picturesque, according to one of its earliest
theorists Uvedale Price, was the intermediate category between the sublime and
the beautiful. In his influential *Essay on the Picturesque* (1794) Price argued
that the work of the great seventeenth-century landscapists, especially Claude
Lorrain, should be used as models for the "improvement of real landscape."
The prototypical Claudian landscape conveyed an idealized, orderly world
organized around a central mountain peak, a body of reflective water before it,
and trees framing the scene. Soon the vogue for "picturesque voyages" further
afield expanded applications of the picturesque beyond the British countryside
to embrace Brazil and Spanish America. These conventions began to serve as a
"civilizing stamp" that the traveler artists imposed on the colonial lands they
began to explore, and subsequently published in books that emerged as a sub-
category of illustrated travel accounts.

Born in Papcastle, Cumberland, Maria Graham grew up in the countryside.
As the daughter of an Admiral, she received a better than average education
for a woman of her day, one that included training in drawing and watercolor
as well as literature and music. In 1793 she moved to the Richmond residence
of her uncle Sir David Dundas, where she would have met leading writers and
painters who gathered there. All of this insured that she was steeped in the
natural world that had inspired Price along with William Gilpin and Richard
Payne Knight, all aestheticians of the Picturesque, and was familiar with their
ideas. When her life of travel commenced in earnest in 1808 with a trip to
India in the company of her father, she possessed the knowledge and ability
to depict visually as well as verbally the world around her. On that three-
year trip she began her career-long habit of keeping both a written diary as
well as a sketchbook of drawings of places of interest on her journeys. Thus
commenced her personal Picturesque Voyage. This dual practice was crucial
to her powers of observation and her skills as a travel writer. Her Brazilian
narrative is punctuated by references to her efforts at drawing what she sees.
From her residence in Catete, to cite one instance, she made an excursion with
several companions to the Botanical Gardens. Afterward they stopped for a
meal and as the others finished dining, she took the opportunity to go off and
make a sketch (p. 165):

> I was soon drawn away from the table by the beauty of the prospect, which
> I endeavored to sketch. The coffee plantations are the only cultivated
> grounds hereabouts; and they are so thickly set with orange trees, lemons,
> and other tall shrubs, that they form in appearance rather a variety in the
> woods, than that mixture of cultivated with wild ground, which might be
> looked for so near a large city, where we expect to see the labour of man
> encroaching in some degree on the wild beauties of nature. But here the
> vegetation is so luxuriant, that even the pruned and grafted tree springs up
> like the native of the forest.

She then reported their return home, bringing some souvenir of the day's outing: "Most of us carried home something. Fruits and flowers attracted some; Langford got a number of diamond beetles, and a magnificent butterfly, and I a most inadequate sketch of the scene from the Padre's house" (p. 166).

Such pictorial recordings were done on the spot, her diary entries made at home after a day's activities, and the text for the book prepared long after the experiences described. Her drawings, therefore, have the impact of imme-diacy. Recording the terrain before her on a sketchbook page forced her to see things she would have otherwise missed, and to take possession of the scene by the sheer act of recording its contours on paper. It was a form of visual note-taking, an aide-de-mémoire that fed and strengthened her writing. Her graphic skills enabled her, with the assistance of professional engravers, to illustrate all her own books: a claim few travel writers could make. When both are created by the same hand, word helps convert picture into a site of meaning. Text and image coexist in her work in a complex symbiosis, fostering the understanding of landscapes of unknown terrain by armchair travelers who would never see them firsthand. Her ability to combine her on-site drawings with text facilitated her accommodation of the Brazilian scenery with the aesthetic category of the Picturesque.

Graham mentions little about Rio's fledgling art scene, but as someone who had access to court and a keen interest in art, she surely must have been aware of—even if she enjoyed little direct contact with—French artist Jean-Baptiste Debret. He had departed Paris for Brazil in 1816 as part of what was later called the French Artistic Mission. Following the arrival of the Portuguese royal family in Brazil, King João VI invited a group of artists from France that included not only Debret but also sculptor Nicolas-Antoine Taunay and archi-tect Joaquin Lebreton. They established what became under the Emperor Dom Pedro I the Imperial Academy of Fine Arts of Rio de Janeiro, where they laid the foundations of an academic style. Unlike most art academies that emphasized figure drawing, here the curriculum included a course on "Landscape, Flowers, and Animals" that assisted in developing a taste for these branches of art. When his compatriots departed for home, Debret remained in Brazil until 1831, and thus would have overlapped with Graham's residence. Cousin of Jacques Louis David, Debret viewed Brazilian life through a neoclassical lens, creating an impressive number of drawings and paintings documenting historic events, landscapes, street scenes, and ethnic types with typical costumes and acces-sories. These became the basis for the three-volume book he produced upon his return to France titled *Voyage pittoreseque et historique au Bresil* (Paris: Firmin Didot frère, 1834–9). Successfully utilized by others including Johan Moritz Rugendas for his Brazilian pictures produced 1827–35, the "Picturesque Voyage" came to constitute a subset of travel literature, one that privileged full-page illustrations over minimal descriptive text and gave viewers the impres-sion of glimpsing everyday life on the streets of a foreign land. Produced a good ten years prior to Debret's publication, Graham's volume is something of a hybrid, located between the expeditionary literature produced by more scien-tifically oriented travelers and the Picturesque Voyage beginning to be created by draftsmen and visual artists for more popular audiences. Graham was a not only a pioneering woman, she was also a pioneering travel writer in this formative historic period in Brazil.

Graham was ahead of her time in her combination of text with 20 pictures (11 full-page plates and nine vignettes).[22] Although some scholars avoid mention of her images and at least one author dismissed them as unoriginal examples of the picturesque, we have to remind ourselves that—published by 1824—they were among the earliest examples of the genre in Brazil.[23] Her pictures helped to establish the travel itinerary in the region, instructing people not only on what to see but how to see it. The Palace of Sao Cristovaõ provides a rare instance where Ender, Debret, and Graham each depicted the same motif, and provides us with a useful case study for understanding just how Graham guided her readers to see things her way.

At the opening of the nineteenth century the area known as the Quinta da Boa Vista (Park of the Nice View) belonged to the wealthy Portuguese merchant Elias Antonio Lopes, who in 1803 built a manor house atop its hill. In 1808 when the Portuguese court was transported to Brazil. Lopes donated the property to King João VI, who spent a good deal of time there. Streets and mansions grew up around it, to accommodate the local aristocracy. As the residence of the Imperial family, the Palace of Saõ Cristovaõ was an important historic site in the Rio vicinity.

In 1817 Austrian painter Thomas Ender selected a distant vantage point, which provide a sweeping transition from the foreground rocks and vegetation to the carriage-filled roadways in the middle distance and on to the palace that sits fortress-like atop the plateau. The effect is imposing, befitting a royal residence, the horse-drawn conveyances on the road a reminder of the business of court. Ender showed the structure when it was a manor house. Then from 1819 to 1821 British architect John Johnson transformed it into a palace, including the installation of the decorative portico imported from England.[24] Afterwards Debret came along and depicted the gateway and palace with its tower stretched across the middle distance, its white façade set against a single bald mountain peak. His foreground is barren, with an improbable cactus here and there, highlighting the building expansion. Graham, who depicted the same phase of construction, sets the stage for her picture (Figure 8.6) via her narrative (p. 246):

> To-day I rode to San Cristovaõ, through a very beautiful country. The palace, which once belonged to a convent, is placed upon a rising ground, and is built rather in the Moresco style, and coloured yellow with white molding. It has a beautiful screen, a gateway of Portland stone, and the court is planted with weeping willows; so that a group of great beauty is formed in the bosom of a valley, surrounded by high and picturesque mountains, the chief of which is the Beco do Perroquito.[25]

Depicting the distinctive structure before its definitive neoclassical intervention (1826–31), she selected a perspective that enhanced the harmony between

Figure 8.6 Edward Finden after Maria Graham, *Palace of San [sic] Cristovaõ*, her plate
IX, to face p. 246. British Museum no. 1871,1111.616. © The Trustees of
the British Museum.

the buildings and surrounding terrain. Trees grow around the man-made
structures, conveying the vitality of tropical nature while simultaneously
underscoring that it can be tamed. Mountains stretch across the horizon. She
admits only one discordant element. In place of the carriages carrying the court
personnel depicted by her male colleagues, she inserted prominently in the central foreground a single figure on the road: an Afro-Brazilian who represented
the troubled element of the population still held in slavery. A proponent of
independence in Brazil, Graham was critical of its institution of slavery and
included references—however subtle —to call attention to it.[26]

Conclusion

Graham's *Journal of a Voyage to Brazil* stands at the historic crossroads when
the countries of Luso- and Spanish America were just gaining independence
from Portugal and Spain in the early 1820s. Thereafter travelers could enjoy
greater access to the region, opening up the floodgates of books and related
pictorial imagery. But in her day she was taking fledgling steps, helping to lay
the groundwork for a new tradition of travel literature in South America.

As a woman traveling alone Graham was restricted physically in where she
could go and what she could do. But she did not allow that to constrain her

intellectually. In Rio she deliberately isolated herself from the English-speaking community, immersed herself in the Portuguese language, devoured available studies on the region, maintained not only a written journal but also an artist's sketchbook that fed her observational practice, and taught herself natural history, especially botany.[27] She broke away from the daily log method of travel writing and developed her text around themes and topics, demonstrating her ability to reimagine the heritage established by her predecessors Humboldt, Spix, and Martius, and others. Her singular accomplishment was in transforming expeditionary literature into a feminine domain.

A drawing entitled *Traveling in Spanish America* (Figure 8.7) appeared in the opening pages of her book on Chile.[28] It represents a carriage moving through the landscape from right to left, against the backdrop of the Andes. A gentleman is seated in the carriage interior and beside him a lady, wearing what appears to be a top hat. It is understood as a portrait of the author-artist. She has replaced the usual turban-like headpiece that she wore in the portrait by Lawrence painted before her departure for Brazil with a black top hat that bestows on her the authority of a man. Expeditionary literature usually contains a portrait of the explorer: almost exclusively male figures shown striding across the landscape, walking stick in hand; seated in a travel chair strapped to the back of a local native; or astride a horse. Graham by contrast

Figure 8.7 Dennis Dighton [?] after Augustus Earle [?], *Traveling in Spanish America*, drawing, British Museum no. 1845,0405.14.146. © The Trustees of the British Museum.

seats herself in the interior of a carriage, progressing across the yet unknown terrain.[29] Significant, too, is the particular care taken to delineate her conveyance. Although sometimes called a "stagecoach," it is more accurately referred to as a "Berlina," a kind of transport that had been used in the German capital from the late eighteenth century on. Spain adopted it and produced several models that were sent to the Americas. Pulled by two horses, it had two or four wheels, closed at the front, and open at the sides.[30] Maria Graham looks directly outward, ready to meet the challenges of what awaits her in this foreign terrain and beckoning her readers to follow. This is how she meant us to remember her, traveling across the landscape, the expert observer of the world around her, gazing out the window with her female eyes on South America.

Notes

1 In later life, as Maria, Lady Callcott (she married Callcott in 1827), she worked behind the scenes with publisher John Murray, who entrusted her with editing George Anson Byron's account of his voyage to the Sandwich Islands. Maria Graham Project, Trent University, Nottingham, provides this background and makes resources on her work available on its website, www.ntu.ac.uk.

2 Although the book narrates activities until 1823 and was published in 1824 she did not actually leave Brazil until 1825 due to difficulties arranging passport and passage back to England.

3 Regina Akel, *Maria Graham: A Literary Biography* (Amherst, NY: Cambria Press, 2009); Jennifer Hayward, "Introduction," in Maria Graham, *Journal of a Residence in Chile* (Charlottesville, VA: University of Virginia Press, 2003).

4 Adriana Méndez Rodenas, *Transatlantic Travels in Nineteenth Century Latin America: European Women Pilgrims* (Lewisburg, PA: Bucknell University Press, 2014); Alicia Lubowski-Jahn, "Picturing the Americas After Humboldt: The Art of Women Travelers," *Review: Literature and Arts of the Americas*, 45, no. 1 (2012): 97–105.

5 Maria Graham, *Journal of a Voyage to Brazil and Residence there, during part of the years 1821, 1822, 1823* (London: Longman, Hurst, Rees, Orme, Brown, & Green, and John Murray, 1824).

6 Lubowki-Jahn, "Picturing the Americas," discusses Humboldt's impact on women's travel narratives.

7 It appears as plate 69 in his *Vues des Cordillères*.

8 Gilberto Ferrez, *O Brasil de Thomas Ender, 1817* (Rio de Janeiro: Fundacão João Salles, 1976).

9 Her earlier account of Chile opened with a 100-page historical overview. See Maria Graham, *Journal of a residence in Chile during the year 1822; And a voyage from Chile to Brazil in 1823* (London: Longman, Hurst, Rees, Orme, Brown, & Green, and John Murray, 1824).

10 In late fall 1823 Graham took her leave to return to England and publish her books, and by August 1824 she was back in Brazil. In the meantime (in Mar. 1824) Dom Pedro had promulgated the first constitution. Regina Akel, "The Journals of Maria Graham (1785–1842)," Ph.D. dissertation, University of Warwick, 2007, p. iii for chronology.

11 Mary Louise Pratt, *Imperial Eyes: Travel Writing and Transculturation* (London, New York: Routledge, 1992).

12 Earle later returned to Brazil in the role of artist on the HMS *Beagle* alongside the young Charles Darwin. See Leonard Bell, "Not Quite Darwin's Artist: The Art and Travel of Augustus Earle," *Journal of Historical Geography* 30 (2013): 1–11.

13 For information on Callcott's gift of the drawings see the British Museum website, consulted July 9, 2019. www.britishmuseum.org/research/collection_online/collection_object_details.aspx?objectId=745115&partId=1&searchText=maria,+lady+callcott&page=1

14 She wrote: "The hedge-rows of the Bencoolen nut (*Vernilzia Montana*) are prodigiously grown: the Norfolk Island pine has shot up like a young giant, and I was glad to find many of the indigenous trees had been placed here; such as the *Andraguoa,* the nut of which is the strongest known purge; the *Cambucá,* whose fruit as large as a russet apple, has the sub-acid taste of the gooseberry, to which its pulp bears a strong resemblance; the *Japatec-caba,* whose fruit is scarcely inferior to the damascene; and the *Grumachama,* whence a liquor, as good as that from cherries, is made: these three last are like laurels, and as beautiful as they are useful" (Sept. 9, p. 296).

15 Betty Hagglund, "The Botanical Writings of Maria Graham," *Journal of Literature and Science* 4 (2011): 44–58, establishes that Graham was both typical in her interest in the popular subject of botany and unusual in her ability to explore that interest in ways that went beyond most of her female contemporaries.

16 Letter from Maria Graham to William Hooker, Apr. 11, 1824 (Royal Botanic Garden, Kew, Archives); quoted by Luciana Martins, "A Bay to be Dreamed Of: British Visions of Rio de Janeiro," *Portuguese Studies* 22 (2006): 30–31.

17 Kew Archive ref: DC 43 f 49.

18 The British Museum acquired an album of her sketches in 1845 (acc. No. 1845,0405.12.1-261). This includes images from her first voyage to Brazil from 1821 to 1823 and the second, from 1824 to 1825.

19 Haggland, "Botanical Writings," 51.

20 Ana Maria Belluzzo, "The Traveller and the Brazilian Landscape," *Portuguese Studies* 23 (2007): 36–54, discusses additional artist-travelers, but they too postdate Graham's work; quote, p. 46.

21 Marilyn Stokstad and Jerry Stannard, *Gardens of the Middle Ages* (Lawrence, KS: University of Kansas, 1983) provides background.

22 Plates in her book (engraved by Edward F. Finden) include:

I-Val Longo, or Slave Market at Rio—to front the title page

II-represents the Great Dragon Tree of Oratava, of which Humboldt has given so interesting an account. He saw it in all its greatest; I drew it after it had lost half its top—to face p. 85

III-View of Count Maurice's Gate at Pernambuco, with the Slave Market—to face p. 107 [drawn by Augustus Earle]

IV-Gamella Tree at Bahia—to face p. 135

V-Larangeiras—to face p. 163

VI-View from Count Hoggendorp's Cottage—to face p. 170

VII-View of Rio from Gloria Hill—to face p. 169

VIII-Corcovado, from Botofogo—to face p. 220

IX-Palace of San [sic] Cristovaõ—to face p. 246

X-Dona Maria de Jesus—to face p. 292 [drawn by Augustus Earle]

XI-English Burial ground—to face p. 307

Vignettes include:

I-That at the head of the Journal, p. 77, represents two young Dragon Trees; that with a single head is twenty years old, and had not, when I saw it, been tapped for the Dragon's Blood. The other is about a century old, and the bark is disfigured by the incisions made into it to procure the gum—to face p. 77

II-Part of Pernambuco, seen from Cocoa-nut Island, within the Reef—to face p. 97

III-Slaves dragging a hogshead in the Streets of Pernambuco—p. 131

IV-Cadeira, or Sedan Chair of Bahia—p. 133

V-Church and Convent of Sant Antonio da Barre at Bahia, as seen from the Roca—p. 157

VI-Sugar-loaf Rock, at the Entrance to the Harbour of Rio de Janeiro—p. 158

VII-The End of an Island in the Harbour of Rio de Janeiro, drawn for the sake of the variety of Vegetation—p. 201

VIII-Convicts carrying Water at Rio de Janeiro—p. 217

IX-Stone Cart at Rio de Janeiro—p. 321.

23 Martins for example states: "There is nothing particularly remarkable in this set of views—they are very much in the manner of the picturesque idiom popular at the time, which was also evident in Graham's sketches of her previous voyages to India and Italy, from 1809 to 1819." See her "A Bay to be Dreamed Of," 30–31.

24 Pedro II was born and raised in the neighborhood and would continue to rule here for half a century. (It currently houses the National Museum of Brazil.)

25 She elaborates on her experiences at the site, including details not evident in her illustration (p. 246):

The view from the palace opens to part of the bay, over an agreeable plain flanked by fertile hills, one of which is crowned with the very handsome barracks that were once a Jesuit establishment. I rode round by the back of the palace to the farm, which appears to be in good order; and the village of the slaves, with its little church, looks more comfortable than I could have believed possible for a village of slaves to do. The Imperial family now live entirely here, and only go to town on formal business or occasions of state.

26 The website Rio de Janeiro Here includes a comparison of her image with those of Ender, Debret, and subsequent photographers, consulted June 2, 2016. See www.riohere.com/imperial-palace-of-quinta-da-boa-vista-at-sao-cristovao.html

27 "Besides which, I speak now less English than Portuguese," she wrote (*Journal of a Voyage to Brazil*, 302).

28 There is some confusion about the authorship of this drawing now in the British Museum (acc. No. 1845,0405.14.146). It is currently identified as "Drawn by Dennis Dighton [?] after Augustus Earle [?]."

29 Adriana Méndez Rodenas, "Women Travelers in Humboldt's New World," *Review 84: Literature and Arts of the Americas* 45 (2012): 176 discusses this self-portrait.

30 Thanks to my colleagues Pablo Diener and Rafael Romero for assisting in the identification of the Berlina.

9 Science, Wonder, and Tourism in the Early Mapping of Yellowstone National Park

James R. Akerman

Since its first systematic explorations in the 1870s, the territory of Yellowstone National Park (geomorphologically, the Yellowstone Plateau, Basin, or Caldera[1]) has been one of the most intensively mapped non-urban regions in the United States. In the half-century following Yellowstone's establishment as a national park in March 1872, it was the object of more than a dozen government expeditions and surveys that produced several hundred topographical and thematic maps concerned with a range of topics embracing geology, hydrology, botany, and zoology, as well as road engineering and military surveys.[2] Private commercial interests also produced a large body of cartography to promote travel to the park, most notably, the Northern Pacific Railroad (NPRR). Maps were also published in travelers' accounts and guidebooks, publications issued by the operators of concessions, hotels, and tourist attractions, and the National Park Service (NPS), and in popular magazines.

In the space of only four years, from 1869 to 1872, Yellowstone was transformed from one of the more prominent blank spots on maps of the American West to one of the best known and most discussed regions of the West. Contemporaries marveled at this, but to a considerable extent it was the result of a conscious and determined effort to explore and develop the region, at first in the hope that it would yield mineral wealth, and then in expectation of its development as a resort. To be sure, Yellowstone was caught up in the post-Civil War drive to complete American exploration and conquest of the Great West, to exploit its mineral and other natural resources, and to displace and assert control over its Indigenous populations.[3] The creation of the park was however an unusual phenomenon within this process. The economic potential of the Yellowstone Plateau as a resort prompted investors in the NPRR and officials in the territories of Montana and Wyoming—who were often one in the same—to take an unusual interest in the early exploration and promotions of the national park. This bound the scientific mapping of the region closely to its promotional mapping. At Yellowstone, the curiosity of the scientist and the first tourists was simultaneously attracted to the same exceptional landscape. Emblematic of this close relationship, they shared a common rhetoric of *wonder*, a word that appears again and again in the narratives of Yellowstone's early travelers and explorers alike, its promotional literature, and its early imagery and cartography.

Figure 9.1 Edwin Hergesheimer, "Yellowstone National Park, from Surveys Made
under the Direction of F. V. Hayden U. S. Geologist, and Other Authorities,"
in Ferdinand Vandeveer Hayden, *Preliminary Report of the United States
Geological Survey of Montana and Portions of Adjacent Territories*, U.S.
42d Cong., 2d Sess., 1871–72. H. Ex. Doc. 326 (Ser. 1520). Library of
Congress, Geography and Map Division. www.loc.gov/item/97683567/

Yellowstone National Park, the world's first, was created by an act of
Congress on March 1, 1872. The first map of the park (Figure 9.1) appeared
nearly simultaneously—not in a guidebook, but in an expeditionary report
by Ferdinand Vandeveer Hayden,[4] who explored the area in the summer of
1871, calculated to provide the evidence of the plateau's geological wonders
necessary to ensure its reservation from unfettered development. Hayden's
account of Yellowstone largely confirmed what other recent expeditionary

accounts had asserted, but it was the first to be extensively cloaked with scientific observations and rhetoric, and the first to include trained topographers, who produced the first authoritative maps, photographs, and views of the plateau's most remarkable features. The publication of these maps and images, the component reports of expeditionary scientists, and Hayden's own florid narrative played an outsized role in promoting the Yellowstone Park as a place most worthy of both scientific and touristic interest. Hayden's map (actually prepared by Edwin Hergesheimer) simultaneously appeared in an article he wrote for the February 1872 issue of *Scribner's Monthly*, which incorporated much of the narrative from his report, and advocated creation of the park at the very moment Congress was considering the matter.[5] Direct copies of the map also appeared in the first guidebooks to the park, Harry J. Norton's *Wonderland Illustrated* (1873) and James Richardson's *Wonders of the Yellowstone Region* (1874).[6] A slightly reduced version also appeared with a note George Crofutt added on the new park ("Latest Wonder in the World") to the 1872 edition of his popular guidebook to the Union Pacific/Central Pacific transcontinental railroad route.[7]

Yellowstone's revelation to the scientific community and the general public was nearly simultaneous, at a time when public attention to the Western expansion was recovering from the shock of the Civil War. Mineral wealth and the agricultural and stock-raising potential of the region was drawing settlers and investment to the West, encouraged by the capital interests of railroads buoyed by generous grants of federal land.[8] The fame of the Yellowstone Plateau in particular was shepherded by the investors and executives of the second transcontinental railroad, the Northern Pacific (begun in 1870 and completed in 1883), whose marketing literature promoted it as a scenic "wonderland."[9]

Since the first descriptions of the Upper Yellowstone region made their way into non-Indigenous accounts, following the Lewis and Clark expedition, the plateau had been cloaked in the rhetoric of mystery and "wonder," a term used frequently to describe the caldera by both scientific and ordinary travelers. The skepticism with which descriptions by trappers and mountain guides was received in the East contributed both to official and popular curiosity; and when these accounts turned out mostly to be true, this skepticism gave way to the rhetoric of the *wondrous*, embedded both in textual descriptions and in maps, official and unofficial. The textual and the pictorial expressions of this rhetoric have been extensively studied, but little attention has been paid to the contribution of early maps to this discourse between the scientist and the tourist.[10]

Wonder operates in the English language as both a noun and a verb. Merriam-Webster defines the noun is "a cause of astonishment or admiration," "the quality of exciting amazed admiration," or "rapt attention or astonishment awesomely mysterious or new to one's experience." The same source defines the verb, *to wonder*, as to "be in a state of wonder" or "to feel surprise," and "to feel curiosity or doubt."[11] A *wonder* is thus both a marvel, something that evokes awe and astonishment, and source of curiosity mixed with skepticism and disbelief. Both aspects explain why wonders—or that is, phenomena that inspire wonder—might simultaneously motivate tourists and scientists to investigate them further. Of course, for the tourist that curiosity might be satisfied by merely seeing, experiencing the wonder. For the scientist, the experience motivates the desire to understand and explain the causes of the wonder, as well perhaps of its effects. In the philosophy of science, the invocation "wonder" as a motivation for research has been alternately accepted and discredited. During the nineteenth century scientists were unabashed in expressing their wonder at new and poorly understood phenomena. In her recent critique of wonder and scientific thought, Lisa Sideris writes that, "René Descartes famously categorized wonder as the first of the passions, an *intellectual* passion that orients toward understanding that object of wonder."[12] By the nineteenth century, wonder was often bound up with the concept of the *sublime,* as it was articulated by the Edmund Burke and Immanuel Kant, an aesthetic mixture of awe, horror, fear, and exhilaration that coincides with the realization that one is in the presence of something that was not merely beautiful, but far larger and more powerful than a single human or humanity itself.[13] Sideris argues that much of modern natural science has developed a version of wonder that is *exclusively* the province of scientific inquiry:

> Some scientists maintain that a hallmark of scientific wonder is that, while the non-scientist may spontaneously wonder at any number of phenomena and think "how strange!", the scientifically minded will cultivate wonder to a "more intellectual height" and then devise explanatory hypotheses that can be tested and verified.[14]

The conduct, writing, and mapping of expeditionary scientists, both military and civilian, and of other travelers who traversed and observed Yellowstone up to the end of the nineteenth century shows that any boundaries between the experience of the tourist, the scientist, and for that matter, the artist, in their reactions to what they saw on and about the plateau were at best indistinct. There was indeed a reluctance to recognize the descriptions of Yellowstone's wonders by untrained and non-scientific travelers until scientifically trained military officers and scientists confirmed them; but the rhetoric of wonder was shared by all. Moreover, until the end of the nineteenth century, and to some extent beyond that, the representations of scientist readily crossed over into the patterns of publications (including map publication) about Yellowstone for more general audiences, including tourists. The commingling of "wonder" in the worlds of science and tourism was as much (if not more) a social phenomenon as it was a philosophical one.

We typically think of scientific mapping—in this context, expeditionary cartography—and tourist mapping as belonging to separate categories, both functionally and aesthetically. On the one hand, the cartography of the nineteenth-century scientific explorer or military surveyor reflected the sensibilities of mapmakers who were professionally trained. Their approach was systematic; committed to careful observation and measurement, and to the skeptical weighing of facts. A typical example of the expeditionary

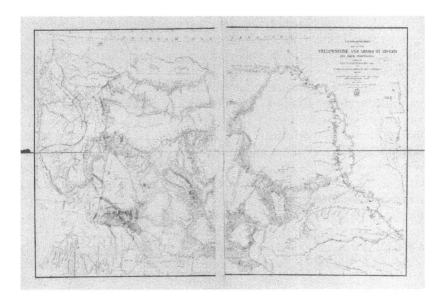

Figure 9.2 William F. Raynolds, "Map of the Yellowstone and Missouri Rivers and
Their Tributaries," in William F. Raynolds, *Report on the Exploration of the
Yellowstone River*, U.S. 40th Cong., 2d. Sess., 1867–68. Sen. Ex. Doc. 77
(Ser. 1317). Library of Congress, Geography and Map Division. www.loc.
gov/item/2010587006/

cartography of the region is the "Map of the Yellowstone and Missouri Rivers
and their Tributaries" by Captain William F. Raynolds (of the Army's Corps
of Topographical Engineers), who led an expedition that explored the upper
reaches of the Missouri and Yellowstone Rivers in 1859–60 (Figure 9.2),
though completion of his report and publication of his map was delayed until
after the Civil War.[15] Drably monochromatic in the style of American military and expeditionary cartography of its day, Raynolds's map was judicious
and skeptical, unwilling to represent what the mapmaker or trusted sources
had not actually seen. It is rich in its topographical description of most of
modern Montana, Wyoming, and adjacent portions of the Dakotas, Idaho,
and Nebraska that official and military expeditions had already explored, but
the portion of the map devoted to what is now Yellowstone National Park is
almost entirely blank. Mountain ranges that Raynolds's expedition had either
traversed or seen enclose a basin in which a wildly inaccurate Yellowstone
Lake is nearly the only feature. Likewise, in keeping with the conventions of
formal reconnaissance mapping, Raynolds marked with dashed lines portions
of the headwaters of the Yellowstone, Gallatin, and Snake Rivers, indicating
that their locations were inferred but which had not been confirmed by expeditionary eyewitness. Scant reference is made to Yellowstone's hydrothermal
oddities, even though Raynolds's guide, the famous trapper and mountain man
Jim Bridger, vouched for their existence. Raynolds believed at least some of

what Bridger told him, but official skepticism prevented him from referring to these on his map based on the untrained eyewitness of Bridger alone. And, because the expedition itself did not succeed in penetrating the mountain wall of the Yellowstone Plateau, the map did not proffer any details of the wonders Bridger described.

Yellowstone's tourist cartography, on the other hand, reflects the sensibilities of the marketer and promoter. Though often highly polished, so as to be more attractive, tourist maps of Yellowstone are more varied in their approach, more concerned, as tourist maps tend to be, with navigation and the identification of salient features of the landscape of particular interest to tourists: hotels, railroad lines, roadside attractions and facilities, hiking trails, campgrounds, and above all, the major scenic attractions of the park itself. Executed roughly on the same scale as the Raynolds map, Herman Haupt's map published in his 1883 guidebook is among the first examples of this approach, which will be familiar to any visitor to the park (Figure 9.3).

Yellow shaded areas highlight the location of the major natural attractions of the park, including its many geothermal features, several waterfalls,

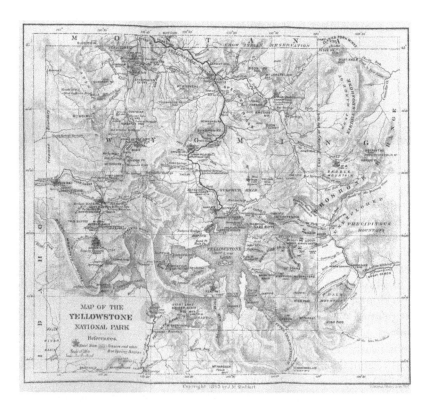

Figure 9.3 J. M. Stoddard, "Map of the Yellowstone National Park," in Herman Haupt, Jr., *The Yellowstone National Park* (New York, Philadelphia, and St. Paul: J. M. Stoddart, 1883). Newberry Library, Chicago, Graff 1820.

Yellowstone Lake, and the Grand Canyon of the Yellowstone. Green stars indicate the location of eleven hotels and camps that have appeared inside the park. Moreover, it is confident in its depiction of Yellowstone geography; what is not yet "known" by scientific explorers is elided. Tourists, the map seems to say, should trust that the map is a reliable source for their own explorations, and more important, that the park can accommodate both their curiosity and their need for comfort and security. That said, the improvement of the topographical knowledge of the Yellowstone Plateau between the publication of Raynolds's and Haupt's maps *was* remarkable; the very features of Yellowstone geography that Raynolds refused to acknowledge dominate Haupt's visualization of the region. What was official *terra incognita* to Raynolds had already been domesticated—or was at least represented as such—for the consumption of tourists.[16]

The transformation of the Yellowstone Plateau from an object of scientific curiosity and skepticism to tourist attraction, however, was neither as stark nor as complete as comparison of these two maps suggests. Between 1868 and 1883 a remarkable barrage of text, map, and image generated, above all, by official scientific reports, but also by journalism, commercial travel accounts, and guidebooks, in which the terms, rhetoric, visualizations, and—most important—cartographic aesthetics associated with archetypical and scientific and touristic publications were freely exchanged and copied. As Hayden's three expeditions to the Yellowstone region in 1871, 1872, and 1878 and their publications (which will be our main focus) illustrate, expeditionary and popular accounts were motivated by a commingling of commercial, official, and scientific sensibilities and goals. The early mapping and exploration of the Yellowstone Plateau offers a fine example of the complicated relationship between the cartographic production of knowledge by nineteenth-century scientific expeditions and the dissemination of that knowledge by a rapidly expanding American popular culture, of which modern tourism and its publications were parts. In respect to Yellowstone at least this relationship is infused with the rhetoric of wonder.

Wonders and Wanderers, on and off the Map

Native Americans, of course, had lived and hunted in the Yellowstone Plateau for centuries, but for non-Indigenous Americans in the mid-nineteenth century the region was among the most inaccessible and poorly understood regions of the West. The interior of the plateau, while not very rugged, rests at high altitude (approximately 8,000 feet above sea level) and is ringed by chains of mountains that rise several thousand feet above the surrounding territory. The passes into the basin are clear of snow for only about five months each year, even in our warmer climate, and were clear for as little as three months most years during the nineteenth century. The great emigrant trails and the Pacific Railroad Surveys passed by the upper Yellowstone to the south and north.[17] Fur trappers visited Yellowstone frequently in the 1810s, 1820s, and 1830s and produced the first accounts of the region by non-natives, but their stories were dismissed by eastern circles as tall tales for which the "mountain men" were famous. After the collapse of the fur trade in the 1840s there was little interest in the area among whites until mining interests arrived in nearby parts of Montana and Idaho in the 1850s.

The plateau made its first significant cartographic impression on William Clark and Samuel Lewis's "Map of Lewis and Clark's Track, across the Western Portion of North America," which was published in the 1814 edition of Meriwether Lewis's history of the Lewis and Clark Expedition.[18] The expedition passed 100 miles north of the plateau, but the map incorporated information gleaned from other sources. Among these was John Colter, a member of the Corps of Discovery who received permission to leave the expedition in 1806 to pursue trapping opportunities. Colter passed through a portion of the plateau in 1807–8 while in the employ of the Spanish-American fur trader Manuel Lisa. Clark and Lewis's published map of their track traces Colter's route through the upper Yellowstone region, noting the rough locations of Yellowstone Lake (Lake Eustis) and Jackson Lake (Lake Biddle) and identifying some "boiling springs" to the east of Lake Eustis.[19] Subsequent maps, both printed and manuscript, often made some reference of the lakes and springs of the Yellowstone region; but the positions, shapes, and orientations of these features, and of adjacent rivers and dividing mountain ranges, were in constant motion on these maps, as the ongoing reports of Indians and trappers were absorbed and weighed against each other by published mapmakers.

The Three Forks (the Jefferson, Gallatin, and Madison Rivers) headwaters of the upper Missouri River was a major focus of trapping activity during the 1820s and 1830s, ensuring that reports of the strange thermal features of the Yellowstone Plateau continued to trickle in. Warren Angus Ferris, a trained surveyor and clerk for the American Fur Company, visited a portion of the geyser basins on a whim in 1834 and recorded his experience. The Yellowstone historian Aubrey Haines describes Ferris as the first tourist to visit the plateau, "because his motive was curiosity rather than business."[20] It will be noted, however, that Ferris's expressions of astonishment, fear, and wonder—"the half was not told me"—were framed within his avowed desire not merely to experience them for himself but to observe and record the phenomena. He writes of the height of the largest geyser's eruption, weighing his judgment against that of a previous party of trappers; of his speculations about the depth of calcareous formations from which the geysers discharge; of the intervals of the eruptions; and of his hand-test of the heat of the water. Ferris also records that his observations confirmed the "testimony" of 20 men who had seen the geysers previously. Whether or not he was the first tourist in Yellowstone, Ferris might be seen as the first scientist, though the publication of his account in the *Western Literary Messenger* a decade later little altered the skepticism of eastern elites.[21]

The tension between official skepticism about and the scientific attraction of Yellowstone's isolated wonders is further illustrated by Raynolds's account of his reconnaissance of 1859–60. He was ordered to find the best possible route from the Wind River, which drains the southeastern slope of the Yellowstone

Plateau, to the economically important Three Forks region. The most direct route would require a transit of the plateau, which no official expedition had previously achieved, or even attempted. Raynolds hired Jim Bridger as his guide but ignored the advice the mountain man offered about the best way to enter the plateau. Approaching the southern rim of the plateau on May 30, 1860, Raynolds writes that his party encountered an impassable basaltic ridge and were forced to content themselves with listening to Bridger's "marvelous tales [of] an immense boiling spring that is a perfect counterpart of the Geysers of Iceland." Raynolds continues:

> As [Bridger] is uneducated, and had probably never heard of the exist-
> ence of such natural marvels elsewhere, I have little doubt that he spoke
> of that which he had actually seen ... Had our attempt to enter this dis-
> trict been made a month later in the season, the snow would have mainly
> disappeared, and there would have been no insurmountable obstacles to
> overcome. I cannot doubt therefore, that at no very distant day the mys-
> teries of this region will be fully revealed, and though small in extent,
> I regard the valley of the upper Yellowstone as the most interesting unex-
> plored district in our widely expanded country."[22]

So it was that on the eve of the Civil War Yellowstone's wonders occupied an uncertain place on official maps of the West. Yellowstone could not be "known" until trained observers had penetrated the Yellowstone country, observed it, and measured it themselves. And yet, as Raynolds's account reveals, like a Shangri-La, the inaccessibility of the plateau only added to its mysterious attraction.

Putting Yellowstone on the Map

The end of the Civil War brought a rapid change in this state of affairs. Gold and silver prospecting activity in the mountains that divide Idaho and Montana, west and northwest of the modern park, brought a new generation of white travelers near and into the Yellowstone Plateau. Among these was Walter Washington De Lacy, a civil engineer, surveyor, and former language instructor at West Point who helped lay out the military road between Fort Benton, Montana, and Walla Walla, Washington, in 1859. An unsuccessful prospecting journey in 1863 took him through the Pitchstone Plateau (west of Yellowstone Lake) and through a portion of the hot springs and geyser basins of the valley of the Firehole River in the southwestern portion of the modern park.[23] Shortly after the establishment of the Territory of Montana in 1864, the territorial legislature engaged De Lacy to make the *Map of the Territory of Montana with Portions of the Adjoining Territories* (1865).[24] The map's main interests in the region were the "gulch diggings" and "quar[tzite] lode" indicated by distinctive red shading astride the Madison and Jefferson forks of the Missouri. But the inclusion of adjacent parts of Wyoming as far south as the Platte River Road and South Pass underscores that the main routes across the Rocky Mountains passed well outside the Yellowstone Plateau. The sole exception were the routes leading from the north to Virginia City, MT, in the heart of the mining region, the approach to the plateau Bridger had recommended to Raynolds. In strictly geographical terms, Raynolds's 1859 (i.e., 1868) map was superior in most respects to De Lacy's, on which Yellowstone Lake is badly displaced, mistakenly east of the crest of the Wind River Range. The western part of the future park, however, benefitted from De Lacy's personal experience. And, most importantly, De Lacy's eyewitness prompted the inclusion of the "Hot Spring Valley" forming a part of the headwaters of the Madison River.[25]

In 1869, several leading citizens of the Montana Territory, including Henry Dana Washburn, the newly appointed Surveyor General for the territory, and businessman Nathaniel P. Langford, the territory's former tax collector and a leading proponent of the NPRR, attempted to organize a large expedition into the region. A flare-up in tensions between whites and Niitsitapi (Blackfeet) required the diversion of the planned military escort for the expeditions, forcing its cancellation, but three of the party, David Folsom, Charles Cook, and William Peterson, undertook an exploration on their own in September and October of that year. Attempts to publish their eyewitness account of the Grand Canyon of Yellowstone, Yellowstone Lake, and the Lower Geyser Basin were rebuffed by several established eastern publishers. It finally was published by a new Chicago journal, the *Western Monthly*, in July 1870, and the public and scientific thirst for information about the plateau began in earnest.[26] Folsom was subsequently employed in the territory's Surveyor General's office and shared his diary and observations (and perhaps a map) with De Lacy, who incorporated the observations in a new version of his map published in 1870.[27]

This second map of Montana and adjacent territories corrected many of the errors of the previous map. De Lacy shows Colter's route and his own 1863 trail path through the region alongside a new route identified as "Cook & Folsom's 1869." Perhaps he was seeking to make a name for himself among the early discoverers of the region's wonders. The map is notable in two other respects. First, it was published by one of the leading commercial map publishers of its time, the Colton family firm in New York. As a Colton issue, it would have had a far larger number of readers in the east than the earlier De Lacy map. The map was also the first to manifest the interest of the Northern Pacific in the Yellowstone Plateau. A large inset in the lower left corner of the map shows the projected route of the railroad, which had just begun construction. Though the map makes no explicit connection between the railroad and the Yellowstone Plateau, by 1870 the railroad—including financier Jay Cooke, whom Langford persuaded to bankroll the new company—had embraced the economic potential of the Yellowstone Plateau as a resort.

Washburn and Langford tried once again to mount an expedition into Yellowstone in 1870. As in 1869, this was to be primarily a civilian undertaking, consisting mostly of business and civic leaders from Helena, the capital of Montana Territory. Langford and Washburn were successful this time, however, in obtaining a small military escort for the expedition, commanded by Lt. Gustavus C. Doane. This proved critical as well to the promotional goals of the expedition, as it added the legitimacy and authority of a West Point-educated officer of the US Army to the enterprise. Doane was obliged to write a formal report of his activities to the Department of War, which was published by Congress in early 1871.[28] Following the established pattern of exploratory reports published by the US Army, the report is scientifically minded, detailed and analytic in its observations and descriptions. But Doane was also a talented narrator; his account was enlivened by his frequent mention of his discomfort with an infected thumb and the search for lost member of the party, Truman C. Everts.[29] In language any guidebook author would be proud of he described the view from the summit of Mt. Washburn, named in honor of the commander of the expedition:

> On the east close beneath our feet, yawns the immense gulf of the Grand Canyon ... The ragged edges of the chasm are from 200 to 500 yards apart, its depth so profound that the river bed is nowhere visible. No sound reaches the ear from the bottom of the abyss; the sun's rays are reflected on the further wall and then lost in the darkness below ...
>
> Turning southward, a strange and new scene bursts upon the view. Filling the whole field of vision, and with its boundaries in the verge of the horizon, lies the great volcanic basin of the Yellowstone. Nearly circular in form, from 50 to 75 miles in diameter, and with a general depression of about 2,000 feet below the summits of the great ranges which forms its outer rim, Mount Washburn lies in the point of the circumference, northeast from the center of the basin. ... Between the south and west points, this vast circle is broken through in many places for the passage of the rivers; but a single glance at the interior slopes of the ranges shows that a former complete connection existed, and that the great basin has been formerly one vast crater.[30]

Doane has been called the inventor of Wonderland,[31] and this passage argues that he might deserve it; for it offers a remarkably vivid overview of the topography and salient attractions of the Yellowstone Plateau, asserting for the first time its identity as a vast volcanic caldera. Doane's astonishment at the wonders before him, juxtaposed with as much scientific description and analysis as his own knowledge and powers of observation allow, is apparent throughout.

Doane prepared a "Map of the Route of the Yellowstone Expedition Commanded by Lieut. G. C. Doane, U.S.A., September 1870."[32] The map indicates the party's route and the major features the Washburn Expedition visited. It also marks the rough circuit of the "Rim of the Great Basin," which he identified from the summit of Mt. Washburn. Though compiled without the benefit of surveying instruments, it represents a considerable improvement over previous maps. Along with a similar map prepared by Washburn it marks the beginning of the long line of maps exclusively focused on the plateau.

The reports emerging from the Washburn-Langford-Doane expedition at last legitimized the earlier accounts of Yellowstone's wonders, and the long-dismissive Eastern press and government circles took notice. Of an early account of the expedition by Washburn, *The New York Times* acknowledged:

"We have said that this record reads like a fairy tale, and readers will this time agree with us. Its official character, however, may be added to the evidence of the simplicity of style ... as earnest of the trustworthiness of the narrative."[33] *Scribner's Monthly* published Langford's account of the expedition in its May and June 1871 issues under the title "The Wonders of the Yellowstone."[34] Both installments were richly illustrated with drawings of events and, for the first time in print, sketches of the natural wonders of the Yellowstone, including the Grand Canyon, the Upper and Lower Falls of the Yellowstone, and several geysers. It was possible for readers to identify the location of these features on a small map based on Washburn's manuscript map, while the interest of the NPRR in the potential of Yellowstone for tourism is discernable by the magazine's insertion of "A Map of the Northern Pacific Railroad and Its Connections" immediately preceding the first installment.[35]

F. V. Hayden, Mapping, and Making the National Park

Before these 1871 articles no images of Yellowstone's falls, canyons, and thermal features had made it into the public eye, and no map leant certainty to their location. Seen in this light, it is easy to understand the revelatory impact of the extensive visual archive, sketched, painted, photographed, and mapped, produced by the members of F. V. Hayden's explorations of 1871 and 1872.[36] The maps, diagrams, and views published by the Hayden expeditions formed only a part of a larger archive devoted to the scenery and natural history of the Great West generated by government explorations, the popular press, railroads, and the tourism industry. But few elements of this archive illustrate so well the convergence of scientific representation and the art of promotion.

Hayden was attached as a geologist to the Raynolds Expedition of 1859–60, and shared Raynolds's disappointment when the expedition had been turned away at the southern gates of the basin. After the Civil War, he ascended to a leading position among scientific explorers of the West. From 1867 until 1878, Hayden persuaded Congress to support annual explorations that ranged widely across the western Great Plains and Rocky Mountains, under the grandiose name of the United States Geological and Geographical Survey of the Territories, one of several large land surveys of the West funded by Congress during this period. Compared to his colleagues and rivals John Wesley Powell, Clarence King, and George Montague Wheeler, Hayden was perhaps the most baldly entrepreneurial. He was criticized by contemporaries for letting special economic interests, such as the railroads, gain undue influence on the scope and direction of his scientific work of his expeditions.[37] In any event, Congressional support allowed Hayden's surveys to approach the scale of the Pacific Railroad Surveys, comprehensive and well staffed with scientists representing many fields. The 1871 party included specialists in entomology, meteorology, botany, mineralogy, and zoology, as well as the topographer Anton Schönborn, the celebrated Western photographer William Henry Jackson, and Henry W. Elliott, the official topographic artist for the expedition. A late addition was Thomas Moran, the renowned landscape artist, who joined the party at the instigation and with the financial support of *Scribner's* and Jay Cooke, chief investor in the Northern Pacific.[38]

The 538-page official report was completed in February 1872, though it was not published by Congress until after the creation of the park. It included the Survey's explorations in Idaho, Montana, and Utah early in 1871,[39] though by far the greatest portion of Hayden's narrative was devoted to description of his party's journey into and through the Yellowstone Plateau. The report incorporated no less than 62 illustrations and diagrams, and seven maps. The largest number of these were simple but evocative sketches prepared by Elliott or Moran of mud pots, vents, springs, and geysers the party encountered (Figure 9.4).

The report also included several of the more polished woodcuts that were published in an article written by Hayden for the February 1872 issue of *Scribner's Monthly,* and supplied by the courtesy of magazine.[40] None of Jackson's photographs were reproduced in this way, although some were models for views printed in later publications.

In the same way that precise drawings in botanical and zoological texts supported taxonomy and the analysis of bodily structures and their functions, photographs and sketches of landscape features, panoramas, and cross-sections supported the classification and analysis of geologic structures and landforms in geographical reports, lending a third dimension and on-the-spot intelligibility to the maps. But just as important, these images served Western explorers and their supporters back east as attractive elements of the

Figure 9.4 "Punch Bowl," in Ferdinand Vandeveer Hayden, *Preliminary Report of the United States Geological Survey of Montana and Portions of Adjacent Territories*, U.S. 42d Cong., 2d Sess., 1871–72. H. Ex. Doc. 326 (Ser. 1520). Newberry Library, Chicago, Govt. 1520, H. Ex. Doc. 326.

"barrage" of publicity that promoted Congressional, commercial, and popular interest in the West and its development.[41] In this context, Moran's inclusion in the 1871 expedition was particularly important. After the expedition's return, Hayden saw to it that Jackson's photographs, Moran's sketches, and his monumental painting of the Grand Canyon of the Yellowstone (see Figure 3.5) were prominently displayed in the Capitol rotunda during the Congressional debate that began in December 1871 considering the creation of Yellowstone National Park.[42] Hayden remained in direct contact with the senators and congressmen advocating the bill, and his report was regularly referenced during the debate.

Narration, description, observation, measurement, and art formed a unity in Hayden's report and its dissemination served well the symbiotic needs of science, publicity, and political activism. Hayden's narrative shifted easily from the measured and precise language of the scientist to the florid prose of a publicist and didact. In the manner of the most engaging travel writers, he was nearly capable of transporting his readers to the spot of his observations—nearly so, because he also conceded that to truly take in a landscape one must be on the spot. Even the talent of a great artist cannot substitute for eyewitness experience:

> [N]o language can do justice to the wonderful grandeur of the Lower Falls; the very nearly vertical walls, slightly sloping down to the water's edge on either side, so that from the summit the river appears like a thread of silver foaming over its rocky bottom; the variegated colors of the sides, yellow, red, brown, white, all intermixed and shading into each other; the Gothic columns of every form standing out from the sides of walls with greater variety and more striking colors than ever adorned a work of human art … Mr. Thomas Moran, a celebrated artist, and noted for his skill as a colorist, exclaimed with a kind of regretful enthusiasm that these beautiful tints were beyond the reach of human art.[43]

Amid all of the attention scholars have given the prose and art produced by the 1871 expedition, its maps have been overlooked. They are modest in number, size, and scope compared to the maps produced by the larger expeditions that followed; the largest folds out to only about 30 × 25cm. In addition to the general map of the park (Figure 9.1), the report included a map of Yellowstone Lake, and five maps of major clusters of hot springs and geysers. Collectively they do not amount to a complete survey of the park, but the serial presentation of these detailed maps set the pattern for all future reports and illustrated guidebooks. Moreover, for the first time the existence of the salient phenomena of the Yellowstone caldera, previously cloaked in mystery or dismissed as mere hearsay, acquired the credibility that mere words and even sketches drawn from life could not provide—they were given the form, substance, and authority of a carefully surveyed and effectively drafted map.

Following the narrative, the reader encounters the maps in the order that the expedition itself—and countless travelers since, entering the region from the north—encountered them, entering the region from Montana by the route leading to the oldest entrance to the modern park: traveling up the Yellowstone and Gardiner Rivers to Mammoth Hot Springs (Hayden's "White Mountain Hot Springs"); then following a clockwise circuit to Tower Falls, Mt. Washburn, and the Grand Canyon of the Yellowstone; up the valley of the Yellowstone River that would later bear Hayden's name, to Yellowstone Lake; and on westward to the geyser basins on the Firehole River.

The first map readers encounter is "White Mountain Hot Springs, Gardiner's River 1871." The party explored this feature, as modern tourists do, by traveling uphill from the Gardiner River. Hayden's account intermingles descriptions of the mammoth spring's dimensions, color, and mechanics with astonishment.[44] Skillful hachuring in the map conveys the general structure and slope of the topography. Each of the features mentioned in the narrative is included—the stream gathering the waters from above; the hill above, its steep sides adorned with the beautifully scalloped semicircular basins; the terrace atop this, with the largest and most active springs, ascending in large steps to the top of the hill, one thousand feet above the river, where may be found several active geysers.

Though one gains a clear idea of the layout and main features of this remarkable landscape from the map, Hayden was frustrated with the inability of the map and accompanying views to entirely capture the scene:

> The annexed illustrations will convey some idea of the form of these bathing-pools as they are arranged one above the other, but the beautiful series of photographs taken by Mr. Jackson are of far greater value. Even the photograph, which is so remarkable for its fidelity to nature, falls far short. It fails to give the completely delicate contrasts of coloring which are so pleasing to the eye.[45]

Another example of Hayden's use of images to convey scientific information comes follows an extensive description of the springs that consists largely of a series of questions concerning the date of their formation, their relationship to volcanic action, and the hydrothermal mechanics at work. Beyond the map and the photographs, a geological cross-section of the springs offers the theory that the heated water, rising from a deposit of trachyte (a volcanic rock) rises through seams in a bed of limestone, which is also the source of the lime-rich deposits on the surface (Figure 9.5).

Hayden's itinerary next took him onto the Yellowstone Plateau itself, via Mt. Washburn. This portion of the journey resulted in two simple topographic maps meant to show "the location of the hills and springs in relation to them," illustrative of the narrative rather than analytic of the phenomena. Next, the party arrived at Yellowstone Lake. Taking a small group, consisting of the topographer Schönborn, the artist Elliott, and the mineralogist for the expedition, Dr. Albert Charles Peale, Hayden conducted a whirlwind tour of the "far-famed geyser basin of the Fire-Hole river," for it was here that he was in closest contact with the volcanism that so fascinated nineteenth-century geologists worldwide.

Figure 9.5 Henry Elliott, "Ideal Section White Mountain Hot Springs," in Ferdinand Vandeveer Hayden, *Preliminary Report of the United States Geological Survey of Montana and Portions of Adjacent Territories*, U.S. 42d Cong., 2d Sess., 1871–72. H. Ex. Doc. 326 (Ser. 1520). Newberry Library, Chicago, Govt. 1520, H. Ex. Doc. 326.

The narrative of his party's encounter with these features, alternates between dispassionately empirical and romantic evocations of wonder.

One map for each basin accompanies the report, compiled by Edwin Hergesheimer, from the notes and sketches taken on the spot by Schönborn and Elliott.[46] Cartographically, these are the most important achievements of the expedition, carefully locating each spring and geyser using measurements made under the supervision of Peale. The representation of topography, though without the benefit of contours, is thorough and provides a fine base for describing the topographic situation of each cluster of hydrothermal features. Only the best-known features, such as Old Faithful and the Giant Geyser, are named on the maps, but we detect on these maps some carefully chosen descriptive terms, including boiling springs, geyser, mud geyser, fissure spring, cauldron, that reflect a movement towards scientific classification (Figure 9.6).

Hayden's and Peale's narratives visit each of the features or clusters of features noted on the map in succession, describing their topography, cones, ejecta, colors, and chemical composition in some detail. They speculate about the life cycle of the features and their subterranean relationships to each other, their sources of water, and the topography. To support this framework, Hayden calls the reader's attention, once again, to an ideal section of the Upper Geyser Basin prepared by Elliott, "which may convey a clearer conception of the way in which we suppose the waters of many of the springs reach the surface."[47] These speculative profiles—already common practice among expeditionary

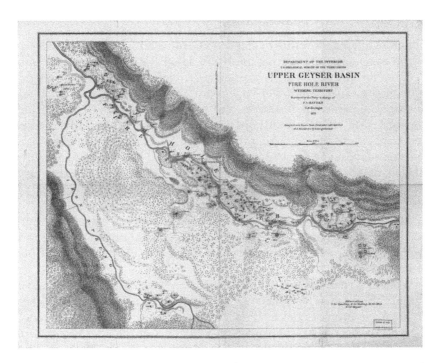

Figure 9.6 Anton Schönborn and Edwin Hergesheimer, "Upper Geyser Basin, Fire Hole River, Wyoming Territory," in Ferdinand Vandeveer Hayden, *Preliminary Report of the United States Geological Survey of Montana and Portions of Adjacent Territories*, U.S. 42d Cong., 2d Sess., 1871–72. H. Ex. Doc. 326 (Ser. 1520). Library of Congress, Geography and Map Division. www.loc. gov/item/97683584/

scientists—would become an especially important tool for theorizing the origins and workings of Yellowstone's hydrothermal features in subsequent reports and, by the end of the nineteenth century, for explaining these features to readers of Yellowstone guidebooks.

Hayden intended his report to serve, alongside the abundant artwork the expedition generated, as an argument for preservation of the Yellowstone Plateau on both recreational and scientific grounds. The rhetoric of wonder that runs through the narrative served both of these motivations. So, too, did his emphasis on the detailed mapping of the hot springs and geyser basins that would become tourist attractions. These maps were just detailed enough to excite curiosity and to lay a topographic foundation for further exploration and research. The cause of science and the needs of the republic had its justi-fication for setting Yellowstone aside—even in the face of national high hopes for the development of the West.

Mapping the Early National Park

Congress funded the return of Hayden's Geological Survey to the Yellowstone region two more times during the 1870s. His 1872 expedition was equipped with a substantially larger contingent of scientists and topographers. The scale of the expedition's 844-page report, published early in 1873, reflects this multiplication of resources and effort.[48] Unlike the report from the previous year, there was little of the romantic in the narrative. Drawings and panoramas of the topographic artist W. H. Holmes depict many of the same landscape features treated previously, but where former reports labeled these with their familiar proper names in early reports, as they might be in tourist guidebooks, they were labeled here with technical terms. Elliott's 1871 drawing of a rock outcrop on the Yellowstone River north of Mammoth Hot Springs, for example, was captioned with the feature's poetic common name, the Devil's Slide. The caption for Holmes's 1872 rendering of the same feature refers to it as a "Trachyte Dike and Columns of Breccia."

While Hayden turned toward other projects, Yellowstone was never out of his mind. His collaboration with the authors and publishers of Yellowstone promotional material continued. Several of the illustrations in the 1873 report were supplied by *Scribner's* and the *Illustrated Christian Weekly.* Harry J. Norton's *Wonder-land Illustrated* (1873), recounting the journey of his own "Geyser Exploring Party" through the new national park in September 1872, incorporated 16 illustrations borrowed from Hayden's two expeditionary reports, and a reprint of Gustav Bechler's 1872 map.[49] The Centennial Exposition at Philadelphia in 1876 presented Hayden with another opportunity to promote his expeditions and Yellowstone. In collaboration with the innovative Boston printer and publisher Louis Prang, he published an album of chromolithographic prints based on watercolors by Moran, "interesting alike to the man of science, the lover of art, and the admirer of nature."[50]

Hayden and his Geological Survey returned to Yellowstone one more time, in 1878, which turned out to be the final year of his funding. He joined forces with the topographer and surveyor Henry Gannett (soon to become the Chief Geographer of the United States Geological Survey). The visual output of the expedition was massive. It included seven panoramas by Holmes, four chromolithographic plates, 12 maps, and more than 100 other figures. Gannett's topographical survey produced the first contoured map of the entire park.[51] His topographic teams also produced detailed maps of seven major hydrothermal districts within the park, the Upper Geyser Basin, Lower Geyser Basin, Mammoth Hot Springs, Shoshone Geyser Basin, Egeria Springs (known today the Grand Prismatic Spring), and the Rustic Geyser Group. They were technically superior to anything published before, larger in scale, and with more extensive inventories of the thermal features (Figure 9.7).

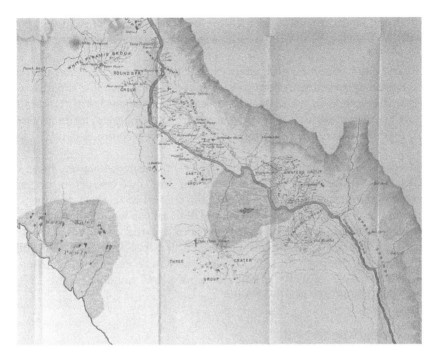

Figure 9.7 Detail, Henry Gannett, "Map of the Upper Geyser Basin, Yellowstone National Park ... 1878," in Ferdinand Vandeveer Hayden, *Twelfth Annual Report of the United States Geological and Geographical Survey of the Territories,* U.S. 47th Cong., 1st Sess., 1881–82. H. Misc. Doc. 62 (Ser. 2057). Newberry Library, Chicago, Govt. 2057, G. Misc. Doc. 62.

In his introduction and narrative of the expedition, Hayden portrayed his survey's exploration and study of Yellowstone as definitive and complete. Of Gannett's topographic work he writes that:

> *little more is left to be done.* All the elevations have been examined with great care, and may be regarded substantially correct. *The descriptions of the mountain ranges and drainage are minute, and the entire report will furnish much valuable matter for a guidebook of the Park.* The maps of the geyser basins are as accurate and complete as will probably ever be needed.[52] [emphasis mine]

Gannett reinforced this point in his own report, and belittled the results of the three surveys organized in the 1870s by Army engineers.[53]

Regardless of Gannett's opinion, the Corps of Engineers expeditions led by Capt. William A. Jones in 1873 and by Capt. William Ludlow in 1875 completed important work reconnoitering possible routes for wagon roads bringing tourists into the region. Ludlow in particular remarked upon the wondrous landscape and lamented the possible dangers posed by unpoliced visitors. However, he noted that with the right kind of supervision:

> The day will come, and it cannot be far distant, when the most interesting region, crowded with marvels and adorned with the most superb scenery, will be rendered accessible to all; and then, thronged with visitors from all over the world, it will be what nature and Congress, for once working together in unison, have declared it should be, a National Park.[54]

Indeed, before the end of the century, private concessionaires, most especially the Northern Pacific, would take the lead in constructing permanent accommodations. The military would take control of the park from its headquarters at Mammoth Hot Springs in 1886, and it would survey and complete the iconic figure-eight of park roads in accordance with its orders. The Northern Pacific would complete a branch line to Gardiner, at the northern boundary of the park in 1883. Consequently, the number of tourists who entered the park annually would rise from a few hundred in the 1870s to approach 10,000 per year by 1900.[55]

Promoting Wonderland

Until the mid-1880s tourists, civilian visitors to the park persisted in comparing themselves to the expeditionary scientists and military personnel with whom they mingled. Most were obliged to fend for themselves or to hire guides to oversee the outfitting and transport of their parties. Though Haupt's 1883 map (Figure 9.3) presented the image of a well-developed network of facilities, the permanent accommodations in the park at that time consisted of little more than tent camps. The first superintendent of the park, the ubiquitous Nathaniel Langford, had no staff and did not live in the park. In 1877 there were several violent encounters between tourists and Nez Perce Indians fleeing an army force commanded by General Oliver Howard. Not surprisingly, Langford's successor, Philetus W. Norris (appointed in 1877) was occupied with Indigenous relations and exploration of the park, and had little money for park maintenance. His fourth annual report to the Secretary of the Interior (1880) is a mixed account of new discoveries in previously unexplored portions of the park, travelogue, and commentary on the poor state of roads and bridges. His explorations of the hoodoos beyond what was then the eastern boundary of the park were incorporated in a new foldout map of the park,[56] the first comprehensive remapping of the entire park since the Hayden-Hergesheimer map of 1872 (as Gannett's 1878 survey had not yet been published). The map is roughly comparable in size and scale to the paper maps routinely distributed at park entrances today. It is similar in content as well; a modern tourist can easily find all of the major tourist attractions of the park, and an emergent network of roads and trails, still largely unimproved. Norris, like the map, is a transitional figure. Echoing Ludlow five years earlier, he complains of vandalism, and both welcomes and fears what was to come. The approach of railroads to the northern and eastern entrances especially concerned him, since there had yet been little investment from the federal government in the infrastructure required to assure the safety of the expected increase in tourism the railroads would bring.[57]

The lack of infrastructure, however, also contributed to Yellowstone's mystique among early tourist accounts and guidebooks, which presented the park as a wild and uncharted wilderness, and compared the authors to explorers. In *The Wonders of the Yellowstone Region in the Rocky Mountains,* James Richardson, arriving at Fort Ellis—vicariously, for he himself never visited the park—declared that:

> Here, on the verge of the Yellow Valley, is the starting-point of the several exploring parties who have made known to the world the wonder of this extraordinary territory; and here, doubtless for many years to come the traveler in quest of the scenes described in these pages will shake hands with the advance guard of civilization before plunging into the wilderness.[58]

William Wyndham-Quin, the Fourth Earl of Dunraven (a powerful Irish Unionist politician and famous game hunter), recalling a journey to the plateau in 1874, felt the need to defend his status as a tourist, half-heartedly, by contrasting his visit with that of a scientific explorer: "I did not undertake the expedition in the cause of science. I do not pretend to anything but a very slight acquaintance with natural history, geology, and mineralogy. I had no instruments for taking measurements."[59]

The completion of the Northern Pacific branch line to the northern entrance of the park in 1883 and the construction of hotels at the railroad's initiative over the next decade were turning points in the commodification of Yellowstone. In 1884, the first full season in which the Northern Pacific provided access to the park, the railroad published a brochure, *Alice's Adventures in the New Wonderland.* The title, explicitly played on Lewis Carroll's popular children's story, published 19 years earlier, but also drew upon previous references to Yellowstone as a "wonderland" in popular accounts, guidebooks, and government reports. The brochure takes the form of a letter, written by a now grown Alice, who has just finished a tour of the park, to her sister Edith back home.

> My Dearest Edith: When Mr. Carroll wrote that funny book about one of my childish dreams, I little thought the time would ever come when I should sit down to describe scenes and incidents in my actual experience every bit as strange and bewildering. Yet, so it is. I am here in a place which, singularly enough, they call Wonderland. Not that the title is by any means inappropriate, for the place is, indeed a land of wonders.[60]

Alice describes each wonder with a thoroughness and passion reminiscent of Doane and Hayden. She finds Yellowstone Lake surrounded by "natural wonders, unequaled in the world and situated amid scenery of enchanting loveliness, neither Como nor Maggiore, in my opinion, approaching it." Her visit to the great geyser basins "were the most memorable of my whole life. There are other scenes, such as the Pyramids, Jerusalem, Venice, Rome, and Niagara Falls, which will forever live in my recollection; but the experiences of those two days will overshadow them all."[61]

On the back of Alice's letter is a large map (Figure 9.8b), by Carl J. Hals and Angus Rydström "compiled from different official explorations and our personal survey, 1882." Hals and Rydström were civil engineers from Norway and Sweden who, according to immigration records, arrived in New York in 1881. Apparently, they were quickly recruited by the Northern Pacific. The topography of the map bears a superficial resemblance to Gannett's 1878 map (Figure 9.7; published in 1883), and there can be little doubt that they had access to it, as well as other previous official maps. It is unclear how extensive their own reconnaissance of the park might have been. In any event, normally we would not expect such words as "official expedition" and "survey" to appear on a tourist map, except perhaps tongue-in-cheek. Their use acknowledges that the line between exploration and tourism was still in flux; even as "Alice's" letter argues that the park was increasingly settled, domesticated, and safe, it was still wild and wonderful:

> We came before long to this hotel, which we have made our headquarters in the Park, and which is a most surprising place in the comfort, and I may say, luxury, which it offered, in the midst of such surroundings. The hotel, and the government roads and bridges are the only artificial things in the Park, everything else being in its natural condition—rude, stern, and wild.[62]

Hals and Rydström rendered relief with hachures and subtle shading, making the map more accessible to a general audience than would a contoured map. And the touring landscape—the emerging system of roads are now prominent, as are the hotels at Mammoth Springs and the Upper Geyser Basin. The continued growth of this infrastructure is documented by subsequent editions of the map issued into the 1890s.

As we have seen, the map by J. M. Stoddard (Figure 9.3) appearing in Herman Haupt's 1883 guidebook, *The Yellowstone National Park*, also promotes the park's infrastructure in the wake of the completion of the North Pacific route to the northern entrance to the park. Haupt was General Manager of the Northern Pacific during the period that the railroad reached Yellowstone, and his guide was the first to include advertisements for outfitters and hotels.[63] Hereafter, the momentum for guidebook publication accelerated, but many of these publications remained nearly as interested in the science of Yellowstone as its spectacle. The renowned French publisher of guidebooks, Hachette, issued its first guidebook to Yellowstone in 1885. Written by the Jules Leclercq, President of the Royal Belgian Geographical Society, *La Terre des Merveilles*, includes 40 engravings gleaned from the scientific reports, including a view of the Firehole Valley, and a general map of the park featuring the road system

Figure 9.8 (a) *Alice's Adventures in the New Wonderland* (b) Carl J. Hals and Angus Rydström, *Map of the Yellowstone National Park, Compiled from Official Explorations and Our Personal Survey, 1882* (Chicago: Poole Bros., for the Northern Pacific Rail Road, 1884). Newberry Library, Chicago, map4F G4262.Y4 .H3.

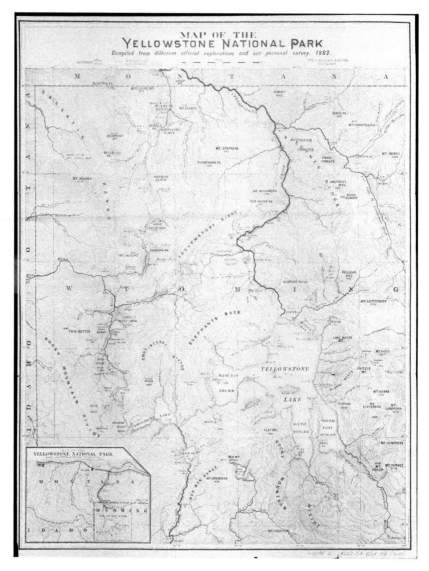

Figure 9.8 Cont.

and major sites. Inaugurating a practice in Yellowstone guidebooks that would carry through to the present day, it included a cross-section showing the inner workings of a geyser, which appeared in chapter devoted to the theory of geysers, based on the work of Peale. The book included as well an extensive bibliography both of scientific reports and popular accounts.[64]

Scientific study of the park, its geology, flora, and fauna has continued unabated since the 1880s, but the rhetoric of wonder has been muted. In 1879,

Hayden's operation merged with those of his rivals to form the United States Geological Survey (USGS).[65] The USGS geologist and surveyor Arnold Hague continued work in Yellowstone in the 1880s and 1890s, producing a geologic and topographic folio of the park in 1896, part of a series of paired topographic and geologic maps produced by the USGS sampling areas selected for their scientific and economic interest.[66] A revised version of the folio published in 1904 was enlarged to include ten special maps of Mammoth Hot Springs, five geyser basins, and Yellowstone Lake.[67] Thus ended what might be called the definitive phase of the scientific mapping of Yellowstone. There was much more to be learned about the ecosystem, but the inventory of the physical geography of the park was now largely complete. Tellingly, the commentaries accompanying both of these works are straightforward descriptive geological history, analyzing rather than reveling in the park's wonders—the word itself is conspicuously absent from the text of both works.

Nevertheless, Hague's 1904 geological atlas felt compelled to include a special sheet on larger scale of the region around Mammoth Hot Springs, so as to allow the depiction of the human features of the park's headquarters and adjacent hotel as well as the needed scientific detail of the hot springs. Humans were now a significant part of Yellowstone's environment (Figure 9.9).

Army engineers supervised the construction of the figure-eight of roads that provided for easy access throughout the park from nearby railheads via stagecoach, and after 1915, by automobiles. The grid of improved roads gained cartographic visibility through railroad publications that were designed inexpensively for wider distribution, and were consequently more rudimentary. These maps emphasized the easy access to the park provided by the expanding western rail network, but since the railroads themselves never entered the park, they left the details of navigating within the park itself to stagecoach concessioners and outfitters, and eventually, guidebooks for serving unescorted motorists.

And yet, the automobile-era guidebooks to Yellowstone responded to a persistent urge to explain the natural history of the region textually and graphically. Many guidebooks, from the early Haynes guides to the present day, include geologic profiles explaining the hydrology and mechanics of hot springs and geyser basins, or the formation of petrified forests. The distance in time, concept, and audience between the nineteenth-century exploratory mapping of Yellowstone and latter-day tourist maps is considerable, but these maps are linked by their motivation and continuous history. For example, the maps of Mammoth Hot Springs and the geyser basins in Janet Chapple's *Yellowstone Treasures* can be compared favorably to those appearing in Hayden's 1871 report. Chapple's maps lack the topographic details but the number of features mentioned are comparable, as they invite visitors to follow systematic and extensive tours through these sites following boardwalk routes and her own detailed descriptions of each geyser that echo the first descriptive tours made by Hayden and his expeditionary colleagues.[68]

The expeditionary explorers of Yellowstone described the region largely in terms of its geology and biology, but their sense of wonder in what they

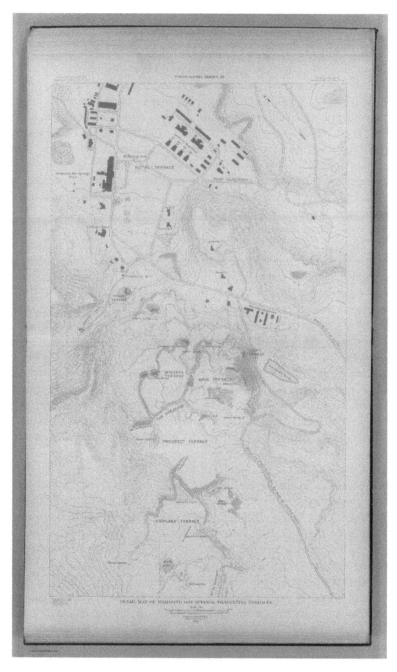

Figure 9.9 Arnold Hague, "Detail Map of Mammoth Hot Springs Travertine Terraces. Topography Sheet XX," in *Atlas to Accompany Monograph XXXII on the Geology of the Yellowstone National Park* (Washington, DC: United States Geological Survey, 1904). Courtesy David Rumsey Historical Map Collection. www.davidrumsey.com.

saw is unmistakable. The tourist may see the park mostly as a network of scenic drives and hikes, but many turn to science to help them appreciate what they see. It turns out that, in Yellowstone at least, the tourist's gaze and the scientist's analytical observation are complementary views of the landscape, not competing ones. Hayden and others like him understood that promotion of the Yellowstone to tourists was, almost paradoxically, essential to its preservation for scientific study. To this end they willingly allied themselves to those who marketed the park to tourists. The textual and graphic record of exploration was implicated directly in the consumption of the park. If Yellowstone's tourist maps pale in technical virtuosity in comparison to the explorers' maps, they are descendants and participants in the same process of western exploration and development. At Yellowstone, perhaps sooner than anywhere else in the West, tourists became consumers of expeditionary science, but they were also its patrons.

Notes

1 To avoid confusion, I will in most instances refer to the geographical region as the Yellowstone Plateau.

2 For a summary of major expeditions, see Jim Walsh, "Yellowstone Park: The First of Many, the Grandest of All," in Jenny Marie Johnson (ed.), *Exploration and Mapping of the National Parks,* Map and Geographical Round Table of the American Library Association, Occasional Paper No. 4 (Winnetka, IL: Speculum Orbis Press, 1994), 253–285. The Yellowstone historian, Aubrey L. Haines, provides an extensive history of early exploration of Yellowstone that is still unsurpassed, *The Yellowstone Story: A History of Our First National Park,* 2 vols (Yellowstone National Park: Yellowstone Library and Museum Association, 1977).

3 On this, see esp., George Black, *Empire of Shadows: The Epic Story of Yellowstone* (New York: St Martin's Press, 2012); also Richard A. Grusin, *Culture, Technology, and the Creation of America's National Parks* (Cambridge and New York: Cambridge University Press, 2004).

4 Ferdinand V. Hayden, *Preliminary Report of the United States Geological Survey of Montana and Portions of Adjacent Territories; being a Fifth Annual Report of Progress* (Washington, DC: Government Printing Office, 1872). U.S. 42d Cong., 2d Sess., 1871–72. H. Ex. Doc. 326 (Ser. 1520).

5 Ferdinand V. Hayden, "Wonders of the West—II; More about Yellowstone," *Scribner's Monthly* 3 (Feb. 1872): 388–396.

6 Harry J. Norton, *Wonder-land Illustrated: or, Horseback Rides through the Yellowstone National Park* (Virginia City, MT: Harry J. Norton, 1873); and James Richardson, *Wonders of the Yellowstone Region in the Rocky Mountains* (London: Blackie & Son, 1874).

7 George A. Crofutt, *Crofutt's Trans-Continental Tourist's Guide,* 3rd annual revision (New York: Geo. A. Crofutt, 1872), 114–115 and opp. 130.

8 See Alfred Runte, *Trains of Discovery: Western Railroads and the National Parks* (Flagstaff, AZ: Northland Press, 1984); J. Valerie Fifer, *American Progress: The Growth of Transport, Tourist, and Information Industries in the Nineteenth-Century West Seen through the Life and Times of George A. Crofutt, Pioneer Publicist of the Transcontinental Age* (Chester, CT: Globe Pequot, 1988); Anne F. Hyde, *An American*

Vision: Far Western Landscape and American Culture, 1820–1920 (New York: New York University Press, 1990); Marquerite S. Shaffer, *See America First: Tourism and National Identity, 1880–1940* (Washington, DC: Smithsonian Institution Press, 2001); and Jerry Musich, "Mapping a Transcontinental Nation: Nineteenth and Early Twentieth-Century American Rail Travel Cartography," in James R. Akerman (ed.), *Cartographies of Travel and Navigation* (Chicago, IL: University of Chicago Press, 2006), 97–150; and Richard White, *Railroaded: The Transcontinentals and the Making of Modern America* (New York: W.W. Norton, 2011).

9   *Wonderland* was in fact the title of its annual magazine issued from 1895 to 1906 to promote transcontinental tourism on its route and entertain passengers.

10   See, e.g., Chris J. Magoc, *Yellowstone: The Creation and Selling of an American Landscape, 1870–1903* (Albuquerque, NM: University of New Mexico Press; Helena, MT: Montana Historical Society Press, 1999); Grusin, *Culture*; Merrill, *Seeing Yellowstone*; Black, *Empire of Shadows*.

11   From Merriam-Webster.com (retrieved Jan. 2019).

12   Lisa H. Sideris, *Consecrating Science: Wonder, Knowledge and the Natural World* (Berkeley, CA: University of California Press, 2017), 14.

13   Most notably, Edmund Burke, *A Philosophical Enquiry into the Origin of Our Ideas of the Sublime and the Beautiful* (London, 1757); Immanuel Kant, *Kritik der Urteilskraft [Critique of Judgment]* (Berlin, 1790).

14   Sideris, *Consecrating Science*, 19.

15   US War Department, "Map of the Yellowstone and Missouri Rivers and their Tributaries explored by Capt. W. F. Raynolds Topl. Engrs. And 1st Lieut. H. E. Maynadier 10th. Infy. Assistant. 1859–60," in W. F. Raynolds, *Report on the Exploration of the Yellowstone River,* U.S. 40th Cong., 2d. Sess., 1867–68. Sen. Ex. Doc. 77 (Ser. 1317). Publication of the map and report was delayed by the Civil War.

16   J. M. Stoddard, "Map of the Yellowstone National Park," in Herman Haupt, Jr., *The Yellowstone National Park: A Complete Guide to and Description of the Wondrous Yellowstone Region of Wyoming and Montana Territories of the United States of America. Illustrated* (New York: J. M. Stoddart, 1883).

17   The most recent summary history of the exploration and creation of Yellowstone National Park is George Black, *Empire of Shadows*. The standard general history of the park is Haines, *Yellowstone Story*. I have relied extensively on these for a general chronology and narrative of the exploration and formation of the region. See also Haines, *Yellowstone National Park: Its Exploration and Establishment* (Washington, DC: National Park Service, 1974), which is available online at www.nps.gov/parkhistory/online_books/haines1/index.htm; and Richard A. Bartlett, *Nature's Yellowstone* (Albuquerque, NM: University of New Mexico Press, 1974), 117–220; and Paul Scullery and Lee Whittlesey, *Myth and History in the Creation of Yellowstone National Park* (Lincoln, NE: University of Nebraska Press, 2003).

18   Meriwether Lewis, *History of the Expedition under the Command of Captains Lewis and Clark, to the sources of the Missouri, thence across the Rocky Mountains and down the River Columbia to the Pacific Ocean, Performed during the Years 1804-5-6* (Philadelphia: Bradford & Inskeep; New York: Abm. H. Inskeep, 1814).

19   These are now widely believed to be hot springs located on the Shoshone River near Cody, not any of the thermal springs in the plateau itself, though we cannot rule out that Colter had seen these features. Some later maps would call this feature "Colter's Hell," which early accounts applied to Yellowstone itself. For a history of Colter's

explorations, see Burton Harris, *John Colter: His Years in the Rockies* (Lincoln, NE: University of Nebraska Press, 1993); and Black, *Empire of Shadows,* 30–38.

20 Haines, *Yellowstone Story,* 1: 47.

21 Warren Angus Ferris, "Life in the Rocky Mountains: A Diary of Wanderings on the Sources of the Rivers Missouri, Columbia, and Colorado, from February, 1830 to 1835," *Western Literary Messenger,* 2, no. 27–3, no. 42 (Jan. 11, 1843–May 4, 1844). Ferris drew a map of the territory through which he traveled over five years, with better accuracy than any of its contemporaries. The map was not published however and was unknown until a new edition of his journal was published in 1940. Warren Angus Ferris, *Life in the Rocky Mountains,* ed. Paul C. Phillips (Denver: F. A. Rosenstock, Old West Publishing Co., 1940). See Carl I. Wheat, *Mapping the Transmississippi West, 1540–1861,* vol. 2, *From Lewis and Clark to Fremont, 1804–1845* (San Francisco, CA: Institute of Historical Cartography, 1958), 150–157.

22 Raynolds, *Report,* 10.

23 De Lacy recounted details of his trip in "A Trip up the South Snake River in 1863," *Contributions to the Historical Society of Montana* 1 (1876): 113–143.

24 Walter Washington De Lacy, *Map of the Territory of Montana with Portions of the Adjoining Territories* (St Louis, MO: Julius Hutawa, [1865?]).

25 Two versions of this map were published almost simultaneously, this one by Hutawa, and one by Rae Smith of New York. See Richard L. Saunders, "W.W. deLacy's *Map of the Territory of Montana,"* *Imago Mundi* 54 (2002): 129–134.

26 Charles W. Cook, "The Valley of the Upper Yellowstone," *Western Monthly* 4 (July 1870): 60–67. Black, *Empire of Shadows,* 226–232. In *Yellowstone National Park,* Haines lists 87 newspaper articles on Yellowstone nationwide published in the period between 1869 and 1870.

27 Walter Washington De Lacy, *Map of the Territory of Montana with Portions of the Adjoining Territories* (New York: G.W. & C.B. Colton, 1870).

28 Gustavus C. Doane, *Report of Lieut. Gustavus C. Doane upon the So-Called Yellowstone Expedition of 1870,* U.S. 41st Cong., 3rd Sess., 1871, S. Ex. Doc. 51 (Serial Set 1440).

29 Given up for lost by the expedition, Everts was found barely alive a month later by local trappers. His account "Thirty-Seven Days of Peril," published in *Scribner's Monthly* in Nov. 1871, was yet another contributor to the Yellowstone media frenzy leading up to the park's creation.

30 Doane, *Report,* 9–10.

31 Attributed by William E. Strong, *A Trip to Yellowstone National Park in July, August, and September 1875* (Norman, OK: University of Oklahoma Press, 1968). In later life Doane greatly resented the credit Hayden received for exploring and promoting the park, which he and many locals felt was attributed at his expense. See Kim Allen Scott, *Yellowstone Denied: The Life of Gustavus Cheyney Doane* (Norman, OK: University of Oklahoma Press, 2007).

32 Described and reproduced in Wheat, *Mapping the Transmississippi West,* 5: 293–294; and in Orrin H. and Lorraine Bonney, *Battle Drums and Geysers: The Life and Journals of Lt. Gustavus Cheyney Doane, Soldier and Explorer of the Yellowstone and Snake River Regions* (Chicago, IL: Sage Books; The Swallow Press, 1970), 199, 399–403.

33 "The Yellowstone Expedition," *The New York Times* (Oct. 14, 1870), 4.

34 Nathaniel P. Langford, "The Wonders of the Yellowstone," *Scribner's Monthly* 2, no. 1 (May 1871): 1–17; and Langford, "The Wonders of the Yellowstone, Second

Article," *Scribner's Monthly* 2, no. 2 (June 1871): 113–128. See Bonney and Bonney, *Battle Drums*, 398–403.

35 Langford, "The Wonders of the Yellowstone, Second Article," 128.

36 See Marlene Deahl Merrill (ed.), *Seeing Yellowstone in 1871: Earliest Descriptions and Images from the Field* (Lincoln, NE: University of Nebraska Press, 2005); and Joni Kinsey, *Thomas Moran and the Surveying of the American West* (Washington, DC: Smithsonian Institution Press, 1992).

37 See Richard A. Bartlett, "Scientific Exploration of the American West, 1865–1900," in John Logan Allen (ed.), *North American Exploration*, vol. 3, *A Continent Comprehended* (Lincoln, NE: University of Nebraska Press, 1997), esp. 467–488; and Mike Foster, *Strange Genius: The Life of Ferdinand Vandeveer Hayden* (Niwot, CO: Roberts Rinehart, 1994).

38 Kinsey, *Thomas Moran*, 48–51, 68–73.

39 Hayden, *Preliminary Report*.

40 Hayden acknowledged and thanked *Scribner's* for allowing him to use them in his *Preliminary Report*, 7.

41 See John B. Krygier, "Envisioning the American West: Maps, the Representational Barrage of 19th Century Expeditions Reports," *Cartography and Geographical Information Science* 24, no. 1 (1997): 27–50; Kinsey, *Thomas Moran*, 49–50.

42 For a concise account of the circumstances of the creation of the park, see Bartlett, *Nature's Yellowstone*, 174–210; and Magoc, *Yellowstone*, 1–20.

43 Hayden, *Preliminary Report*, 83–84.

44 Ibid., 64–66.

45 Ibid., 66. There are eight illustrations, all wood engravings, included in this portion of the narrative. Some are signed by artists not directly associated with the expedition. They were likely employed by *Scribner's* and produced from sketches and photographs by the expedition's artists.

46 The four specialized maps were all prepared by E. Hergesheimer from notes left by Schönborn, who tragically committed suicide on his return east.

47 Hayden, *Preliminary Report*, 125–26.

48 F.V. Hayden, *Sixth Annual Report of the United States Geological Survey of the Territories ... being a report of the progress of the explorations for the year 1872*, U.S. 42nd Cong. 3rd Sess., 1873–74, H. Misc. Doc. 112 (SS 1573).

49 *Wonder-land Illustrated: or, Horseback Rides through the Yellowstone National Park* (Virginia City, MT: Harry J. Norton, 1873).

50 F.V. Hayden, *The Yellowstone National Park* (Boston, MA: L. Prang & Co., 1876).

51 Ferdinand Vandeveer Hayden, *Twelfth Annual Report of the United States Geological and Geographical Survey of the Territories*, U.S. 47th Cong., 1st Sess., 1881–82. H. Misc. Doc. 62 (Ser. 2057).

52 Ibid., xx–xxiv.

53 Henry E. Gannett, "Geographical Fieldwork of the Yellowstone Expedition," ibid., 457–459.

54 Ibid., 36–37.

55 Estimates of annual park visitation may be found at *Yellowstone Up Close and Personal* (www.yellowstone.co/stats.htm), viewed Mar. 2020.

56 This area would be added to the park in 1929.

57 Philetus W. Norris, *Annual Report of the Superintendant of the Yellowstone National Park*, U.S. 46th Cong., 3rd Sess., 1879–80. H. Exec. Doc. 1, pt. 5, vol. 2 (serial set 1960), 573–631.

58 Richardson, *Wonders of Yellowstone*, v.

59 William Wyndham-Quin, *Travels in the Upper Yellowstone in the Summer of 1874* (New York: Scribner, Welford, & Armstrong, 1876), xi–xv.

60 *Alice's Adventures in the New Wonderland. The Yellowstone National Park* (St Paul, MN: Northern Pacific Rail Road, 1884).

61 Ibid.

62 Ibid.

63 Herman Haupt, Jr., *The Yellowstone National Park: A Complete Guide to and Description of the Wondrous Yellowstone Region of Wyoming and Montana Territories of the United States of America* (New York: J. M. Stoddart, 1883).

64 Jules Leclerc, *La Terre des Merveilles promenade au Parc National de l'Amérique du Nord* (Paris: Librairie Hachette & Cie., 1886).

65 Hayden lobbied for the position of the survey's director, but was passed up in favor of Clarence King, who was followed by Powell in 1880. See Foster, *Strange Genius,* 283–322; and Bartlett, "Scientific Exploration," 461–520.

66 *Geologic Atlas of the United States, Yellowstone National Park Folio, Wyoming* (Washington, DC: US Geological Survey, 1896).

67 Arnold Hague, *Atlas to Accompany Monograph XXXII on the Geology of the Yellowstone National Park* (Washington, DC: United States Geological Survey, 1904).

68 Janet Chapple, Beth Chapple, Bruno J. Giletti, and Jo-Ann Sherwin, *Yellowstone Treasures: The Traveler's Companion to the Park,* 6th ed. (Lake Forest, WA: Granite Peak Publications, 2020).

Part III

Art and the Expeditionary Impulse

10 Delineating Land

Art, Mapping, and the Work of Frederic Edwin Church

Julia B. Rosenbaum

In his 1867 *Book of the Artists*, a compendium of American artistic output, the well-known writer and art critic Henry Tuckerman used the words "indomitable explorative enterprise" to open his section on Frederic Edwin Church. Throughout the 1850s, Church had been on the move, trekking to northern and southern wilderness areas of the American continent from Labrador to Ecuador. Church sketched continuously on these travels and the large-scale paintings that resulted, among them *Niagara* (1857), *Heart of the Andes* (1859), and *The Icebergs* (1861), catapulted him to celebrity status and established him as a renowned landscapist. Critics remarked on the decidedly empirical bent to his work. Tuckerman in his 1867 biographical piece repeatedly turned to the adjective "scientific" to describe Church and his paintings, praising him as one of the few artists to study earth and sky so deeply.[1]

These twin subjects occupied Church his entire life and took form not only on paper and on canvas but also in actual land. Church's purchase over several years of 250 acres overlooking the Hudson River in mid-state New York became a decades-long creative project that reconceived art as kinesthetic movement more than passive spectatorship. To see Olana, Church's name for the property, was to experience natural elements, to discover meadows, mountains, woods, and water, along the five miles of artist-designed paths. This negotiation of terrain is what anthropologist Tim Ingold has suggestively termed "ambulatory knowing."[2] Looking back on Church's artwork today, both the monumental paintings and the site of Olana, what stands out is not merely an "explorative," scientific interest but an artistic practice deeply engaged with expeditionary ideas and tools of nineteenth-century investigations of the natural world. Church's efforts underscore the challenges, for artists and cartographers alike, of delineating land in pursuit of meaning.

Church matured in an era marked by continuous exploratory expeditions and cartographic surveys that had as their aim the gridding, graphing, and charting of the American continent. Legendary among them was Alexander von Humboldt's five-year journey through South America and Mexico from 1799 to 1804. Humboldt, the eminent Prussian natural scientist, had dedicated his life to understanding the physical geography and phenomena of the world and to publishing his findings. Toward the end of his career he wrote his

Figure 10.1 Frederic Edwin Church, *Heart of the Andes*, 1859, oil on canvas, 66″ × 119¼ in. (168 × 302.9 cm), The Metropolitan Museum of Art, Bequest of Margaret E. Dows, 1909 (09.95).

synthetic work, the multi-volume *Cosmos: A Sketch of a Physical Description of the Universe* (1845–62), whose very title captures its ambitious scope and subject. Church owned not only the English translation of the text, as well as several of Humboldt's earlier travel/science narratives, but also a painted portrait of the scientist, which Church displayed prominently in his house. He had acquired it on a trip to South America that itself aimed to retrace parts of Humboldt's itinerary. The importance of Humboldt to Church registered also in reviews of Church's art; in 1859 when his equatorial painting *Heart of the Andes* (Figure 10.1) went on tour, critics saw a direct connection, "a pictorial counterpart," as Tuckerman would later put it, to Humboldt's exploration and research.[3]

In its joining of sweeping panorama and minute detail, the painting seemed to capture a fundamental point Humboldt expressed in the first volume of *Cosmos*: the importance of recognizing the interconnectedness of natural forces and the idea that nature "considered *rationally* … is a unity in diversity of phenomena; a harmony, blending together all created things, however dissimilar in form and attributes."[4] Humboldt further advocated for the visual arts as a critical tool in the meaningful appreciation of nature, promoting not simply repositories of artwork such as museums but more popular visual entertainments such as panoramas. The medium of the panorama offered a compelling way for the public to have access to "alternating pictures of landscapes of different geographical latitudes and from different zones of elevation."[5] Over his lifetime and in collaboration with artists, Humboldt considered multiple graphic strategies—charts, diagrams, graphs, sections, maps—to convey the inter-related patterns and systems of the natural world, an effort to find, as history of science scholar Anne Marie Claire Godlewska has described, "a more analytical spatial language that would allow the almost intuitive transfer of understanding from one graphic genre to another and from one specialist body of knowledge to another."[6]

One of Humboldt's most innovative pictorial experiments was a color plate published in his and Aimé Bonpland's *Essay on the Geography of Plants* (1807). Utilizing typical European landscape elements (horizon line, single-point perspective), the image transmutes scientific data into an artistic composition to visualize in this case the connection between elevation and plant distribution. Oriented horizontally, *Géographie des plantes équinoxiales: Tableau physique des Andes et pays voisins*, is part landscape, part scientific table, part thematic map (see Figure 1.1). In its attempt at breadth, the image not only compresses geographic space but mixes perspectives as well. There is both a vivid profile view of Andean volcanoes (singled out as Chimborazo and Cotopaxi by the nearby text in the sky) and a planar view immediately to the right, a cross-section filled with specific plant names. While echoing the form of the mountain profiles, this flattened space marked by text is meant to evoke the horizontal spread of land across the equatorial Andes, as described in the very title of the plate.[7] To this composed scene of land and sky, Humboldt appended on each side multiple columns of text, registering empirical facts that detail meteorological, hydrological, geological, and chemical occurrences.

Humboldt considered equatorial regions, such as those of South America, especially rich areas in which to observe the diversity of natural phenomena, and therefore ideal candidates for pictorial representation. He specifically entreated landscape artists "to seize, with the genuine freshness of a pure and youthful spirit, on the true image of the varied forms of nature."[8] This call motivated Church, who in 1853 and again in 1857 undertook, like Humboldt, expeditions to Colombia and Ecuador, seeking there the geologic formations, flora, and fauna the scientist had highlighted in his publications. Church's small, detailed sketches with close observations of nature developed into large oil paintings such as *The Cordilleras: Sunrise*; *Falls of Tequendama, near Bogotá, New Granada*; *The Andes of Ecuador*; *Cotopaxi*, and the blockbuster *Heart of the Andes*. Church worked to merge topographic verisimilitude with a broad composite vision, akin to Humboldt's holistic efforts in the *Tableau physique*.

Humboldt, in describing his working process, acknowledged the inherent conflict he faced between, what he referred to as, exactitude and appearance; his need to convey accurate detail and fact and his need to engage attention and spark imagination at the same time.[9] To accommodate these diverging demands, Humboldt employed the panoramic landscape perspective. So, too, did Church in his paintings. But confined to the pictorial, he also turned to the Humboldtian device of the thematic map. Similar to *Tableau physique*, Church's 1855 *Cotopaxi* (Figure 10.2), for example, is structured through geographic zones laid out horizontally, from the lush, meticulously rendered tropical environment of the palms in the crystalline foreground to the barren altitude of Cotopaxi in the hazy background. A serpentine line of striking

Figure 10.2 Frederic Edwin Church, *Cotopaxi*, 1855, oil on canvas, 30 × 46 7/16 in. (76.2 × 118 cm). The Museum of Fine Arts Houston, Museum purchase funded by the Hogg Brothers Collection, gift of Miss Ima Hogg, by exchange, 74.58.

white features extends down the left side, an artistic conceit to emphatically show the interrelation of natural forces, from volcanism in the sharp outline of the snow-crusted peak in the distance to erosion in the spray of rushing water of the middle ground to the aquifers in the chalky pool below. A snow-white horse and a rider mark the foreground, an element of scale but also an acknowledgment of humans as part of this interrelationship, a subject Humboldt addressed throughout his writings.

Church again plotted out geologic and ecological zones in his *Heart of the Andes*, the enormous—5½′ by almost 10′—composite vista of the Andean cordilleras. It was this grand painting the artist had specifically wanted to exhibit in Berlin so that Humboldt, by then an old man, could see it. Humboldt, however, died the very month the work made its inaugural debut in New York.[10] Church's depiction moves between comprehensive whole and minute particular. Jagged outlines of snow-covered peaks turn into arid slopes and more temperate plateaus that open up in the foreground onto topographical minutiae such as tangles of crisply rendered botanical and geological specimens. Critics mentioned viewers using opera glasses and rolled tubes of paper so as to better apprehend the fine parts of the intricate scene.[11] Mark Twain's comment about "straining" to absorb the fullness of the image, even as he referred to it as "the most wonderfully beautiful painting which this city [St. Louis] has ever seen" makes clear the struggle for both Humboldt and Church to present legibly, but also evocatively, the terrestrial in all its complexity.[12]

The density of Church's image may account for the published texts that were also a part of the May 1859 New York exhibition. Writers Louis Legrand Noble and Theodore Winthrop, close friends of Church, each produced a pamphlet that verbally elucidated the Andean geography depicted. These commentaries decoded the signs (in this case the natural features or regions) of the landscape in an effort to serve as a guide through the painting as well as to attempt a fuller understanding of equatorial phenomena. They hearken back to Humboldt's saturated visual field in *Tableau physique*, in which he strategically amalgamated diverse information through the deployment of text both within the landscape scene as well as flanking it. Indeed Noble launched his piece, as art historian Katherine Manthorne has pointed out, not with reference to the painting but with a stirring paragraph on geologic forces.[13] Noble went on to discuss the work through three fundamental natural elements—earth; trees and verdure; and air and light. Similarly, Winthrop laid out ten distinct terrestrial and celestial regions of the painting. Part way through his narrative, he then paused, as a surveyor might do, to assess the distance covered: "What have we done? Where are we? Let us review our mountain work before we go among the groves and flowers of Arcady."[14] These travelogue texts, along with the painting itself, accentuated the expeditionary and the revelatory; they bid a reader/viewer to imaginatively retread Church's sojourn through the Andes, which itself had been a reiteration of Humboldt's exploration of the area.

Critical responses at the time and on both sides of the Atlantic to *Heart of the Andes* were overwhelmingly positive and enthusiastic. Clearly the work struck a chord in 1859, in large part due to the way it was seen to intertwine art and scientific knowledge so effortlessly. If science rests on rigorous empirical observation, demonstrated facts, and accuracy of detail, art-making privileges imaginative conception. Such competing emphases established a spectrum in the nineteenth century stretching from the scalar, mathematical efforts of the topographer/surveyor to the landscape artist. As cartographic technologies and relief representation developed and advanced in the context of Western imperial efforts through the eighteenth and early nineteenth centuries, so too did categorizations for knowing and visualizing landscapes.[15]

How scientific study related to artistic composition was a question the English art critic John Ruskin addressed at length in his influential *Modern Painters* (a copy of which Church also owned). Ruskin insisted on the importance of the facts, or truth, of nature, asserting that it was "the imperative duty of the landscape painter, to descend to the lowest details with undiminished attention ... Nor is it of herbs and flowers alone that such scientific representation is required. Every class of rock, every kind of earth, every form of cloud, must be studied with equal industry, and rendered with equal precision."[16] But scrupulous attention to detail and specificity did not make an artist. As the art historian Rebecca Bedell elegantly summarized Ruskin's point, "True greatness lies in moving beyond fidelity to detail, or rather using this faithfully perceived detail to convey the artist's impressions, his interpretations of his subject."[17]

Observation and imagination, according to Ruskin, could not be separated: "The rapid and powerful artist necessarily looks with such contempt on those who seek minutiae of detail *rather* than grandeur of impression, that it is almost impossible for him to conceive of the great last step in art by which both become compatible."[18] The difficulty of achieving that synthesis and the degree to which Church managed it in *Heart of the Andes* was expressed by a Boston critic in his review:

> This may sound strange and rhapsodical, perhaps, to the reader who has not seen it and felt its influence; but it is true, nevertheless ... The varied and diverse features which it presents—magnificent and perpetual summer on the one hand, graduating from thence to a temperate region, and further up to the extreme of Arctic winter, were so designed by the artist to display at one glance the genuine character of the scenery of the Andes. It is, therefore, a representative picture.[19]

Part of Church's success was to deliver a work of aesthetic sublimity that simultaneously registered the scientific data and topographic clarity underpinning the principle of the interconnectedness of natural phenomena.

By the 1870s, the ready melding of empirical fact and conceptual vision achieved by Church in *Heart of the Andes* and attendant in Humboldt and Ruskin proved more difficult. The case in point is Church's 1870 *Jerusalem from the Mount of Olives* (Figure 10.3). The subject emerged from Church's travels to the Near East a year or two before. The painting was first exhibited

Figure 10.3 Frederic Edwin Church, *Jerusalem from the Mount of Olives*, 1870, oil on canvas, 54 ¼ × 84 3/8 inches (137.8 × 214.3 cm). The Nelson-Atkins Museum of Art, Kansas City, Missouri. Gift of the Enid and Crosby Kemper Foundation, F77-40/1. Photo: Jamison Miller.

in 1871 and Church's mapping proclivities immediately met critical resistance. Carefully delineated and bathed in light, the city of Jerusalem extends strip-like across the upper middle of the painting. The majority of the 4½′ × 7′ canvas is divided between a luminescent sky filled with roiling clouds and a deep foreground featuring a stony, arid landscape. But critics tended to fixate on the narrow portion depicting Jerusalem, hesitating about the genre of the painting: was it artwork or topographical survey map?

Appleton's Journal was blunt: "It presents an excellent topographical panorama of the site and surroundings of the Holy City, but has few of the merits which make a really fine work of art."[20] While the reviewer from the *New York Daily Tribune* made a point to praise Church and his fine handling of the sky, he similarly balked at the painting's empirical, quasi-scientific elements: "It is, in a certain sense, a map of Jerusalem and its suburbs. The artist has been too conscientious in the treatment of his rich and tempting material." He went on to compare the viewer's besieged eye to "an engineer officer reconnoitering a difficult field."[21] The survey/map quality of the work was further underscored at the gallery exhibit by an accompanying "Key to 'Jerusalem from the Mount of Olives'" (1870–71). Much like a map in fact, the engraving not only accurately oriented a potential viewer in time and space—"The spectator is supposed to stand in the early spring, on the Mount of Olives, facing the west"—it also numbered and identified specific landmarks, 17 sites and buildings, so they could be readily picked out in the painting (Figure 10.4).

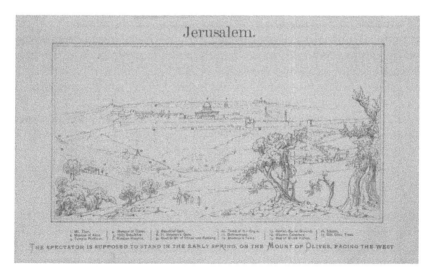

Figure 10.4 Key to *Jerusalem from the Mount of Olives*, American, 1870–71. Engraving, 6 × 9½ in. (15.2 × 24.1 cm). The Nelson-Atkins Museum of Art, Kansas City, Missouri. Gift of the Enid and Crosby Kemper Foundation, F77-40/2. Photo: Matt Pearson.

This pointed criticism of Church's inclusion of topographic exactitude and specificity as somehow too scientific—that is, too cartographic—and not sufficiently imaginative became full-blown in George W. Sheldon's assessment of Church's work in his 1879 *American Painters*. Here Sheldon circled back to Church's South American paintings after his second trip, singling them out as defective despite their extraordinary popularity and artistry:

> It is scarcely necessary to stop here and explain what their principal defect is, because, by this time, that defect must have been recognized by almost every intelligent American lover of art. It consists in the elaboration of details at the expense of the unity and force of sentiment. Some of Church's pictures, if reduced, would make capital illustrations for Humboldt's "Cosmos," or any similar text-book of natural science—for Agassiz's works on Brazil, for instance. They are faithful and beautiful, but they are not so rich as they might be in the poetry, the aroma, of art. The higher and spiritual verities of Nature are the true home of landscape art.[22]

What critics had earlier perceived as a pictorial apotheosis in Church's work, Sheldon now reduced to mere geographical transcription. In Sheldon's eyes, Church's South American canvases, chief among them *Heart of the Andes*, turned the artist from painter into a kind of topographer (an ironic twist given Humboldt's own aesthetic principle that landscape painting while grounded in accurate details must be generated from "feeling" and "from the force of idealizing mental power").[23] Such critical response in the later nineteenth century suggests how much the aesthetic and the empirical had hardened into discrete categories, provoked in part by the advent of photography and the mechanical capacity to produce exact likenesses, along with a viewing public made far more scientifically literate through the mass circulation of maps, geology and geography textbooks, survey reports, and photographs. In an era of transformative technologies and increasing professionalization in both the arts and the sciences, what constituted artistic creativity and what it meant to be an artist were being reimagined.

Church's response to these shifts—and to the limits of painting—brought him to physical land as an artistic medium. The result was Olana. Returning to the Hudson River Valley where he had sketched as a young artist, Church in 1860 purchased an initial long, sharp slope of 126 acres just south of Hudson, New York. Six years later he acquired its summit, then added several additional parcels to make a total of 250 acres. Olana became an integrated artwork as Church over the years transformed the property: expansively planting trees, shaping a lake out of a swamp, designing over five miles of dramatically staged carriage drives through woods and meadows, framing spectacular vistas of the Catskill mountain range, and constructing a house at the top of the property's steep escarpment that featured panoramic southern and western views overlooking the Hudson River (Figure 10.5). With Olana, Church gave living form to dynamics of the exploratory and the revelatory that he had earlier experimented with in his two-dimensional art.

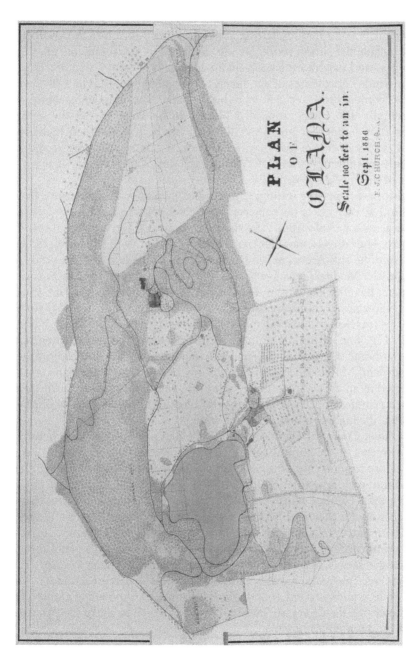

Figure 10.5 Frederic Joseph Church, *Plan of Olana*, September 1886. Ink, watercolor on paper, 22" × 36¼ in. OL.1984.39.A. Courtesy of Olana State Historic Site, New York State Office of Parks, Recreation and Historic Preservation.

In the very design of the house, Church evoked mapping elements. Through reference to cardinal points of a map, Church, working with the architect Calvert Vaux, devised a central floor plan based on intersecting axes at 90 degrees. The house aligns almost exactly along north/south and east/west points.[24] Church literally suggested a map by setting a metal compass rose into the floor of the piazza outside the sitting room. He also kept height measurements of "Olana Mountain" and neighboring peaks in an address book along with the latitude and longitude coordinates of the highest point of the house, the bell tower.[25] Church's compass rose at the heart of his property thus oriented his world both sentimentally and cartographically. Writing to his close friend, the sculptor Erastus Dow Palmer, in July 1869 shortly after he had returned home from abroad (and before the house was yet built), Church exuberantly, and perhaps only half-jokingly, claimed: "Almost an hour of this side of Albany is the Center of the World—I own it."[26]

In this basecamp-like setting, Church also maintained an extensive library of natural science texts on subjects from geography to botany, as well as a diverse array of exploration reports, surveys, and travel accounts spanning the globe. They complement his own earlier expeditions to the southern hemisphere and the sub-Arctic, as well as his travels in the late 1860s to the Near East and the Mediterranean, where he had sought out historic sites such as Jerusalem, Baalbek, Damascus, Petra, and Athens. Throughout his life Church regularly journeyed to distant and out-of-the way locations; in the 1880s and 1890s he traveled for several months each year to Mexico, often based in Mexico City but setting off to more secluded sites in the surrounding states. Closer to home, Church made repeated wilderness trips to the Adirondacks, Vermont, and Maine. In 1878, not only was one of these adventures notably chronicled in an article in *Scribner's Monthly*, but that same year Church also bought a remote property on Millinocket Lake in Maine with a view of Mount Katahdin, the highest mountain in the state.[27]

At Olana, Church drew on techniques he had perfected in his paintings to bring elements of the natural world into sharp focus. He positioned windows in the house to showcase sweeping views akin to a basic Euro-American landscape paradigm; clear foreground details, middle ground water elements, and distant peaks. He then wittily created elaborate frames around those window scenes as though they had become painted canvas (Figure 10.6). Outside the house, through tree plantings, particularly placed viewsheds, and carefully thought-out carriage drives, Church continued to lay out—one could say, map out—nature scenes, accentuating his private mountain site as a realm of discovery. Over the years, visitors remarked on this aspect of Church's work. Susan Hale, a family friend, found Olana "real woodsy and wild" and in a later letter described the drives as "invented by Mr. Church to make the place seem as large and remote as possible."[28]

Church constructed six main drives (or roads, as he liked to call them) through Olana, each detailing different aspects of the natural setting. Ridge Road, for instance, (Figure 10.7) skirts under forest canopies, opens onto meadows, and offers viewers stunning panoramic vistas of the Catskills to

Figure 10.6 Larry Lederman, View south from the Churches' second-floor bedroom
window. Courtesy of Larry Lederman © all rights reserved.

Figure 10.7 Larry Lederman, View of Ridge Road opening onto a vista of the Catskill
Mountains. Courtesy of Larry Lederman © all rights reserved.

Figure 10.8 Larry Lederman, View of North Road switchbacks. Courtesy of Larry Lederman © all rights reserved.

the west and the Hudson River north to Albany. Across the property, Lake Road, as the name suggests, highlights the contours of the large body of water the artist constructed from a swampy depression. North Road, a series of switchbacks (Figure 10.8), keeps a visitor immersed in dense woods, as does Bethune Road, which also traces the forest floor and outlines the sharp pitch of the escarpment leading up to the house. Together, these human pathways set in relief the diverse ecological features of this Hudson River Valley locale, plunging a visitor deep into the thick of nature and back out to wide prospects.

As in the pictorial work discussed above, Church in his landscaping orchestrated compositional zones to bring attention to diversity within a larger unity. A viewer is meant to oscillate between the panoramic survey of natural features and the close observation of terrestrial and atmospheric conditions. Referring to the different degrees of contemplating nature, from the pure impression of its grandeur to greater awareness and analysis of its diverse and specific features, Humboldt had stated: "Graphic delineations of nature, arranged according to systematic views, are not only suited to please the imagination, but may also, when properly considered, indicate the grades of the impressions of which I have spoken."[29] Church's construction of carriage drives suggests Humboldt's "systematic views": they offer multiple opportunities to encounter and examine geographic and environmental phenomena. While Church dredged a lake and planted thousands of trees over the years, he largely let nature portray or reveal itself, a tacit rejection of any notion of improvement or cultivation typical of picturesque landscaping.

Church's comments in letters to artist friends underscore the exploratory quality of Olana, a place for Church and visitors to observe, study, and delight in natural events whether climatic, ecologic, or celestial. To fellow artist Martin Johnson Heade, he wrote in 1870: "We are having splendid Meteoric displays— Magnificent sunsets and Auroras ... I have actually been drawn away from my usual steady devotion to the new house to sketch some of the fine things hung in the sky—."[30] The nature observable from his perch continued to inspire, and divert, him through the years, as seen in his confession to close friend Erastus Dow Palmer about how hopelessly absent-minded his letter to him had become "owing to the magnificent effects this morning—beautiful clouds, an opalescent atmosphere, and lovely tints in the landscape distract me every minute."[31]

In designing Olana, Church was free to contemplate the science of nature at the same time as he could aesthetically compose it. Landscaping liberated him from constraints of scale. Working in the three-dimensional made it possible for him to engage real time as an artistic technique. These strategies offered yet another avenue to experiment with the communicative challenge brought on by nineteenth-century expeditions and articulated by Humboldt back in 1807: how to convey effectively not only the empirical study of terrain but imaginative understanding of it as well. Church's artistic forays along these lines began with mimetic representation but ultimately expanded—or rather necessitated his move—into lived experience. Olana offered Church a local means to know as well as to revel in the magnificence of material facts.

Acknowledgments

My thanks to *American Art*, where some of the material included here appeared in "Frederic Edwin Church in an Era of Expedition," *American Art* 29, no. 2 (summer 2015): 26–33. © 2015 Smithsonian Institution. www.journals. uchicago.edu/doi/abs/10.1086/683349?mobileUi=0&journalCode=amart

Notes

1 Henry T. Tuckerman, *Book of the Artists: American Artist Life, Comprising Biographical and Critical Sketches of American Artists ...*, 2nd ed. (New York: G. P. Putnam & Son, 1870), 370 and 371. Among his wide sampling of artists, Tuckerman used the descriptor "scientific" almost exclusively for Church.

2 Tim Ingold, "Footprints through the Weather-World: Walking, Breathing, Knowing," *Journal of the Royal Anthropological Institute* 16, *Making Knowledge* (2010): S122.

3 Tuckerman, *Book of the Artists*, 372. For other critics who also referenced Humboldt in their reviews of Church's works, see "Editor's Easy Chair," *Harper's New Monthly Magazine* 19, no. 110 (July 1859): 271; "The Heart of the Andes, Church's Great Picture," unidentified Boston newspaper marked Dec. 1859, photocopy of Clippings Scrapbook, (14) 15, and unidentified Philadelphia newspaper marked Feb. 7, 1860, photocopy of Clippings Scrapbook, p. (22) 23, Olana Research Collection, Olana State Historic Site, New York State Office of Parks, Recreation and Historic

Preservation (hereafter Olana State Historic Site). Kevin J. Avery, *Church's Great Picture: The Heart of the Andes* (New York: The Metropolitan Museum of Art, 1993), 33–44, gives a detailed account of the picture's reception. On Humboldt's portrait, see Karen Zukowski, *The Historic Furnishings Report for Olana State Historic Site*, vol. 1 (Hudson, NY: The Olana Partnership, New York State Office of Parks, Recreation and Historic Preservation, Olana State Historic Site, Apr. 2001), 65.

4 Alexander von Humboldt, *Cosmos: A Sketch of a Physical Description of the Universe*, trans. E. C. Otté, 5 vols (New York: Harper & Brothers, 1870), 1: 24, see also 23. Church owned the earlier London publication.

5 Humboldt, *Cosmos*, 2: 98. Earlier in the volume, he identified landscape painting, along with literature and plant cultivation, as the three main "inducements" to an appreciation of nature (2: 19). For a succinct discussion of Humboldt's aesthetic philosophy and connections to Church, see Stephen Jay Gould, "Church, Humboldt, and Darwin: The Tension and Harmony of Art and Science" (1989), reprinted in William H. Beezley and Linda A. Curcio-Nagy (eds), *Latin American Popular Culture since Independence: An Introduction*, 2nd ed. (Lanham, MD: Rowman & Littlefield, 2012), 36–51, particularly 40–42. See also Alicia Eve Lubowski, "The Picture of Nature: Alexander von Humboldt and the Tropical American Landscape" (Ph.D. dissertation, New York University, 2009), and for the broader context of ideas about the relationship between science and landscape painting in Germany, Timothy F. Mitchell, *Art and Science in German Landscape Paintings, 1770–1840* (Oxford: Clarendon Press, 1993).

6 Anne Marie Claire Godlewska, "From Enlightenment Vision to Modern Science? Humboldt's Visual Thinking," in David N. Livingstone and Charles W.J. Withers (eds), *Geography and Enlightenment* (Chicago, IL: University of Chicago Press, 1999), 252. See also Susan Schulten, *Mapping the Nation: History and Cartography in Nineteenth-Century America* (Chicago, IL: University of Chicago Press, 2012), 80–86.

7 Humboldt spends several pages discussing the necessity for abstractions and compressions in rendering this image of the equatorial Andes that includes more than just the mountains of Chimborazo and Cotopaxi; see Alexander von Humboldt and Aimé Bonpland, *Essay on the Geography of Plants*, ed. Stephen T. Jackson, trans. Sylvie Romanowski (Chicago, IL: University of Chicago Press, 2009), 79–87. Karl S. Zimmerer provides a concise description of the image and its context in "Mapping Mountains," in Jordana Dym and Karl Offen (eds), *Mapping Latin America: A Cartographic Reader* (Chicago, IL: University of Chicago Press, 2011), 125–128.

8 Humboldt, *Cosmos*, 2: 93. He expressed similar thoughts in *Cosmos*, 1: 33.

9 Humboldt and Bonpland, *Essay on the Geography of Plants*, 81, as well as 79–80, which also addresses the artists and botanists who helped Humboldt render the *Tableau physique*.

10 Avery, *Church's Great Picture*, 39. Church expressed his desire for Humboldt to see his painting in a letter to Bayard Taylor, May 9, 1859, Bayard Taylor Correspondence, Letters to Taylor, Box A-Cr, letter #1, Cornell Regional Archives, Cornell University, Ithaca, NY (transcription in Olana Research Collection, Olana State Historic Site).

11 Unidentified Boston newspaper marked Dec. 17 1859, photocopy of Clippings Scrapbook, (12) 13, Olana Research Collection, Olana State Historic Site; and "The Heart of the Andes," *Boston Evening Transcript* (Dec. 15, 1859), 2.

12 Samuel L. Clemens to Orion Clemens, Mar. 18, 1861, published in *Mark Twain's Letters*, vol. 1, online at: www.marktwainproject.org/xtf/search?category=letters;r mode=landing_letters;style=mtp. In *Frederic Church: The Art and Science of Detail* (New Haven, CT: Yale University Press, 2015), 66–68, Jennifer Raab raises the issue of parts—that is, Church's profusion of detail—overwhelming the whole and in fact resisting comprehension and knowing.

13 Katherine E. Manthorne, "Legible Landscapes: Text and Image in the Expeditionary Art of Frederic Church," in Edward C. Carter II (ed.), *Surveying the Record: North American Scientific Exploration to 1930* (Philadelphia, PA: American Philosophical Society, 1999), 143. Revd Louis L. Noble, *Church's Painting: The Heart of the Andes* (New York: D. Appleton & Co., 1859). For a discussion of the pamphlets, see Kevin Avery, "'The Heart of the Andes' Exhibited: Frederic E. Church's Window on the Equatorial World," *American Art Journal* 18, no. 1 (Winter 1986): 52–72.

14 Theodore Winthrop, *A Companion to The Heart of the Andes* (New York: D. Appleton & Co., 1859), 28. Winthrop lists on p. 13 the ten regions he would explore.

15 Classic histories of topographic map-making include P.D.A. Harvey, *The History of Topographic Maps: Symbols, Pictures, and Surveys* (London: Thames & Hudson, 1980) and Eduard Imhof, *Cartographic Relief Presentation* (Redlands, CA: ESRI Press, 2007 reprint of 1982 English trans.). See also Ernesto Capello, "Mapping Mountains," *Brill Research Perspectives in Map History* 2, no. 1 (2020).

16 John Ruskin, *Modern Painters*, vol. 1, *Of General Principles, and of Truth* (Sunnyside, Orpington: George Allen, 1888), preface to 2nd ed,, xxx–xxxi. Ruskin first published the volume in 1843 but added a major preface in 1844, which was published in all subsequent editions. Church owned a copy from 1856.

17 Rebecca Bedell, *The Anatomy of Nature: Geology and American Landscape Painting, 1825–1875* (Princeton, NJ: Princeton University Press, 2001), 127. For confluences in Ruskin's and Humboldt's aesthetic thinking, see Alicia Lubowski-Jahn, "A Comparative Analysis of the Landscape Aesthetics of Alexander von Humboldt and John Ruskin," *British Journal of Aesthetics* 51, no. 3 (July 2011): 321–333.

18 Ruskin, *Modern Painters* 1: preface to 2nd ed., xxix. Ruskin expressed the inherent tension for artists in addressing both particular truth and general conception: "I repeat then, generalization, as the word is commonly understood, is the act of a vulgar, incapable, and unthinking mind. To see in all mountains nothing but similar heaps of earth; in all rocks, nothing but similar concretions of solid matter; in all trees, nothing but similar accumulations of leaves, is no sign of high feeling or extended thought. The more we know, and the more we feel, the more we separate; we separate to obtain a more perfect unity" (xxxiii).

19 Unidentified Boston newspaper marked Dec. 17, 1859, photocopy of Clippings Scrapbook, (12) 13, Olana Research Collection, Olana State Historic Site. See also the *Boston Courier* review, Dec. 16, 1859, (10) 11–(12) 13 in the same collection for a similarly fervent review, along with "Mr Church's New Picture," *The New York Times* (Apr. 28, 1859), 4–5.

20 "Art Notes," *Appletons' Journal* 5, no. 115 (June 10, 1871): 688.

21 "Fine-Arts: Church's Jerusalem," *New-York Daily Tribune* (Mar. 31, 1871), 5. John Davis notes a similar response in the *Hartford Evening Post* in *The Landscape of Belief: Encountering the Holy Land in Nineteenth-Century American Art and Culture* (Princeton, NJ: Princeton University Press, 1996), 189.

22 G[eorge] W. Sheldon, *American Painters* (New York: D. Appleton & Co., 1879), 13.

23 Humboldt, *Cosmos*, 2: 95. See also Gould, "Church, Humboldt, and Darwin," 43.

24 Vaux had designed one similar house in 1851–2, as Francis Kowsky points out in *Country, Park and City: The Architecture and Life of Calvert Vaux* (New York: Oxford University Press, 1998), 212. For the plan and description of the house, see Calvert Vaux, *Villas and Cottages: A Series of Designs Prepared for Execution in the United States* (1864; repr. New York: Dover Publications, 1970), 198–202.

25 Both measurements and coordinates appear on the first page of the address book, which is not securely dated but appears to be before 1891 (OL.1994.18, Collection Olana State Historic Site). Church's 1888 addition of a studio and corridor off the west side of the building did not change the basic sight lines of the original plan. For details on the house and its construction, see James Anthony Ryan, *Frederic Church's Olana: Architecture and Landscape as Art* (Hensonville, NY: Black Dome, 2001), chs. 4 and 5.

26 Frederic Edwin Church to Erastus Dow Palmer, July 7, 1869, Collection Albany Institute of History & Art Library (transcription in Olana Research Collection, Olana State Historic Site).

27 Arbor Ilex [A. L. Holley], "Camps and Tramps about Ktaadn," *Scribner's Monthly* 16, no. 1 (May 1878): 33–47. Jervis McEntee's diaries relate trips with Church to Maine, Aug. 9, 1877; Aug. 28, 1878; Aug. 9, 1879. Jervis McEntee papers, 1796, 1848–1905. Archives of American Art, Smithsonian Institution, www.aa.si.edu/collections/diaries/mcentee. Theodore Winthrop in *Life in the Open Air and Other Papers* (Boston, MA: Ticknor & Fields, 1863) details his and Church's 1856 Maine expedition. For a chronology of Church's travels, see John K. Howat, *Frederic Church* (New Haven, CT: Yale University Press, 2005), 189–190.

28 Susan Hale to Lucretia P. Hale, June 29, 1884 in *Letters of Susan Hale*, ed. Caroline P. Atkinson (Boston, MA: Marshall Jones Co., 1919), 140 (transcription in Olana Research Collection, Olana State Historic Site); and Susan Hale to Edward Hale, Nov. 15, 1903, Susan Hale Collection, Special Collection 1842–1934, Mss. Gr. 88, University of Rhode Island Special Collections (transcription in Olana Research Collection, Olana State Historic Site).

29 Humboldt, *Cosmos*, 1: 27–28.

30 Frederic Edwin Church to Martin Johnson Heade, Oct. 24, 1870, Martin Johnson Heade Papers, 1853–1904. Archives of American Art, Smithsonian Institution, www.aaa.si.edu/collections/martin-johnson-heade-papers-7699/series-1

31 Frederic Edwin Church to Erastus Dow Palmer, Apr. 19, 1891, Collection Albany Institute of History & Art Library (transcription in Olana Research Collection, Olana State Historic Site).

11 Albert Operti

An Arctic Historical Painter and the Popular Sublime

Ernesto Capello

Albert Operti found himself at a crossroads in 1909. His longtime employment as a scenic painter for the Metropolitan Opera in New York had slowly dwindled. While he strongly desired to parlay his experience as Arctic explorer Robert Peary's former expeditionary artist into a position at the Museum of Natural History, his entreaties were politely rebuffed.[1] With theatrical opportunities limited, Operti faced an uncertain future and potential financial ruin. That spring, however, Peary finally reached the North Pole.

Operti's earlier ties to Peary opened up new possibilities to keep the loan sharks at bay. Over the next several years, Operti increasingly worked in a variety of popular media with themes related to the far northern regions (Figure 11.1). This included illustrating two series of Arctic exploration themed cards for Hassan Tobacco, expanding a series of "Oilette" postcards of the frigid north, and even illustrating a novel. Operti also collaborated with Peary on a polar-themed travel exhibit at Grand Central Station, part of a series sponsored by the Museum of Natural History. The strong reviews the exhibit received, likely coupled with sympathy given the recent passing of his wife Martha, helped Operti finally receive his commission to the Museum of Natural History. There he began his final artistic endeavor, the painting of the panoramic backdrops that adorned the museum's celebrated dioramas.[2]

Operti's extensive output during this period thematically echoes what many scholars have termed the "Arctic sublime," a particular subgenre of painting and literature that emerged across Britain, the United States, and Canada in the nineteenth century.[3] While often linked to scientific and imperial exploration, by the turn of the century the Arctic had largely been mapped, painting had given way to photography as the scientific illustration of choice, and all that remained was the race to the Pole. For literary scholar and explorer Chauncey Loomis, this situation led to the fading of the "Arctic Sublime"—after all, "the Sublime cannot be mapped."[4] The popularity of Operti's work, however, seems to indicate the perpetuation of a "popular sublime" in which vernacular visual culture—postcards, tobacco cards, dioramas, travel exhibits—served as a means to translate the continued public fascination with the Far North into a consumable form.

Figure 11.1 Albert Operti, popular media imagery. a: Arctic Landscape Cards. National Archives. 200 (S) AA-73 to 200 (S) AA-81. b: Danish Woman. National Archives. 200 (S) AA-35. c: Aurora with Polar Bear. National Archives. 200 (S) AA-35. d: Baffin Bay. National Archives. 200 (S) AA-35.

Figure 11.1 Cont.

This chapter seeks to locate Albert Operti's work within the broader history of a popularly expressed and especially popularly consumed sublime. While this history dovetails with the canvasses of master painters like Frederic Edwin Church or Edwin Landseer, its greatest reach came from vernacular imagery such as naval illustration, panoramas, magazine illustrations, or the penny tobacco cards of Operti himself. These media translated the sublime from aesthetic discourse to entertainment while also transforming explorers such as John Franklin, Elijah Kent Kane, or Robert Peary into household names. Operti considered himself an "Arctic historical painter" and, as such, he carefully crafted a visual corpus that sought to both document contemporary heroism while memorializing past exploration. His project bolstered the public imaginary of the Arctic as a sublime landscape even as the region became more mapped and more accessible. And while his works helped shape public opinion, they were themselves shaped by the public's expectations for an accessible and easily understood sublime.

Operti drew on decades of artistic attempts to visualize the Arctic that developed in tandem with expanding exploration across the nineteenth century. This began when John Barrow rebooted the Royal Navy's Arctic program in 1818 in part to justify a budget that appeared bloated during peacetime and to "display the virtues that legitimated [Britain's] global position."[5] The scores of expeditions that followed over the next several decades thus identified a new series of naval heroes for an eager public, with figures like William Parry and Trafalgar veteran John Franklin becoming household names. The territorial implications of British exploration were not lost on other European powers, stimulating a slow-burning race for the Arctic that paralleled the more dramatic scramble for Africa. Russian Arctic exploration increased particularly rapidly, as Count Nikolai Rumyantsev served as Barrow's counterpart in propelling various expeditions designed to cement control over both northern Siberia and Alaska.[6]

An expansion of visual technologies of representation and dissemination paralleled this upsurge in Arctic exploration. As Russell Potter and Hester Blum have noted, the public consumption of Arctic reportage proved highly mediated, incorporating a variety of visual spectacles that relied upon theatricality and narrative as much as illustration and painting. The legitimacy of these representations soon came to dovetail with broader considerations of exploratory authenticity as well as a recursive engagement with the fruits of earlier expeditions. As such, Blum has discussed the emergence of a "polar ecomedia" that was layered onto the northern landscape itself in materials such as ship's newspapers or messages in stone cairns.[7] These items, both in their original environmental context and in mediated reportage in cities from London to New York, helped to shape the relationship of Euro-American society with the Arctic. Moreover, as I will discuss further below, engaging with the vestiges of previous explorers altered and shaped future discourses of representation.

The difficulties proved particularly strenuous for artists and illustrators attempting to showcase the dramatic aspects of the Arctic terrain. Potter has underscored that the far north remained "largely unseen" for metropolitan artists and their public, which made the representation of its "unimaginable" features doubly difficult. An early and effective visual strategy arrived with the development of the Arctic panorama, which offered a colossal three-dimensional strategy designed to awe spectators. One of the first, Henry Baker's "View of the North Coast of Spitzbergen" (1819–20), presented attempts by naval ships to escape a sea of ice on a massive scale featuring an 80 ft. canvas exhibited in a circular rotunda. The vastness of the vista, with viewers some 40 ft. away, accentuated the hyperreality of a scene involving monstrous walruses and ship-sized icebergs that dwarfed the intrepid naval party.[8]

While panoramas highlighted the enormity of the Arctic, further exploration also brought greater familiarity and commensurate artistic attempts to reduce its immensity to a human scale. Talk of developing a "summer residence" in the Arctic emerged as early as 1820 with John Franklin's establishment of Fort Enterprise on a beautiful site in the Canadian Northwest Territories.[9] By the 1830s, British amateurs could pursue tourist safaris into the Norwegian Arctic, which itself developed trade in animal trophies for public or private display.[10] Artists followed suit and by the 1840s began to imagine a picturesque Arctic that challenged notions of its sublime grandeur (and terror).

Somewhat paradoxically, these picturesque views expanded following the high-profile disappearance of John Franklin's 1845 expedition, whose fate is worth briefly discussing. Despite being extraordinarily well equipped—with over 100 personnel and two state-of-the-art ships in the HMS *Erebus* and *Terror*—two years passed without any word from the veteran of three previous northern journeys. After receiving numerous petitions from his wife, Lady Jane Franklin, the Admiralty outfitted a rescue mission in 1848, which itself returned a year later without any new information. Further search parties also failed to find a trace. Lady Franklin's grief became world famous, inspiring poetry, theatre, panoramas, and landscape paintings. Matters came to a head following a Hudson Bay Company expedition in 1854, headed by Dr. John Rae, who reported that Inuit peoples he had encountered had knowledge of white men having perished near King William Island. Rae's report proved all the more shocking because of rumors that the sailors had resorted to cannibalism to fend off starvation in the harsh Arctic winter. Four years later, another expedition led by Leopold McClintock confirmed the location of the corpses as well as John Franklin's early demise.[11]

The domesticated views of the Arctic that emerged in the 1840s can thus be read in part as a meditation on the future of the British Arctic program. Works like J. Coventry's "Assistance Bay 24th February 1851, The Coldest Day, Mercury Frozen" deploy a human scale, in this case presenting laboring seamen with the sun hidden on the horizon in a conventional picturesque trope.[12] As Ellen Boucher has highlighted, such views emphasize the possibilities of survival so as to overcome the challenge to British masculinity symbolized by Franklin's disappearance. Eventually, an argument emerged blaming the Franklin debacle on a lack of adequate tools and technologies. Somewhat paradoxically, Boucher notes that British interest in the Arctic began to fade once these new technologies had been developed.[13]

One way to make sense of this shifting interest may stem from the paradoxical contours of the sublime. As noted by Loomis in his classic essay on the "Arctic Sublime,"

> The Natural Sublime, suggesting in its magnitude the immensity of creation, and in its irregularity a natural order that is beyond man's ken, strains the soul of the observer. Part of him goes out to it in rapture; part

of him withdraws from it in fear. It simultaneously reminds him of his own responsive vastness of soul, and of his mortal smallness in the universe. Exultation and terror, liberation and acrophobia, a mixed sense of triumph and defeat ...[14]

There are two elements to this analysis. The first concerns the nature of the sublime itself, which can be considered as a dialectic between the awesomeness of creation and an irrationality that eclipses Reason and unleashes the potential for despair. Loomis underscores this ironic juxtaposition in his examination of Caspar David Friedrich's *The Sea of Ice*, also known as *The Wreck of Hope* (1824), which emphasizes shards jutting from an ice sheet, broken by the impact of a shipwreck slowly sinking beneath their weight. The shards and the ship all rest at oblique angles, in effect creating both a pseudo mausoleum as well as the illusion of unity between the manmade object (the ship) and sublime nature (the ice). As Loomis notes, the ship is dwarfed by the slabs of ice and the pinnacled icebergs in the background, to the point that any sense of "hope" seems at best overwhelmed by the lifelessness of the scene.[15]

Loomis also underscores that Friedrich's image of lifelessness belies the existing greenery, animal life, and human populations of the Arctic.[16] For Loomis, obscuring the presence of mundane survival forces the observer to contemplate their "mortal smallness" and "mixed sense of triumph and defeat," revealing the sublime. In the case of Friedrich's painting, this mortal smallness is not only a function of the vast scope of the ice but, perhaps most important, of the near invisibility of the shipwreck. As such, any potential for survival disappears as the ship will momentarily.

By the time of Franklin's mid-century disappearance, however, the contours of the Arctic were much better known, making it more difficult for artists to convincingly represent the region as uninhabitable and barren. The extended media attention the search for Franklin received, culminating in revelations of starvation and cannibalism, may also have led to oversaturation and eventual indifference among the public. A further challenge for artists stemmed from the decline of the sublime as a popular aesthetic in the midst of the Pre-Raphaelite preoccupation with beauty and eminent critic John Ruskin's championship of their endeavors. While by 1853 Ruskin would accept the sublime as a separate aesthetic category, Alison Smith has argued that he continued to refute Edmund Burke's concept of a "terrible sublimity." As such, Ruskin advocated reducing the sublime to depictions of "a manifestation of divine power and moral judgement working through nature." Otherwise, "[the sublime] risked being merely horrid, incapable of elevating the mind or the imagination."[17]

Regardless of the validity of Ruskin's critique, the sensibility he espoused can illuminate the public's reaction to varied strategies of depicting the Arctic at mid-century. Take, for instance, the strikingly distinct responses to two of the most celebrated artistic representations of the loss of the Franklin expedition, namely Frederic Edwin Church's *The Icebergs* (Figure 11.2) from 1861 and Edwin Landseer's 1864 masterpiece *Man Proposes, God Disposes*

Figure 11.2 Frederic Edwin Church, *The Icebergs*, 1861, oil on canvas; 64½ × 112½ in. Dallas Museum of Art, gift of Norma and Lamar Hunt. 1979.28.

Figure 11.3 Edwin Henry Landseer. *Man Proposes, God Disposes*, 1864. Oil on canvas; 36 × 95.9 in. Royal Holloway, University of London.

(Figure 11.3). Each of these responded to Friedrich's earlier composition by highlighting the overwhelming presence of ice and sea. Each also rejected Friedrich's attempt to obscure his shipwreck by foregrounding portions of the masthead of Franklin's lost ships. However, there the similarities end.

Church's painting presents a still moment of the late afternoon with two icebergs simply floating in the Arctic sea. Dominated by the white massifs, the painting explores the shimmering colors of the frigid sunset, with wisps of greens, blues, and reds reflected on the ice. Its New York and Boston exhibits received mixed reviews, in part because of its still and muted view of nature.

Before the painting travelled to London, Church added a single masthead in the foreground, which scholars agree likely referenced the Franklin expedition and added a narrative element previously lacking.[18] The public responded as the 1863 London exhibit proved a triumph. The press compared Church to Turner in laudatory reviews, with the *Manchester Guardian* describing it as "a most weird and beautiful picture; one to affect the imagination powerfully by virtue of its grand and simple truth."[19] An opening gala was attended by the great Arctic celebrities of the day, including well-known explorers like McClintock and Rae but also Lady Franklin herself. The exhibit also proved financially rewarding, in part due to color lithograph reproductions sold as souvenirs but mostly because Church finally found a buyer, the Manchester railway magnate Sir Edward Watkin, who had himself visited Canada's icy north.[20]

In contrast, Edwin Landseer's dramatic *Man Proposes, God Disposes*, which premiered at the Royal Academy the following year, drew mixed reviews and even a pointed snub from Lady Franklin.[21] This reaction stemmed from the composition, which features two naturalistic polar bears clambering upon a mast while tearing apart the red ensign of the Royal Navy that had served as a shroud for a skeletal figure, whose bare ribcage is being savored by one of the animals. The sensibility could not be further from Church's, even as the ontological narrative is similar. Rather than present a serene acceptance of the sublime province of God, Landseer highlights the materiality and violence of the scene, while also incorporating specific elements depicting authority—the ensign, a blue serge coat and a crushed brass telescope, which would have been the tool of a captain. However, as Donald has noted, perhaps the greatest shock value of the piece stems from the very barrenness of the landscape in which the viewer is led to imagine the tenuous state of even the bear's survival. After all, the bones are bare and perhaps the bear too is starving. [22]

Both Church and Landseer's paintings appeared following the heyday of the British sublime, at a moment dominated by the Pre-Raphaelites and an emerging tension within the aesthetics of the scientific as Darwinian theories began to filter into the visual.[23] Each work, however, illustrated the powerful pull of the sublime's ability to inspire terror in dramatically different ways. Detractors criticized a nihilistic post-Darwinian vision of nature. Even Church's critics complained especially of the uniformity of the icy landscape that almost appeared "too cold," in which humanity would be reduced to the base cycles of life, death, and eating highlighted by Landseer. And hence unpalatable.

However much the sublime may have been in the midst of a crisis within the art world, the image of a transcendental harshness continued to bear fruit in the broader public sphere. This was particularly the case in the United States, which now began to take the lead in polar exploration. And while vast scores of explorers, photographers, scientists, and artists played a hand in this maintenance of a visible, popular, and ultimately palatable sublime, none experimented with as vast an array of forms as Albert Operti.

Born in Turin in 1852, Operti spent his formative years in London where his father Giuseppe served as musical director for the Italian Opera Company. The

young Albert embraced England's maritime culture as a child, reading extensively in its history and joining the Naval School in Portsmouth at age 12. He
abandoned the sea to embrace the arts, beginning his education at the Glasgow
Institute of Art in 1870 before following his family to New York in 1875 to
study under Matthew Morgan at the Art Student League. Like Morgan, Operti
would embrace the versatility of a popular artist, engaging fields as diverse as
cartoons, scenic painting, illustration, and "great" pictures over the course of
his career.[24]

Operti concluded his studies in 1880 and soon distinguished himself as a
scenic painter of great promise. His early pieces were commissioned by his
father's new theatre, Niblo's Garden, but beginning with its foundation in
1883 he also received regular employment from the Metropolitan Opera.
During this era, he met and married Martha Greene, from Albion in upstate
New York, and seemingly settled into a comfortable existence. But he also
began to follow the expanding cycle of polar exploration that would come to
mark his mature years as an artist.

Indeed, polar exploration entered a new phase in the late 1870s as competi-
tion to reach farthest north began to heat up globally. For figures like the Austro-
Hungarian Karl Weyprecht, the still extant tinge of imperialism detracted from
this essentially scientific pursuit.[25] Weyprecht's advocacy for an International
Polar Year bore fruit in 1882–3, unfortunately after his passing. The United
States initiated the efforts with an expedition led by Adolphus Greely to Lady
Franklin Bay in Greenland in June 1881, an expedition that merged the desire
for American colonization with the scientific pursuits of the International Polar
Year. Greely's team conducted extensive magnetic observations during the
summer of 1882 and survived the following two winters despite relief teams
being unable to reach them. While the most extensive measurements were made
by the German expedition in Baffin Bay, Greely's tribulations dimly echoed the
loss of Franklin decades earlier and captivated an international public. When
he was finally found at Cape Sabine by General Commander Wilfield Scott
Schley in June 1884, a collective sigh of relief was heard across the Atlantic.

Somewhat ironically, the Greely saga helped shift polar exploration away
from scientific pursuits. Greely himself was dogged by accusations of having
executed a man for stealing food while rumors of cannibalism arose anew. The
fascination of the press with these sensational stories sapped the US public's
engagement with scientific exploration. Greely and his supporters countered
these scandals by recounting tales of manly suffering, yet his intellectual out-
look and emaciated physique countered the public's desire for a more rugged
hero. Ultimately, this scandal also laid bare the need for Arctic explorers to
carefully curate their image in a fashion befitting Gilded Age masculinity, in the
mold of boisterous figures such as Theodore Roosevelt and, eventually, Robert
E. Peary.[26]

Albert Operti's engagement with polar image-making emerged in this context. Having just returned from his first trip to the Arctic, a summer 1884
journey to Lapland, Operti reached out to US secretary of war William
Chandler with an offer to draw on his knowledge of Arctic landscapes to

picture the Greely expedition and the special role played by the US military.[27] Chandler offered to fund the commission, after which Operti contacted both Greely and his fellow survivor Sergeant David L. Brainard for descriptions of their rescue. The resulting works, *The Rescue of the Greely Party* and *Farthest North*, were each completed in June 1885 and were subsequently displayed at the War Department.[28] These pictures feature the dramatic quality of the Arctic landscape but simultaneously emphasize intimate moments of human scale. *Farthest North*, for example, features a moment in which Lieutenant James Lockwood and Sergeant Brainard take measurements at 83° 24′ N, in effect capturing both the mundane quality of measurement—signaled perhaps most succinctly in simple concentration and downcast eyes of Brainard recording entries in a field notebook—even amid the harshness of the fully icebound slope where a circle of huskies eagerly await a third figure clutching some form of food as he emerges from an igloo adorned with an American flag (Figure 11.4a). *The Rescue of the Greely Party*, for its part, also features a dialectic between a forlorn landscape and American nationalism, featuring the arrival of Commander Schley's forces at Cape Sabine the night of June 22, 1884 (Figure 11.4b). The painting's visual drama stems from the barren slopes still dotted by extensive ice even in the heart of the summer. The actors, portrayed in muted blue uniforms and carrying gray stretchers or tents, nearly fade into the dusky browns of the earth. These two paintings thus present an Arctic terrain that emerges somewhere in between the sublime wasteland of a Church or a Landseer and the picturesque "holiday" destination of Coventry.

However, what is perhaps most striking about these earliest representations is the degree to which Operti features the interaction between individuals and the landscape. Operti not only contacted Greely and Brainard but also pursued extensive research in diaries, "one poor photograph," and correspondence with other rescuers and rescued. These efforts resulted in an accompanying "Key to Rescue" that identified the specific individuals depicted as well as their role in the Greely or Schley expeditions.[29] It is this emphasis on the individual and landscape as historic subjects that distinguishes these efforts from those of Operti's artistic predecessors, even as it links him to popular imagery more broadly.

Indeed, Operti's paintings form part of the broader corpus of Arctic ecomedia as described by Hester Blum. Alongside the panoramas, periodical illustrations, and paintings exhibited in the urban halls of London, New York, or Boston, the exploration of the Arctic also led to a variety of site-specific exploration representations from ship newspapers, to deckside dramas, and, most visibly, a series of stone cairns holding documentation of exploration and measurement.[30] These cairns proffered a modicum of solidity and permanence to the essentially transient nature of exploration by linking the activities of specific group of people with a specific time and place. Operti's insistence on rooting his paintings within a specific location and moment ("The rescue" is identified as occurring at 11:00 pm) echoes this form of emplacement. He even evoked the figure of the cairn itself in a cartoon depiction of Brainard celebrating his arrival at farthest north (Figure 11.4c). As in the great paintings,

Figure 11.4 Albert Jasper Ludwig Operti. (a) *Farthest North*, 1886, oil on canvas, 90 × 120 in. Collection of Shelburne Museum, museum Purchase. 1961-1111. (b) *Rescue of the Greely Party*, 1886, oil on canvas. The Explorers Club Research Collections. Photo: Ernesto Capello. (c) *Ecce Homo: Brainard Expedition*, 1885. Courtesy of the Frick Art Reference Library.

Figure 11.4 Cont.

Brainard appears as a specific individual, in this case perched atop a cairn marking the transition of "farthest north" measurements across the nineteenth century.

Over the next five years, Operti expanded his attention to what he began to consider his "arctic historical paintings."[31] Having received Secretary of War Chandler's promise, ultimately unfulfilled, to pay $15,000 for his first two paintings, Operti began to pursue other possible commissions.[32] These included at least five "great pictures" depicting over 40 years of Arctic exploration. Several focused on the search for Franklin, including *Farewell* (1889), which depicts the moment the second Grinnell expedition (1853–5), led by Dr Elisha Kent Kane, abandoned their ship. Operti also developed two pieces picturing the Jeannette expedition (1879–81) for which he was advised by George Melville, its chief engineer. With the support of the American Geographical Society, he also painted *The Last Franklin Search* (1894), which prominently features a Netchillik woman named Ahlangyah, surrounded by her family, as she advises Lieutenant Schwatka as to the possible whereabouts of remains of Franklin's men during Schwatka's 1879–80 expedition (Figure 11.5). In each of these cases, Operti consulted various field notes, reviewed photographs if available, and, with the possible exception of *Farewell*, also interviewed expedition personnel. Moreover, each also features the kind of specific attention to time, place, and actors that had been demonstrated in his Greely paintings, in effect cementing the motives of an Operti Arctic historical painting. Following their exhibit at the War Department, both *Farthest North* and *The Rescue of the Greely Party* were exhibited at the Columbian Exposition in Chicago in 1893 where they were seen by thousands of visitors. Operti also designed a diorama of the Greely party for the Exposition—complete with waxworks of huskies, icebergs, and figures like Greely, Brainard, and Schley—further adding to his visibility.[33]

The Chicago installation deepened Operti's connections with prominent artic explorers such as US Navy Lieutenant Robert E. Peary whom he had known for several years through their connections at the Kane Lodge. As Peary prepared for an 1896 expedition to remove a meteorite he had discovered the previous year, the two were in regular contact about how to

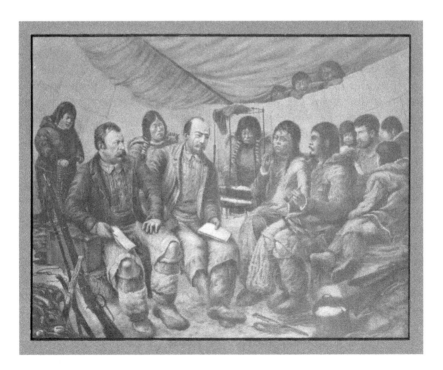

Figure 11.5 Albert Operti, *The Last Franklin Search*, 1894. American Geographical Society Library. University of Wisconsin-Milwaukee Libraries.

visually present the expedition to the public. Operti was particularly eager to share his collaborations with Edward von Kilanyi on the "Glyptorama," a new form of *tableau vivant* featuring movable mechanical backdrops based on historic landscapes that anticipated the cinema.[34] It is unclear whether Peary saw the Glyptorama, but during its run he offered Operti the chance to develop an installation documenting Inuit means of securing iron ore from the meteorite for spears, knives, and other tools.[35] As such, Operti was among the crew that sailed on the *Hope* for Greenland that July, armed with pencils, oils, drafting paper along with barrels of plaster, vaseline, and over 200 pounds of modeling clay to produce casts of the local inhabitants for Peary's imagined installation.[36]

Ostensibly focused on the plaster casts of Inuit, Operti also produced hundreds of sketches, color studies, landscape profiles in his role as expeditionary artist during the two-month excursion.[37] These works bolstered his later ethnographic credentials and also began his shift away from the relatively dark color palette of his early paintings. The vast majority focus on the everyday life of the expedition near their base camp on the Nugsuak Peninsula. Operti produced scores of shore profiles, documented native clothing and tools, took rubbings of everyday objects such as oars and knives, and illustrated daily activities. The quotidian is well represented, including team tasks such as the building of igloos as well as several individual portraits of Peary engaged in tasks such as hanging laundry or reading on deck. Operti also emphasized more dramatic moments as in a series of views documenting the capture of a polar bear. He also included several images of a storm that Peary termed "a night of such savage wildness" while remarking that Operti unceasingly ran onto the deck to be able to capture the horizontal driving snow and wind.[38] Operti was also attentive to those elements of permanence in the harsh environment, including images of the stone cairns erected by the expedition as well as stone graves of earlier explorers. Each of these elements would accentuate the naturalistic representation of bodies and foliage in his later works on the Arctic.

Upon returning to New York in September 1896, Operti suddenly found himself awash in celebrity. Early accounts of Peary's return highlighted the "unique" nature of the collection of Inuit casts and Operti's role in procuring them.[39] On October 11, 1896, the *New York Herald* published a full-page spread detailing his account of the expedition. It also reproduced four of his sketches including a view of the aforementioned storm and Peary bagging a polar bear. The *Herald* reporter identifies Operti as having traveled further north than any previous artist and describes his apartment as "almost filled with Arctic curios ... walrus tusks, miniature canoes, spears, moccasin quartz." Operti's description of his journeys echoes the florid prose of its day, incorporating extensive discussion of the chase across the snows to pursue two polar bear cubs, vivid descriptions of an arctic gale, and a relatively warm evaluation of the trusting nature of the Inuit subjects for his plaster busts alongside vaguely racist evaluations of their primitive simplicity.[40]

In the interview, Operti also discussed the nature of color, seeking to walk a middle ground between scientific observation and aesthetic wonder. In a lengthy aside, Operti critiques earlier claims of the multitude of colors that exist in the northern ice, asserting instead that ice has no hue on its own but merely reflects the surrounding environment. As he puts it,

> The prevailing idea is that ice has various colors, and in all Arctic books you will read of green ice and blue ice and ice of other colors. But ice has no color of its own; it has merely a reflection of colors caught from the water and the sky. The deeper the water the greener the color of the ice; the fresher the water the bluer the ice. The more opaque the ice the whiter and greener it seems; the more transparent the ice the bluer the tones. The colors mainly reflected in ice are emerald and malachite greens, cobalt and turquoise blues. It is my intention to produce artificial icebergs and glaciers for the American museums of natural history by the use of electric lights. I shall also reproduce lifelike figures of the Esquimaux.[41]

This extended reflection, beyond demonstrating his continued commitment to theatrically pursuing the panorama that Peary had envisioned, most dramatically illustrates the importance that a naturalistic yet still vibrant color scheme played in Operti's vision of the Arctic. In contrast with the refracted light on the ice, he also notes just how distinct the reality of the landscape was from the expectations that he brought with him. And indeed, in available color studies produced during the 1896 voyage, the prevailing palette emphasizes various greys, simple whites, and dark browns in the earth. Operti's huskies are uniformly grey and black and the skies tend to be stormy, with perhaps the only major emergence of vibrant primary colors coming in the form of budding flowers.[42]

I am highlighting this relatively severe palette for two reasons. The first is to demonstrate the naturalistic fidelity that Operti appears to have attempted to achieve in his depiction of the Arctic landscape. The second is to underscore the gap between Operti's fidelity to nature in his use of color and the expectations of the wider public, expectations that he himself had shared prior to his visit north. This tension came to a head during a February 1898 exhibit of his oils and some of his sketches, which was held at the Truth Gallery in Manhattan. While it is unclear which pieces were exhibited, *The New York Times* commended Operti's attention to detail but critiqued the color scheme, which the reviewer found "thin and hard."[43]

For Operti's late nineteenth-century audience, a spectacular color scheme therefore had become part of the narrative and imaginary of the Arctic for the British and American publics. Besides the dangerous temperatures, it was the sense of awe and wonder from the regularly reported extremes of color and light, particularly vivid in the summer months when most explorers visited the north, which marked the Arctic as sublime. Shane McCorristine has recently noted that these extremes of light themselves impacted the narrative schema of exploration reports and Arctic visual culture, while narratives of the spectral, the dreamlike, and the magical prevailed. While decidedly linked to colonial pretensions, in which Indigenous people disappear or appear as ancillary characters to support the framework of "heroic man versus harsh environment," the physiological effects of extreme light patterns and commensurate sleepiness or wakefulness beg further consideration.[44] So too does the importance of mediating technologies in establishing a certain consumed understanding of Arctic light defined as vivid spectacle, from the panoramas of mid-century to the larger-than-life landscapes of Church or Landseer to even Operti's imagined electric lights beneath artificial icebergs and glaciers.[45]

In this imagined landscape, Operti's relatively mild palette in his 1898 paintings would have seemed an anathema even as his credentials as the first trained artist to venture farthest north gave him a certain respectability and celebrity.[46] He furthered this reputation with the occasional newspaper article tackling subjects like the graves of Arctic explorers or Peary's new goal to reach the North Pole. These included simple line drawings as illustrations, with Operti identified as "artist of the Peary expedition." However, in the early years of the twentieth century, the theatrical engagements began to dry up and Operti began to re-explore alternate possibilities to make ends meet with a renewed attention to color, spectacle, and the bolstering of his personal bona fides as an explorer. That is to say, he attempted to meet the expectations of his audience and thus turned to more deliberate engagement with the eye-catching and the spectacular.

These tendencies were foreshadowed in Operti's work for *The White World*, a 1902 collection of essays by living Arctic explorers edited by Rudolph Kersting. Operti provided eight paintings, including his Greely paintings along with the frontispiece, "Lost on the Icecap," which features the kind of ghostly snow that he had enthusiastically drawn during the aforementioned arctic gale in 1896. The book also includes his essay "An Artist in the Frozen Zone," which highlights his methods for obtaining the Inuit plaster casts as well as his more extensive collection of sketches and oil studies. Unlike the 1896 *Herald* interview, however, Operti also stresses the dramatic lighting and incredible colors that he viewed during his Arctic journeys, noting that "the regions are replete with color, form, and never-ending variety." This enthusiasm is tempered, however, by his highlighting the need "for perfect health" and the sorrow that he felt at viewing the graves of those explorers he had read about and painting "the barren rocks, the scene of their suffering, in that great region of awful solitude."[47]

This dialectic, between the "never-ending variety" of color and the sorrow of "that great region of awful solitude," would animate the majority of Operti's late activities as he moved into developing forms evoking an Arctic sublime for popular consumption. As in his earlier years, these activities also featured his ability to transcend genre and benefitted from the increasing availability of color images or high-quality photographs in weekly magazines, postcards, and other venues, images that complemented his commentary and extended the reach of his theories on color and his conceptualization of the historical element of his work.

Operti first began this experimentation in earnest in 1903 during one of the recurring financial crises that would dot his later years. Without theatrical work to fall back on, Operti at first focused on entertainments, developing a Coney Island amusement titled "A Trip to the North Pole."[48] Though photographs or reviews have not surfaced, a likely mock-up found in the Explorer's Club features a plan with massive icebergs around a central lake that would have likely included waxworks of polar bears, walrus, and Inuit.[49] Indeed, a similar theme underscored Robert E. Peary's Arctic diorama for the 1904 Louisiana Purchase Exposition in Saint Louis, on which the explorer had consulted Operti about how best to prepare artificial snow and ice. Operti sent his friend detailed instructions along with a loose design for a panoramic igloo. Peary's final design echoed Operti's idea of a cavernous world of ice, however, it failed to incorporate features like the igloo bricks or the anthropomorphic polar bears that Operti had somewhat fancifully envisioned.[50] However, the success of these two endeavors appears to have inspired Operti, who in June 1904 would send the first of scores of requests for employment to the Museum of Natural History.[51] As noted above, it would only be upon completing yet another exhibit with Peary in 1912 that Operti would finally receive his employment with the museum.

Besides entertainments, Operti largely focused his creative energies on writing, penning a number of essays on Arctic themes between 1904 and 1912 in weekly magazines such as *The Christian Herald* and the *Sunday Magazine*.[52] These expanded on his theories of color and history in the Arctic context, while also shifting to a more populist and imperialist vein, particularly with regard to his depiction of the Inuit. This new framework first appeared in "The Great White World," published in the *Sunday Magazine* on March 13, 1904. The essay features two main themes—an ethnographic description of the "Eskimo" and a series of ruminations on Arctic color and Operti's artistic adventures. It is pitched with a humorous and vaguely racist tone, epitomized by the opening questions, which include: "Why should those of earth's children who are indubitably the happiest be incomparably the dirtiest?" Operti also cites anthropological observations by figures like Peary and Middleton Smith and echoes colonial tropes, describing the Inuit as "happy children" and "extremely superstitious." He also emphasizes how absurd his artistic attempts to produce plaster casts seemed to his Inuit models, particularly given the logistical hurdles. Wryly, he parodies himself, noting that, "covered with white powder as I appeared, [...] I am known to this day in the northland as Opixuah, or 'The Great White Owl.'"[53]

The real star of the piece, however, is the interplay between this ethnographic description and Operti's renewed engagement with the "panorama of the most wonderful colors in the world." This begins with two portraits, one of a "Danish-Greenland Eskimo" and then another of a "Danish-Greenland Eskimo woman." Each is depicted in gaily patterned, sumptuous garb, with the man enjoying a pipe and the woman in somewhat ceremonial attire, holding a fish. The vibrancy of their clothing belies Operti's comments about their dirtiness even as it conforms to anthropological "type" illustrations.

These portraits also echo a series of landscape vistas surrounding them in the text as well as Operti's mid-essay rhapsody on the mutability of the Arctic palette, in which "the deep, translucent purple of the ice mountains … may be raspberry, or burnished copper, or gold, or whatever may come in the changing lights and weathers."[54] Like the vibrancy of the woman's attire, the portraits showcase a variable sky from the grays and light peaches of the twilight to the deep red and burning gold of "the sun above the horizon at midnight," an image presumably inspired by the midsummer days Operti witnessed. As such, they delineate the shifting and deeply uncertain colors of the Arctic landscape itself and the difficulties for the artist—precisely the kind of ghostly and spectral qualities that McCorristine has identified as central to traditional visions of the Arctic sublime. It is worth noting that it is indeed possible that some of these images may even be reproductions of the paintings exhibited in 1898, here reframed textually to conform to a spectrum of light and adventure rather than presented as a definitive view.

Besides expanding to a more vibrant color palette in both prose and image, Operti's other experiments from 1904 also seek to more fully delineate a historical approach. For example, he published a more polished version of his earlier essay on the graves of explorers in *The Christian Herald*, which incorporates fully realized paintings based on his earlier sketches alongside an account of being overwhelmed by emotion at "the utter loneliness and desolation of it all" on encountering these graves.[55] This article, one of an Arctic series, was accompanied by a new ethnographic piece on the 'Eskimo" echoing themes from his earlier *Sunday Magazine* piece but this time illustrated by some of Peary's photographs including an image of Operti himself in full Arctic gear. Peary himself makes two appearances, including in a short overview of his upcoming polar excursion, an essay he wrote as a favor to his artist friend, and, most important, in a portrait for the magazine cover.

Operti had described the painting to Peary as early as February 5, 1904 as a "portrait of yourself in bearskin trousers, seal garment, a pocket folded map, or rather, unfolded, showing the latest connected coastline of Greenland and Polar basin."[56] Working in watercolor, Operti's painting, the original of which is held at the Smithsonian (Figure 11.6a), explores a complicated composition that lays somewhere in between classical sublime and picturesque modes. There are indecisive nods to Renaissance perspective with a series of undulating blue lines in the ice to Peary's right that, coupled with the low level of the ice shelf and the almost melting drip of the map, appear to lead to a vanishing point somewhere behind Peary's groin. This horizon line, however, is undercut by various alternate light sources across the canvas, mostly from an oblique point somewhere slightly above and to the left of Peary's head, though possibly cast in part from the barely obscured sun visible above Peary's hat. The uneven nature of the terrain, the vague and curved lines of the sun's shadows in the upper background, and even the multicolored hue of Peary's "seal garment" potently underscore the instability of the Arctic light. As such, Peary's grasping of the limp map and the sled, with its curved whalebone support, almost appear desperate. Indeed, perhaps Peary's expedition even seems dependent upon the

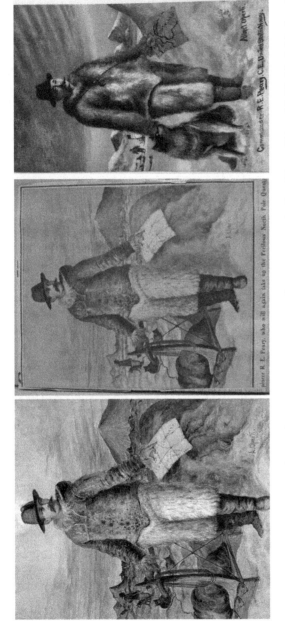

Figure 11.6 (a) Albert Operti, *Robert Edwin Peary*, 1904, watercolor on paper, 45.7 × 37 cm (18 × 14 9/16 in.). National Portrait Gallery, Smithsonian Institution. (b) Albert Operti, *Robert Edwin Peary*, 1904. Cover of *The Christian Herald*. The Explorers Club Research Collections. Photo: Ernesto Capello. (c) Albert Operti, *Commander R.E. Peary, CE United States Navy*, c.1905–6. Raphael Tuck Company Oilette Postcard. National Archives. 200 (S) AA-35.

partly obscured huskies and unidentified fellow explorer in a similar felt hat in the near left background.

In dramatic contrast, the final magazine cover eliminates nearly all of these liminal elements to present a relatively mundane vision of Arctic exploration largely at odds with Operti's artistic vision (Figure 11.6b). These include a series of alterations that reframe Operti's work as a picturesque image, in which Peary's upcoming success in finding the pole is a foregone narrative conclusion. While Operti decried these changes as a function of "the recent Lithographic strike," the alteration is far too dramatic and too explicit to have been a simple consequence of a rushed job and thus likely reflected the publisher's sense of audience expectations. For example, not only is the color palette dramatically softened across the image, but specific alterations erase the liminality of the original image as well. The undulating blue lines across the ice are eliminated, for instance, which not only erases the suggestion of a vanishing point at Peary's groin but also stabilizes the map. A single vanishing point is suggested by softening the chiaroscuros of the original by homogenizing the ice's color. This has the perhaps unintended effect of raising the ice shelf to rest more decidedly at Peary's torso and the commensurate impact of shifting the potential vanishing point suggested by the lower right boulder, itself flattened and homogenized, at Peary's torso rather than at his hips or groin. The flattening of the traces of the setting sun's rays, and the elimination of the suggestion of a solar halo above Perry's head, similarly contribute to a singular vanishing point at Peary's back, obscuring a single point of light directly behind the explorer. While there is no evidence that Operti's successful attempt to integrate his aesthetic and his historical views of Arctic exploration was in any way deliberately compromised, there is no question that the end result betrayed the subtlety of his original intent.

Over the next several years, Operti expanded his attention to popular media, in particular through developing a number of 5½″ xy 8″ watercolor paintings of Arctic scenes for the Raphael Tuck Company's "Wide, wide world" series of Oilette postcards.[57] The Oilette postcard first appeared in 1903 and employed a patented process to produce high-quality reproductions mimicking an oil palette. Their 'Wide, wide world" series debuted in 1905 but it is unclear precisely when Operti began his pieces, though it was likely before Peary's 1906 polar expedition. The vast majority of his postcards represented scenes from the Arctic environment, depicted with heightened color and majesty in a luxurious palette echoing classic sublime tenets. These included tempestuous seas, a view of the vertical ice of the Humboldt glacier, colorful sunsets, a polar bear gazing at the Aurora, and drab crevasses. Only a few featured humans, mostly anonymous "Arctic highlanders," including a reformulation of the Inuit woman from the 1904 *Sunday Magazine* article smiling coquettishly in front of a simple stone abode. Operti reworked his Peary portrait from *The Christian Herald* to avoid the reproduction issues he had encountered previously (Figure 11.6c). This included bluntly evoking the sublime in its dramatic chiaroscuros, restoring the curves of the setting sun, altering the headgear of Peary's companion in the background to suggest a native origin, and replacing the narwhal boned sled of the original with a husky to further accentuate the isolation of the region. Perhaps the most effective shift, though, was relatively simple: moving Peary's hand from pointing at the coast of Greenland to grasping and hence obscuring the North Pole. While still laying claim to cartographic knowledge, the gesture emphasizes the unknown and daunting aspects of Peary's quest.

When first Frederick Cook, and then Peary, claimed to have reached the Pole in 1909, Operti continued to engage popular media. This began with an Oilette postcard dedicated to Cook, identified as having claimed to be the first to reach the North Pole "and as the first to arrive at this goal his name must stand high on the roll of Polar Exploration." Operti would later acknowledge Peary's accomplishment and would deploy his association with the explorer to expand his market. One of the more extensive new projects was the securing of contracts with Hassan Tobacco to prepare images of explorers and of course the Arctic. I will turn to these in their own right momentarily, but before doing so want to explore how Operti once again paired these new works with a significant essay further clarifying his theories on Arctic color and splendor.

Operti's essay, "Splendors of the Arctic," appeared in November 1909 in the *Sunday Magazine*. More directly than his earlier pieces, it formally engages the spectral and sublime elements of the light and color of the Arctic from both aesthetic and scientific perspectives. An early passage establishes the stakes involved:

> But I was compelled to admit that the realities of the polar world, the extraordinary and unparalleled effects of light, of color and of background, are far beyond the limits of palette and brush. It is a world of color so brilliant that the hand falls hopeless; of magnificences so grand that all idea of reproducing them is lost in the awe which they inspire. Before the strange results of prismatic light upon ice and snow the artist sighs vainly. Before the universe of fire, in the celestial kaleidoscope of the aurora, he simply can hold his breath and gaze in wonder.[58]

While this passage decidedly laments Operti's inability to capture the variety of these vistas, it also roots his subsequent elaborations on this shifting visuality within the aesthetics of the sublime. He underscores this sense of awe and wonder despite the best efforts of mankind by subsequently deploying scientific studies on subjects like mirages and the lightshow of the Aurora rather than simply describing his own experience, as he had in earlier pieces. At times, he adopts quite technical language, as in his consideration of the role of argon gas in the Aurora, which had been shown in the 1890s to reproduce the visual lightshow in laboratory conditions. In this particular case, Operti fails to note that his account follows an 1895 article from the *New York World* almost verbatim.[59] While it is highly unlikely this near plagiarism would have been noted at the time, Operti's deployment of such scientific language seems to have afforded a single purpose, that of legitimating his singular understanding of the scientific terrain of the Arctic, presumably in service of his aesthetic (and historical) judgment. Needless to say, there is no "Eskimo" present in this essay unlike in his earlier efforts. Only Albert Operti, a luminary in a dark land, or, to paraphrase McCorristine, a "heroic man [in a] harsh environment."[60]

Similarly, the Hassan Tobacco cards, divided into two series—"The World's Greatest Explorers" and an untitled Arctic themed series—also evoke imperialist motifs in their representation of sublime landscapes. While there are some decided differences in the two series, such as the incorporation of a modicum of non-Arctic but decidedly mainstream figures like David Livingstone and Henry Hudson in the Explorers series, each features distinctive visual elements marked by vibrant colors, sharp chiaroscuros, and the vertical composition or low horizons typical of the classic sublime.[61] Both series are also highly colonial in their approach to human agency. To be sure, each card depicts an inhabited land, but one inhabited mostly by the great explorers themselves along with their signed interlocutor, "Albert Operti, F.N.A.G.S."[62]

The rhetorical impact of this representation appears particularly acute when considering the Arctic series, where the only discernible live figures are "Eskimo dogs," some playing "Eskimo children" and an "Eskimo woman." None of these are represented with exaggerated features and they are shown in drab dress without any of the specificity of his previous work. As such, they may well represent Operti's final nod to the expectations of his target audience. It is perhaps significant to note that the set of cards in the US National Archives, which belonged to the collection of Operti's mentor, friend, and fellow Arctic traveler, David Brainard, is only missing two cards—those depicting Eskimo children and the Eskimo woman.[63] While those two cards may have been lost, I personally wonder whether either Brainard or, more likely Operti, would have omitted these images precisely because they are caricatures, bereft of the colorful gaiety and relative dignity of his earlier illustrations and therefore unworthy to share.[64]

Operti's move toward popular entertainments and popular media stemmed in part from necessity but also challenges Loomis's sense of the demise of the Arctic sublime following the region's mapping. Instead, Operti seems to have been employing his particular expertise to present a vision of the sublime for popular consumption. Rather than fading into obscurity, in his work the Arctic sublime expanded its reach and its audience precisely at the moment of greatest triumph of the lengthy course of nineteenth-century exploration. While Operti's heroic explorers may not all have met the fates of Friedrich's or Church's ice-ridden vessels, their graves and resting places abound in his work even alongside triumphant figures like Peary, certainly as portrayed in the 1904 watercolor and the 1905 Oilette portrait. Nor is it an accident that Operti redoubled his credentials as an artist of the sublime precisely at the moment of Peary's greatest triumph—after all, without his claim to singular knowledge of the colors and grandeur of the artic skies, ice, rocks, and plants, his fortunes and his passions would have been severely compromised.

One of the key elements of Operti's work, in spite of his late career turn toward a more traditional engagement with the aesthetics of the sublime, was the incorporation of naturalistic bodies into an Arctic sublime. This also included an acknowledgment of the original inhabitants of the region, particularly as illustrated in *The Last Franklin Search*, but also in his numerous writings and illustrations from 1896 onward, even if this acknowledgment often repeated racist tropes. In 1910, Operti synthesized this conception of the inhabited Arctic in a study for a monument to celebrate Peary's arrival at the pole. Unlike the memorial that would eventually be erected in Greenland, which consisted of a 60 ft. brick obelisk emblazoned with the letter "P" on four sides, Operti imagined a structure that would incorporate the bodies of the people and animals that resided in the Arctic as accompaniments to the pedestaled figure of Peary in his exploring furs (Figures 11.7a and 11.7b).[65] The piece imagines Peary atop the globe, which emerges from an iceberg on which threatening polar bears reminiscent of Landseer's *Man Proposes, God Disposes* maraud. The monument would also incorporate other Arctic creatures such as a musk ox and various walrus busts and, most noticeably, five Inuit at the base engaged in the kind of traditional activities whose documentation had been at the heart of Peary's invitation to the artist to join the 1896 expedition. The final figure is likely Matt Henson, Peary's African-American colleague whom Peary claimed reached the Pole first.

I see this piece as an apotheosis of Operti's several decades of Arctic historical painting and sculpture, one which attempts to reconcile his fascination with the sublime qualities of both art and the Arctic landscape with the acknowledgment of the region's vernacular qualities, its environment, and even the prejudiced mediascape. While never built, it indicates the degree to which Operti's inventive mind attempted to conceive of the human qualities at the heart of exploration. As such, it is fitting that Operti would ultimately spend his final years exploring such theatrical approaches to the representation of an inhabited nature as a diorama artist at the Museum of Natural History, where he would produce panscopic murals representing the habitats of animals from the king penguin to the baboon or the muskrat group. His polar projects included the exhibition of an Arctic map with national flags tracking Roald Amundsen and Richard Byrd's early 1920s attempts to fly to the North Pole. Perhaps most fitting, one of his most lasting diorama paintings would be a reproduction of Frederic Church's *The Icebergs*, long the only way to see Church's masterpiece which was sequestered in a private collection in England until the 1980s. Operti's version, though, also included an extra element—a ship named *Roosevelt*, on which Peary had sailed toward the North Pole.[66] Operti thus rejected Church's anonymous lament of Franklin's demise and presented a historically specific (if counterfactual) vision of an inhabited and human Arctic while also celebrating both his mentor's exploratory triumphs and his own.

Figure 11.7 (a–b) Albert Operti, *Study for Peary Monument*, 1910. The Explorers Club Research Collection.

Figure 11.7 Cont.

Notes

1 Douglas W. Wamsley, "Albert L. Operti: Chronicler of Arctic Exploration," *Polar Record* 52, no. 264 (2016): 286, 292.

2 National Archives and Reference Administration (NARA): Rear Adm. Robert E. Peary Papers/ Letters and Telegrams Received, Box 48 (XP:48), Albert Operti 1912. See also Wamsley, "Operti," 291–292.

3 Chauncey C. Loomis, "The Arctic Sublime," in U.C. Knoephflmacher and G.B. Tennyson (eds) *Nature and the Victorian Imagination* (Berkeley, CA: University of California Press, 1977), 95–112; Russell A. Potter, *Arctic Spectacles: The Frozen North in Visual Culture, 1818–1875* (Seattle, WA: University of Washington Press, 2007).

4 Loomis, "Arctic Sublime," 112.

5 Shane McCorristine, *The Spectral Arctic: A History of Dreams and Ghosts in Polar Exploration* (London: UCL Press, 2018), 35. On the Admiralty's program see also Adriana Craciun, "What is an Explorer?" *Eighteenth-Century Studies* 45, no. 1 (2011): 32; Huw Lewis-Jones, *Imagining the Arctic: Heroism, Spectacle and Polar Exploration* (London and New York: I. B. Tauris: 2017), 28; and John McCannon, *A History of the Arctic: Nature, Exploration and Exploitation* (London: Reaktion Books, 2012), 127–128.

6 The best overview of this era in Arctic exploration can be found in McCannon, *History of the Arctic,* 127–34.

7 Hester Blum, *The News at the Ends of the Earth: The Print Culture of Polar Exploration* (Durham, NC: Duke University Press, 2019), 5–7, 29–35.

8 Potter, *Arctic Spectacles*, 41–44.

9 I.S. MacLaren, "The Aesthetic Map of the North, 1845–1859," *Arctic* 38, no. 2 (June 1985): 90.

10 Lena Aarekol, "Arctic Trophy Hunters, Tourism and Masculinities, 1827–1914," *Acta Borealia* 33, no. 2 (2016), 123.

11 Loomis, "Arctic Sublime," 106–110.

12 MacLaren, "Aesthetic Map," 95.

13 Ellen Boucher, "Arctic Mysteries and Imperial Ambitions: The Hunt for Sir John Franklin and the Victorian Culture of Survival," *Journal of Modern History* 90 (Mar. 2018): 40–75.

14 Loomis, "Arctic Sublime," 98.

15 Loomis, "Arctic Sublime," 103–105.

16 Loomis, "Arctic Sublime," 104.

17 Alison Smith, "The Sublime in Crisis: Landscape Painting After Turner," in Nigel Llewellyn and Christine Riding (eds), *The Art of the Sublime*, Tate Research Publication, Jan. 2013, www.tate.org.uk/art/research-publications/the-sublime/ alison-smith-the-sublime-in-crisis-landscape-painting-after-turner-r1109220, accessed Feb. 2020.

18 Diana Donald, for instance, argues the masthead represents Church's view of the Arctic as "the sublime dwelling-place of God, into which humans venture at their peril." See Diana Donald, "The Arctic Fantasies of Edwin Landseer and Briton Riviere: Polar Bears, Wilderness and Notions of the Sublime," in Llewellyn and Riding, *Art of the Sublime,* www.tate.org.uk/art/research-publications/the-sublime/ diana-donald-the-arctic-fantasies-of-edwin-landseer-and-briton-riviere-polar-bears-r1136829, accessed Feb. 2020.

19 Quoted in Potter, *Arctic Spectacles*, 187.

20 Andrew Wilton and Tim Barringer, *American Sublime: Landscape Painting in the United States 1820–1880* (Princeton, NJ: Princeton University Press, 2003), 226.

21 Potter, *Arctic Spectacles*, 166.

22 Donald, "Arctic Fantasies." See also, Andrew Moore, "Sir Edwin Landseer's 'Man Proposes, God Disposes': And the Fate of Franklin," *British Art Journal* 9, no. 3 (Spring 2009): 32–35.

23 Smith, "The Sublime in Crisis." On Darwin see Diana Donald, *Endless Forms: Charles Darwin, Natural Science and the Visual Arts* (Cambridge: Fitzwilliam Museum, 2009).

24 Wamsley, "Operti," 276–277.

25 Trevor H. Levere, *Science and the Canadian Arctic: A Century of Exploration, 1818–1918* (Cambridge: Cambridge University Press, 2003), ch. 8.

26 Michael F. Robinson, *The Coldest Crucible: Artic Exploration and American Culture* (Chicago, IL: University of Chicago Press, 2006), ch. 4.

27 Some of Operti's Lapland drawings would eventually be republished as illustrations for an article in *The Illustrated* American by W.H. Gilder. See W.H. Gilder, "Some Popular Fallacies about Siberia," *The Illustrated American* (Dec. 8, 1894). Archived at Explorers Club (EC), Albert J. Operti Collection (AJO), Drawer 2.

28 Wamsley, "Operti," 278–279. The full saga of Operti's difficulties with his payment is covered pp. 279–80. See also "Paintings for the Departments," *Washington Post* (Feb. 28, 1888), 2.

29 "Picturing Greely's Camp," *The New York Times* (July 19, 1885), 1. See also Wamsley, "Operti," 278.

30 Blum, *News*, 24, 29–35, ch. 4.

31 Wamsley, "Operti," 279–286.

32 Despite his growing reputation, Operti's financial fortunes remained stagnant. Not only did he not receive the promised $15,000 from the US government as Chandler failed to push the appropriation through Congress, but he also failed to collect a $500 commission from the American Geographical Society for the "Last Franklin Search." Since he had also donated his painting of "Farewell" to the Kane Lodge in New York, his income still relied on scenic painting and periodic external commissions. As noted below, this situation would almost lead to his having to refuse the invitation join Peary's 1896 expedition. On his financial fortunes, see Walmsley, "Operti."

33 "Panorama of the Greely Expedition." EC: AJO/2.

34 NARA, (XP:12) Rear Adm. Robert E. Peary Papers, Box 12, Letters Received Albert Operti 1896; Operti to Peary, Jan. 5, 1896; On the Glyptorama, see William Paul, *When Movies Were Theater: Architecture, Exhibition, and the Evolution of American Film* (New York: Columbia University Press, 2016), 31–36. See also Lynda Nead, *The Haunted Gallery: Painting, Photography, Film c. 1900* (New Haven, CT: Yale University Press, 2007), 73–74.

35 The invitation caught Operti unawares. As he already had a commitment to a scenery contract, he originally declined in a terse telegram. He later wrote a letter lamenting this decision while also explaining the extended timeline of theatrical contracts. Possibly with Peary's help (and certainly with the pull of fellow masonic "brothers") Operti ultimately was able to break his contract. NARA, XP:12, Operti to Peary, May 20, 1896; May 30, 1896. See also Robert E. Peary, *Northward Over the "Great Ice": A Narrative of Life and Work along the Shores and upon the Interior Ice-Cap of Northern Greenland in the Years 1886 and 1891–1897*, vol. 2 (New York: Frederick A. Stokes Co., 1898), 614.

36   Albert Operti, "An Artist in the Frozen Zone," in Rudolf Kersting (ed.), *The White World: Life and Adventures within the Arctic Circle Portrayed by Famous Living Explorers* (New York: Lewis, Scribner & Co, 1902), 297.

37   NARA, (XP-XPAR) Drawings and Sketches by Robert E. Peary and Albert Operti Relating to Polar Explorations, 1880–1912, Box 1, Folders 6, 9, 10; Box 2, Folders 10, 11.

38   NARA, XP-XPAR/1:6. See also Peary, *Northward*, 573.

39   "Return of Liet. Peary: Bring Back Fine Specimens from the North …" *The New York Times* (Oct. 3, 1896), 3.

40   Operti's account of the Inuit varies across his multiple publications. In general they are depicted as "simple" people whose trust needed to be earned for him to pursue his artistic objectives but who eagerly cooperated once shown that plaster casting was harmless. Some further discussion can be seen below but a more extensive study is merited.

41   "Incidents of the Last Peary Expedition," *New York Herald* (Oct. 11, 1896), 6: 3. Archived in EC: AJO/2.

42   EC: AJO/2; and NARA, XP-XPAR:1–2.

43   Wamsley, "Operti," 289. See also "The Week in the Art World: Events in Studio and Gallery—Landscapes, Hunting Scenes, and Portraits …," *The New York Times* (Mar. 5, 1898).

44   McCorristine, *The Spectral Arctic*, 4, 64.

45   Ibid., 119–120.

46   Over the next several years Operti would take advantage of this celebrity, expanding his scenic design work, in places as far flung as San Diego, where he designed the scenery for the Carnegie Lyceum's production of Aeschylus's "Eumenides" in November 1898. "Activities," *New Century* (1897–1903); Oct. 22, 1898; 2, 3; "The Personnel of 'Eumenides,'" *New Century* (1897–1903); Nov. 12, 1898; 2, 6; ProQuest.

47   Albert Operti, "An Artist in the Frozen Zone," in Rudolph Kersting (ed.), *The White World. Life and Adventures within the Arctic Circle Portrayed by Famous Living Explorers* (New York: Lewis, Scribner & Co., 1902), 304.

48   Wamsley, "Operti," 289. See also *The New York Tribune* (May 24, 1903), 9.

49   EC: AJO/2.

50   AO to RP, Mar. 16, 1904; Mar. 19, 1904; NARA: XP/Letters/23.

51   AO to RP, undated (prob. June 27, 1904); NARA: XP/Letters/23. This includes Operti's draft of his letter to the MNH.

52   EC: AJO/2; NARA, XP: 23, 1904.

53   Albert Operti, "The Great White World," *Sunday Magazine* (Mar. 13, 1904), 4–5, 14. EC: AJO/2.

54   Ibid., 4.

55   Albert Operti, "Buried Hope in the Arctic," *The Christian Herald* (Apr. 20, 1904). EC: AJO/2. The series of articles he was writing for *The Christian Herald* is also described in AO to RP, Feb. 26, 1904; NARA: XP/Letters/23.

56   AO to RP, Feb. 5, 1904; NARA: XP/Letters/23.

57   Several of the originals can be found alongside the postcard reproductions in the National Archives' Brainard collection. See NARA: DLB-AA/1. See also Wamsley, "Operti," 290.

58   Albert Operti, "Splendors of the Arctic," *Sunday Magazine* (Nov. 7, 1909), 8. EC: AJO/2.

59   Ibid., 17.

60 McCorristine, *Spectral Arctic*, 16.

61 mostly full set of these cards can be found at NARA: Brainard Collection of Arctic Exploration, Series AA (DLB-AA), Box 1: Folder 3.

62 It is unclear what the "N" stands for—Operti usually would sign materials around this era with "F.A.G. S." which stood for Fellow of the American Geographical Society. The "N" may mean National as he also had an affiliation with the National Geographic Society given his connections to Peary.

63 For a full representation, see the Trading Card Database, at www.tradingcarddb. com/Checklist.cfm/sid/168229, accessed Dec. 2019.

64 Again, this is an issue that deserves further reflection. Operti's photographs of the Inuit during the 1896 and 1897 expeditions tend toward respectful portraits even while incorporating periodic signals of the power dynamics of such semi-colonial situations. See in particular the photographic albums in EC: AJO, some of which have been reproduced in Wamsley, "Operti."

65 EC: AJO/9.

66 Wamsley, "Operti," 291–292.

Index

Lightning Source UK Ltd.
Milton Keynes UK
UKHW020803010822
406672UK00010B/1291